D1499090

THE HARVEY LECTURES

WILLIAM HARVEY

BORN APRIL 1, 1578–DIED JUNE 3, 1657

THE HARVEY LECTURES

DELIVERED UNDER THE AUSPICES OF

The HARVEY SOCIETY of NEW YORK

1983–1984

———

BY

RICHARD AXEL   STUART F. SCHLOSSMAN
WAI YIU CHEUNG   LOUIS SOKOLOFF
IRWIN FRIDOVICH   HAROLD WEINTRAUB
ROBERT C. GALLO   JEAN D. WILSON

SERIES 79

1985

ACADEMIC PRESS, INC.
Harcourt Brace Jovanovich, Publishers
Orlando San Diego New York
Austin London Montreal Sydney
Tokyo Toronto

ACADEMIC PRESS, INC.
Orlando, Florida 32887

United Kingdom Edition published by
ACADEMIC PRESS INC. (LONDON) LTD.
24–28 Oval Road, London NW1 7DX

LIBRARY OF CONGRESS CATALOG CARD NUMBER: 7-2726

ISBN 0–12–312079–9

PRINTED IN THE UNITED STATES OF AMERICA

85 86 87 88   9 8 7 6 5 4 3 2 1

CONTENTS

HARVEY LECTURES 1983–1984

*Manuscript not received.

THE HARVEY SOCIETY*

A SOCIETY FOR THE DIFFUSION OF KNOWLEDGE
OF THE MEDICAL SCIENCES

CONSTITUTION

I

This Society shall be named the Harvey Society.

II

The object of this Society shall be the diffusion of scientific knowledge in selected chapters in anatomy, physiology, pathology, bacteriology, pharmacology, and physiological and pathological chemistry, through the medium of public lectures by men and women who are workers in the subjects presented.

III

The members of the Society shall constitute two classes: Active and Honorary members. Active members shall be workers in the medical or biological sciences, residing in the metropolitan New York area, who have personally contributed to the advancement of these sciences. Active members who leave New York to reside elsewhere may retain their membership. Honorary members shall be those who have delivered lectures before the Society and who are not Active members. Honorary members shall not be eligible to office, nor shall they be entitled to a vote.

Active members shall be elected by ballot. They shall be nominated to the Executive Committee and the names of the nominees shall accompany the notice of the meeting at which the vote for their election will be taken.

IV

The management of the Society shall be vested in an Executive Committee to consist of a President, a Vice-President, a Secretary, a Treasurer, and

*The Constitution is reprinted here for historical interest only; its essential features have been included in the Articles of Incorporation and By-Laws.

three other members, these officers to be elected by ballot at each annual meeting of the Society to serve one year.

V

The Annual Meeting of the Society shall be held at a stated date in January of each year at a time and place to be determined by the Executive Committee. Special meetings may be held at such times and places as the Executive Committee may determine. At all meetings ten members shall constitute a quorum.

VI

Changes in the Constitution may be made at any meeting of the Society by a majority vote of those present after previous notification to the members in writing.

THE HARVEY SOCIETY, INC.

A SOCIETY FOR THE DIFFUSION OF KNOWLEDGE
OF THE MEDICAL SCIENCES

BY-LAWS

ARTICLE I

Name and Purposes of the Society

SECTION 1. The name of the Society as recorded in the Constitution at the time of its founding in 1905 was the Harvey Society. In 1955, it was incorporated in the State of New York as The Harvey Society, Inc.

SECTION 2. The purposes for which this Society is formed are those set forth in its original Constitution and modified in its Certificate of Incorporation as from time to time amended. The purposes of the Society shall be to foster the diffusion of scientific knowledge in selected chapters of the biological sciences and related areas of knowledge through the medium of public delivery and printed publication of lectures by men and women who are workers in the subjects presented, and to promote the development of these sciences.

It is not organized for pecuniary profit, and no part of the net earnings, contributions, or other corporate funds of the Society shall inure to the benefit of any private member or individual, and no substantial part of its activities shall be carrying on propaganda, or otherwise attempting, to influence legislation.

ARTICLE II

Offices of the Society

SECTION 1. The main office and place of business of the Society shall be in the City and County of New York. The Board of Directors may designate additional offices.

ARTICLE III

Members

SECTION 1. The members of the Society shall consist of the incorporators, members of the hitherto unincorporated Harvey Society, and persons elected from time to time. The members of the Society shall constitute two classes: Active and Honorary Members. Active members shall be individuals with either the Ph.D. or the M.D. degree or its equivalent, residing or carrying on a major part of their work in the New York metropolitan area at the time of their election, who are personally making original contributions to the literature of the medical or biological sciences. Honorary members shall be those who have delivered a lecture before the Society and who are not Active members. Honorary members shall be exempted from the payment of dues. Active members who have remained in good standing for 35 years or who have reached the age of 65 and have remained in good standing for 25 years shall be designated Life members. They shall retain all the privileges of their class of membership without further payment of dues. Honorary members shall not be eligible to office, nor shall they be entitled to participate by voting in the affairs of the Society. Volumes of The Harvey Lectures will be circulated only to Active and Life members. Honorary members will receive only the volume containing their lecture. New Active members shall be nominated in writing to the Board of Directors by an Active member and seconded by another Active member. They shall be elected at the Annual Meeting of the Society by a vote of the majority of the Active members present at the meeting. Members who leave New York to reside elsewhere may retain their membership. Active members who have given a Harvey Lecture and who have moved out of the New York metropolitan area may, if they wish, become Honorary members. Membership in the Society shall terminate on the death, resignation, or removal of the member.

SECTION 2. Members may be suspended or expelled from the Society by the vote of a majority of the members present at any meeting of members at which a quorum is present, for refusing or failing to comply with the By-Laws, or for other good and sufficient cause.

SECTION 3. Members may resign from the Society by written declaration, which shall take effect upon the filing thereof with the Secretary.

ARTICLE IV

Meetings of the Members of the Society

SECTION 1. The Society shall hold its annual meeting of Active members for the election of officers and directors, and for the transaction of such other business as may come before the meeting in the month of January or

February in each year, at a place within the City of New York, and on a date and at an hour to be specified in the notice of such meeting.

SECTION 2. Special meetings of members shall be called by the Secretary upon the request of the President or Vice-President or of the Board of Directors, or on written request of twenty-five of the Active members.

SECTION 3. Notice of all meetings of Active members shall be mailed or delivered personally to each member not less than ten nor more than sixty days before the meeting. Like notice shall be given with respect to lectures.

SECTION 4. At all meetings of Active members of the Society ten Active members, present in person, shall constitute a quorum, but less than a quorum shall have power to adjourn from time to time until a quorum be present.

ARTICLE V

Board of Directors

SECTION 1. The number of directors constituting The Board of Directors shall be seven: the President, the Vice-President, the Secretary, and the Treasurer of the Society, and the three members of the Council. The number of directors may be increased or reduced by amendments of the By-Laws as hereinafter provided, within the maximum and minimum numbers fixed in the Certificate of Incorporation or any amendment thereto.

SECTION 2. The Board of Directors shall hold an annual meeting shortly before the annual meeting of the Society.

Special meetings of the Board of Directors shall be called at any time by the Secretary upon the request of the President or Vice-President or of one-fourth of the directors then in office.

SECTION 3. Notice of all regular annual meetings of the Board shall be given to each director at least seven days before the meeting and notice of special meetings, at least one day before. Meetings may be held at any place within the City of New York designated in the notice of the meeting.

SECTION 4. The Board of Directors shall have the immediate charge, management, and control of the activities and affairs of the Society, and it shall have full power, in the intervals between the annual meetings of the Active members, to do any and all things in relation to the affairs of the Society.

SECTION 5. Council members shall be elected by the members of the Society at the Annual Meeting. One Council member is elected each year to serve for three years, there being three Council members at all times. Vacancies occurring on the Council for any cause may be filled for the unexpired term by the majority vote of the directors present at any meeting at which a quorum is present. Only Active members of the Society shall be eligible for membership on the Council.

SECTION 6. A majority of the Board as from time to time constituted shall be necessary to constitute a quorum, but less than a quorum shall have power to adjourn from time to time until a quorum be present.

SECTION 7. The Board shall have power to appoint individual or corporate trustees and their successors of any or all of the property of the Society, and to confer upon them such of the powers, duties, or obligations of the directors in relation to the care, custody, or management of such property as may be deemed advisable.

SECTION 8. The directors shall present at the Annual Meeting a report, verified by the President and Treasurer, or by a majority of the directors, showing the whole amount of real and personal property owned by the Society, where located, and where and how invested, the amount and nature of the property acquired during the year immediately preceding the date of the report and the manner of the acquisition; the amount applied, appropriated, or expended during the year immediately preceding such date, and the purposes, objects, or persons to or for which such applications, appropriations, or expenditures have been made; and the names of the persons who have been admitted to membership in the Society during such year, which report shall be filed with the records of the Society and an abstract thereof entered in the minutes of the proceedings of the Annual Meeting.

ARTICLE VI

Committees

SECTION 1. The Board of Directors may appoint from time to time such committees as it deems advisable, and each such committee shall exercise such powers and perform such duties as may be conferred upon it by the Board of Directors subject to its continuing direction and control.

ARTICLE VII

Officers

SECTION 1. The officers of the Society shall consist of a President, a Vice-President, a Secretary, and a Treasurer, and such other officers as the Board of Directors may from time to time determine. All of the officers of the Society shall be members of the Board of Directors.

SECTION 2. The President shall be the chief executive officer of the Society and shall be in charge of the direction of its affairs, acting with the advice of the Board of Directors. The other officers of the Society shall have the powers and perform the duties that usually pertain to their respective offices, or as may from time to time be prescribed by the Board of Directors.

SECTION 3. The officers and the directors shall not receive, directly or indirectly, any salary or other compensation from the Society, unless authorized by the concurring vote of two-thirds of all the directors.

SECTION 4. The officers shall be elected at the Annual Meeting of the Active members. All officers shall hold office until the next Annual Meeting and until their successors are elected or until removed by vote of a majority vote of the directors. Vacancies occurring among the officers for any cause may be filled for the unexpired term by the majority vote of the directors present at any meeting at which a quorum is present. Officers must be Active members of the Society.

ARTICLE VIII

Fiscal Year—Seal

SECTION 1. The fiscal year of the Society shall be the calendar year.

SECTION 2. The seal of the Society shall be circular in form and shall bear the words "The Harvey Society, Inc., New York, New York, Corporate Seal."

ARTICLE IX

Amendments

SECTION 1. These By-Laws may be added to, amended, or repealed, in whole or in part, by the Active members or by the Board of Directors, in each case by a majority vote at any meeting at which a quorum is present, provided that notice of the proposed addition, amendment, or repeal has been given to each member or director, as the case may be, in the notice of such meeting.

NEUROPEPTIDE GENES MEDIATING COMPLEX BEHAVIOR IN *Aplysia**

RICHARD AXEL

Institute of Cancer Research
Columbia University
New York, New York

N ERVOUS systems consist of diverse populations of neurons that are anatomically and functionally distinct. Specific neurons, or groups of neurons, are called into play by the action of neurotransmitters to generate specific behaviors at the appropriate time. The diversity of nerve cells and the precision with which they are interconnected suggest that specific genes or gene sets are activated in some neurons but not expressed in others. We have examined the expression of specific genes in individual neurons to ask what genes encode patterns of behavior and how the products of a gene interact with the individual components of the nervous system to coordinate a precisely defined behavioral sequence.

It should already be apparent that I have tacitly assumed a genetic component to behavior, that certain forms of behavior are indeed innate. Convincing support for this assumption, for the inheritance of behavioral patterns, was provided over 100 years ago in Darwin's treatise, "The Descent of Man" (1871). Darwin applied to behavioral patterns the very same principles of comparative evolutionary biology that he applied to morphological structures, to argue that every animal is born with a repertoire of instinctual behaviors as characteristic of a species as morphologic features. Certain behavioral patterns evolved in much the same way as structures, as wings or heads, and obeyed the same laws: the evolution of fitter variants through natural selection. To the extent that one considers the gene as the substrate for mutability or change in evolutionary time, we may now consider certain behaviors, at least in part, dictated by genes, and changes in behavior in different

---

*Lecture delivered September 15, 1983.

species may therefore be associated with changes in genes. At the cell and molecular level, however, this problem is complicated by the fact that the central nervous system integrates and filters the dictates of the genes in a manner that is often experimentally inaccessible. For this reason numerous investigators have chosen the relatively simple nervous system of invertebrates as model systems for the study of the cellular and molecular basis of behavior.

I. THE NERVOUS SYSTEM OF THE SNAIL

The simple nervous system of the invertebrate *Aplysia californica,* a marine snail, is particularly suitable for analyzing specific gene expression because it contains only about 20,000 central nerve cells which are collected into 4 pairs of symmetric ganglia and a single asymmetric abdominal ganglion. Moreover, several of the neurons in these ganglia may be recognized by highly reproducible characteristics such as size, shape, position, pigmentation, and function (for review see Kandel, 1979). The cells of the abdominal ganglion are illustrated in Fig. 1. In addition to being few in number, neurons in *Aplysia* can be quite large, up to 1 mm in diameter. Most of these large cells are polyploid and contain as much as 1 μg of DNA, more than 10^5 times the content of the haploid genome (Coggeshall *et al.,* 1971; Lasek and Dower, 1971). Furthermore, our data indicate that mRNA content is also proportional to cell size such that the largest of cells contains up to 5 ng of mRNA. This numerical simplification has made it possible to relate the function of particular cells to specific patterns of behavior and may permit us to attribute neuronal function to the expression of specific genes. The behavioral function of several invariant cells has been identified (for review see Kandel, 1979). For example, the largest cell in the animal, R2, connects to the mucous glands of the foot controlling walking; the peptidergic neuron R15 controls water balance; and a cluster of smaller neurons, the bag cells, mediates a complex behavioral repertoire involved in egg laying.

It is now possible to dissect out these neurons and examine the activity of individual genes in a single cell. Fig. 2 reveals the diversity of proteins expressed in individual cells of the ganglia. These profiles result from ^{35}S labeling of proteins synthesized in single cells and reveal several striking differences among the proteins of individual neurons.

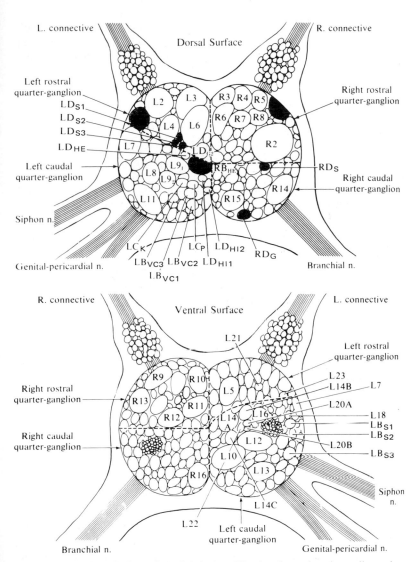

FIG. 1. The abdominal ganglion of *Aplysia californica*. Large invariant cells are labeled L or R, designating left or right hemiganglion with an identifying number. The two clusters of bag cell neurons are observed surrounding both the right and left connectives rostral to the ganglia. For reference, the largest cell in the ganglion, R2, can be as large as 0.5 mm in diameter. Reprinted with permission from Kandel (1979).

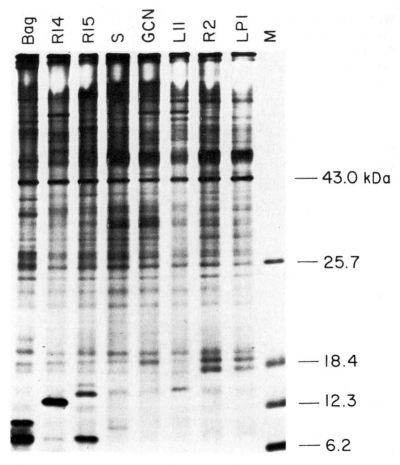

Fig. 2. Analysis of proteins synthesized in individual neurons or small clusters of neurons. Isolated ganglia were incubated *in vitro* with [³⁵S]methionine for 6 hours. Individual neurons were dissected, solubilized in SDS under reducing conditions, and subjected to SDS–polyacrylamide gel electrophoresis. The symbols above each lane denote the cell in which the proteins were synthesized. R14, R15, L11, R2, and S (a small group of serotinergic neurons in the left upper quadrant) all reside within the abdominal ganglion. GCN denotes a giant cerebral neuron of the cerebral ganglion. LPl is a large neuron thought to be the asymmetric counterpart of R2 in the left pleural ganglion. Lane M contains molecular weight standards whose sizes ($\times 10^{-3}$) are noted on the right.

We have also constructed both a genomic library and a library of cDNA clones expressed in the abdominal ganglion and have screened these libraries with probes synthesized from the mRNA of individual neurons. These procedures now permit the identification of genes whose expression is restricted to unique and identified nerve cells of known function. At the limit, with the largest neurons, screening for prevalent sequences can be performed with the cDNA synthesized from a single cell. When these procedures are applied to nerve cells that express prevalent gene products such as peptidergic neurons, clones encoding multiple behavioral neuropeptides can be isolated. In this manner, we have isolated the genes encoding a set of neuropeptides mediating egg-laying behavior and, more recently, a gene that encodes a peptide involved in water balance.

II. THE GENES CONTROLLING EGG-LAYING BEHAVIOR

Our studies on the relation between the expression of specific genes and the generation of specific behavioral patterns initially focused on egg laying. In *Aplysia,* egg laying consists of a stereotyped, fixed action pattern, aspects of which are understood at both the cellular and molecular level. *Aplysia* are annual, non-self-fertilizing hermaphrodites which culminate their life cycle with egg laying. Fertilization occurs internally within a reproductive organ, the large hermaphroditic duct, while development of the fertilized egg occurs externally in the sea. The process of egg laying consists of an elaborate but totally stereotyped behavioral pattern. The egg string is a long, 3-ft ribbon, containing over one million fertilized eggs. As the egg string emerges via contraction of the muscles of the duct, the animal stops walking and eating and its heart and respiratory rate increase. The egg string is then caught in the mouth and with a series of characteristic head-waving motions, it is helped out of the organism and wound into a tight, irregular mass. A small gland in the mouth then secretes a sticky mucoid substance which attaches to the string and with one forceful head wave the entire mass of eggs is stuck to a solid substrate such as a rock. Thus, a series of discrete and seemingly unrelated behaviors come together in a rigidly coordinated sequence which together serve a common function, the deposition and protection of fertilized eggs.

This stereotyped behavioral array has been termed a fixed action pattern. The innate behavior is thought to be generated by a "central nervous system program," in an all-or-none fashion, such that the individual elements either occur together in a coordinated sequence or do not occur at all. The characteristic form of such behaviors is often not modified by experience or learning. Thus each animal inherits a repertory of fixed action patterns characteristic of the species (Lorenz, 1965).

The behavioral array associated with egg laying is thought to be initiated by the release of peptides from the atrial gland, a secretory organ of the reproductive tract. The atrial gland releases two closely related 34-amino acid peptides, A and B peptide (Heller *et al.*, 1980). These peptides may, either directly or indirectly, initiate the excitation of the bag cells, a collection of neurons clustered on the connectives leading to the abdominal ganglion (see Fig. 1). Once activated, the bag cells coordinately release a battery of peptides onto the vascularized sheath and abdominal ganglion (Frazier *et al.*, 1967; Arch, 1972; Loh *et al.*, 1975; Stuart and Strumwasser, 1980). These neuroactive peptides then diffuse into the circulation (Kupfermann, 1970) and onto the neurons mediating the physiological behavioral events responsible for egg laying (Branton *et al.*, 1978a).

Perhaps the best characterized of this peptide set is the egg-laying hormone, ELH. This 36-amino acid peptide (Chiu *et al.*, 1979) acts as a neurotransmitter on cells of the abdominal ganglion, altering the activity of specific neurons (Branton *et al.*, 1978b; Mayeri and Rothman, 1982; Stuart and Strumwasser, 1980), and at the same time diffuses into the hemolymph, where it is dispersed through the organism and acts as a hormone. When ELH reaches the ovotestis, it causes contraction of the smooth muscle follicles, facilitating the expulsion of the egg string (Dudek and Tobe, 1979; Rothman *et al.*, 1982).

The entire repertory of behaviors associated with egg laying cannot simply be elicited by ELH alone. Additional neuroactive peptides present along with ELH in extracts of bag cells also modulate the activity of specific neurons controlling respiratory movements and cardiac output (Mayeri *et al.*, 1979a). ELH alone can duplicate some of these responses, but the full complement requires additional neuroactive peptides which have been characterized in bag cell extracts (Rothman *et al.*, 1983; Scheller *et al.*, 1983a,b). These observations suggest that this combination of peptides may be responsible for the entire behavioral array associated with egg laying.

During the egg-laying season more than half of the protein synthetic machinery of the bag is devoted to the production of ELH. Richard Scheller, James Jackson, and Linda McAllister in my laboratory, in collaboration with Eric Kandel and James Schwartz, have exploited the abundance of ELH mRNA to isolate a family of ELH genes by differential screening procedures. We have isolated three different members of a small gene family which are homologous to ELH mRNA. These cloned genes have been characterized by detailed restriction endonuclease mapping, heteroduplex analysis, transcript mapping, and partial nucleotide sequencing. The sequences of these genes suggest several possible mechanisms whereby nerve cells can utilize polyproteins and gene families to generate diverse sets of neuroactive peptides (Scheller *et al.*, 1982, 1983a).

A schematic of the protein sequence, deduced from the nucleotide sequence of the ELH gene, is shown in Fig. 3. The gene for ELH expressed in the bag cells encodes a protein consisting of 271 amino acid residues while the ELH peptide itself consists of only 36 amino acids. Thus, ELH is synthesized as part of a larger precursor molecule, and its release requires cleavage at pairs of basic residues that flank the ELH sequence. The precursor, however, contains eight additional pairs of basic residues that may serve as cleavage sites flanking putative neuroactive peptides. We therefore asked whether these sites are in fact recognized and cleaved; whether the precursor is actually a polyprotein generating multiple peptides? Three peptides, alpha and beta bag cell factors, as well as the acidic peptide, have been isolated from extracts of bag cells and appear to be coordinately released with ELH (Mayeri *et al.*, 1983; Scheller *et al.*, 1983b). We have found that each of these peptides is encoded in the ELH precursor and is bounded by cleavage sites (Fig. 3).

What are the physiologic functions of these peptides? The entire array of behaviors associated with egg laying can be elicited by excitation of the bag cells. ELH alone, however, cannot elicit the full array of behaviors (S. Mackey and T. Carew; B. S. Rothman and E. Mayeri; both personal communications), indicating that additional factors produced by the bag cells are essential in mediating this behavioral repertoire.

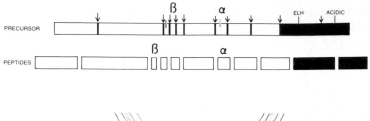

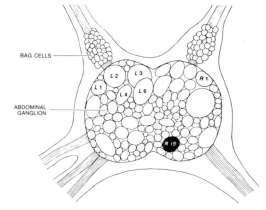

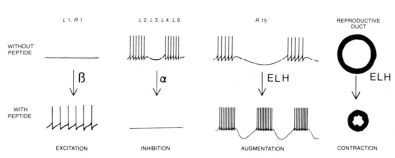

FIG. 3. A schematic of the ELH precursor, the peptides derived from it, and their site of action. The ELH precursor is synthesized as a polyprotein and contains 10 potential Lys-Arg cleavage sites. Four of the peptides known to be released by the bag cells, beta and alpha bag cell factors (β and α BCF), ELH, and an acidic peptide are noted. Three of these peptides alter the activity of specific abdominal ganglion neurons. Beta bag cell factor excites cells L1 and R1. Alpha bag cell factor inhibits cells L2, L3, L4, and L6, while ELH augments the firing of R15. ELH also enters the circulation and acts as a neurohormone causing contraction of hermaphroditic duct.

These observations suggested the possibility the companion peptides to ELH could perhaps be responsible for mediating the other element of egg-laying behavior.

Electrophysiologic experiments have demonstrated that three of the four peptides present within bag cell extracts interact with specific identified neurons in the abdominal ganglion where they act as neurotransmitters or "neuromodulators" (Mayeri *et al.*, 1979a,b). These peptides and the neurons with which they interact are shown in Fig. 3. Let us first consider the neuropeptide, ELH. ELH acts as an excitatory transmitter augmenting the firing of a specific neuron, R15. At the same time, ELH diffuses into the circulatory system and excites the smooth muscle cells responsible for the contraction of the hermaphroditic duct, expelling the egg string. A second, small peptide, beta bag cell factor, causes the transient excitation of two symmetric neurons, L1 and R1. Finally, a third neuropeptide, alpha bag cell factor, inhibits the firing of a defined cluster of neurons of unknown function in the left upper quadrant of the abdominal ganglion. Interestingly, this peptide released by the bag cells also is capable of depolarizing the bag cells. This self-excitatory property taken together with the relatively slow but long-lasting activity of alpha bag cell factor may be responsible for the prolonged excitation of the bag cell cluster.

The specific association of these individual peptides, each derived from a single gene, with the activity of individual neurons suggests a possible mechanism for the generation of the complex pattern of behaviors associated with egg laying. A single gene generates a long protein which is cut into several small, biologically active peptides. Although far from proven, it is possible that individual components of the behavioral array may be mediated by individual peptides or small groups of peptides encoded by only one gene. Since all the behavioral peptides must therefore be synthesized as part of a single precursor protein, the appearance of individual behaviors would be rigidly coordinated. Further, since one peptide cannot be synthesized in the absence of the others, the repertoire of behaviors would occur in an all-or-none fashion. In this manner, a single gene encoding multiple neuroactive peptides could dictate a complex repertoire of innate behaviors: a fixed action pattern.

III. The ELH Gene Is a Member of a Multigene Family Expressing Several Peptides

The ELH gene expressed by the bag cells is only one member of a small family of genes. We next asked whether the other member genes were also expressed and whether they encoded products involved in the egg-laying process. In initial experiments we demonstrated that each member gene could hybridize efficiently with RNA either from bag cells or from the reproductive exocrine organ, the atrial gland. This created an apparent paradox since the member genes were over 90% homologous, yet the bag cells expressed only ELH, while the atrial gland expressed the A and B peptides but no active ELH. Thus, a set of genes which share over 90% sequence homology appears to generate nonoverlapping sets of neuroactive peptides in different tissues. The manner by which this is accomplished is apparent upon examination of the nucleotide sequence of three members of the egg-laying gene family: the genes encoding A and B peptides expressed in the atrial gland and the gene encoding ELH expressed in the bag cells.

A comparison of the protein sequences deduced from the nucleotide sequences of the three genes is schematically illustrated in Fig. 4. It is perhaps worth noting the general features shared by each of the three gene sequences before describing the detailed organization of the individual genes. Each gene encodes a protein precursor in which the active peptides are flanked by basic amino acid residues which permit cleavage to liberate small internal peptides. All three genes begin with a small hydrophobic signal sequence which is often required for membrane association, vesiculation, and ultimate secretion. Each of the three genes consists of sequences homologous to A or B peptide as well as ELH. Finally, although these genes share significant nucleotide sequence homology, they have diverged by single base changes, deletions, and insertions, to generate a functionally related set of nonoverlapping peptides.

IV. The A and B Peptide Genes

Let us first consider the genes encoding the two hormones, A and B peptides, which are expressed by the atrial gland, and are capable of

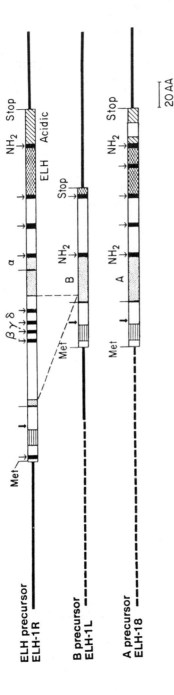

Fig. 4. Schematic comparing the precursors encoding the ELH, alpha, and beta peptides, deduced from the nucleotide sequences of the peptide genes. Each of the three proteins is initiated by a methionine, followed by a hydrophobic region (▦). (↓) Putative site of cleavage of the signal sequence. Lines above the sequence (|) represent potential cleavages at single arginine residues. (↓) Potential or known cleavage at dibasic, tribasic, or tetrabasic residues; if carboxyl terminal amidation is believed to occur, an NH₂ appears above the arrow. (▒) A/B peptide homology; (▨) ELH homology; (▩) acidic peptide homology. (—) Sequenced noncoding regions; (– – –) regions not sequenced. (Reprinted with permission from Scheller et al., 1983a.)

initiating the egg-laying process (Fig. 4). If we begin at the 5′ terminus of the sequence encoding both the A and B peptides, we observe that the amino terminal end of the protein consists of a stretch of 15 amino acids with features characteristic of signal sequences. Thirty-four amino acids from the start of translation, we observe a single arginine, followed in the B peptide gene by the complete amino acid sequence of the 34-residue B peptide, and in the A gene by the 34-amino acid sequence comprising the A peptide. These peptides differ by only two amino acids. The carboxyl terminal amino acid of these peptides is followed by the residues glycine-lysine-arginine (Gly-Lys-Arg). The sequence Gly-Lys-Arg not only signals cleavage, but in addition, the glycine serves as a signal for destructive transamidation. After cleavage at the Lys-Arg, the C terminal glycine is destroyed with subsequent trans-amidation of the carboxyl group of the amino acid preceding the glycine. The resulting peptide therefore contains a blocked carboxyl terminal which may be essential for the biological activity of the peptide and further, may protect it from the action of carboxypeptidases. Thus, the active A and B peptides are released from their respective precursors by appropriate internal cleavages.

We next observe a stretch of 141 nucleotides encoding 47 amino acids which do not share homology with any known peptides. At this point, in both the A and B precursor, we observe another cleavage site, Lys-Arg. Immediately following this site, we observe a region encoding the amino terminal residues of egg-laying hormone. However, the atrial gland does not synthesize intact egg-laying hormone. In the B precursor there is a deletion of a single cytosine residue from the triplet encoding the sixth amino acid of ELH. The resulting frame shift generates a nonsense codon, terminating translation at the sixth amino acid of the ELH peptide. Quite a different change occurs in the region encoding ELH in the A peptide precursor. The A peptide precursor encodes the first 22 amino acids of ELH. A single base change occurs in triplet for amino acid 23, changing the amino acid sequence to Arg-Arg-Arg, generating a new cleavage site at this position. Cleavage at this site would generate a truncated ELH peptide, presumably without the biological properties of the intact 36-amino acid ELH. Thus the genes encoding A and B peptides, peptides which cause release of ELH, also encode a segment of ELH itself, but in a biologically inactive form.

V. THE ELH GENE

The nucleotide sequence of the gene encoding the egg laying precursor expressed in the bag cells shares over 90% homology with the genes encoding A or B peptide. However, as described earlier, this gene encodes a nonoverlapping set of peptides which are required for the mediation of the behavioral repertoire associated with egg laying. This is accomplished by small differences involving single base changes in insertions and deletions which dramatically alter the coding potential of this gene.

The ELH gene is homologous to the peptide gene up to the fifth amino acid of B peptide. At this point, however, the ELH gene diverges dramatically from the atrial gland genes and contains a 240-nucleotide stretch encoding 80 amino acids not present in the A or B peptide precursors. Following this insertion, the sequence of the A and B peptides resumes at the sixth amino acid. Thus, the insertion in the bag cell gene does not alter the reading frame from that observed for the atrial gland genes. This insert contains at least one of the neuroactive peptides thought to be involved in modulating egg-laying behavior. Within the insert, we observe four pairs of basic residues flanking the peptide sequences of beta, gamma, and delta bag cell factors. After the insert, the sequence resumes in phase to generate a stretch of incomplete homology, with the COOH terminal sequences of the A and B peptides. The divergence within this sequence is significant, however, and generates yet another nine-amino acid peptide, alpha bag cell factor, which is also released upon excitation of the bag cells and as described earlier serves as an inhibitory neuropeptide in the abdominal ganglia. Thus, an in-phase insertion in the precursor introduces a new set of peptides unique to the bag cell which as we have already seen is likely to be involved in mediating the egg-laying behaviors.

Moving further in a C-terminal direction, we observe yet another cleavage site, Lys-Arg, which precedes the amino terminus of the 36-amino acid peptide, egg-laying hormone. The carboxyl terminus of this neuroactive peptide, like those of A and B peptides, is followed by the sequence Gly-Lys-Arg, again signaling cleavage with amidation of the C-terminal residue. This peptide, ELH, acts locally as a neurotransmitter, and at a distance, as a neurohormone. Twenty-seven amino acids remain between the carboxyl terminal cleavage site of ELH and the codon dictating the stop of translation. This 27-amino acid peptide is coreleased with ELH upon depolarization of the bag cells.

Thus, three homologous members of a small family of genes have diverged to express functionally related sets of neuroactive peptides. The A and B peptide precursors encode either intact A or B peptide along with variable portions of the amino terminal region of egg-laying hormone. A and B peptides are capable of initiating egg laying by causing excitation of the bag cells and release of the peptide products of yet a third member of the gene family, the ELH gene. The ELH precursor, however, has diverged significantly from the members of the gene family expressed in the atrial gland to generate a unique set of neuroactive peptides including ELH and alpha and beta bag cell factors, which mediate the behavioral array associated with egg laying. Thus the peptides capable of initiating the behavioral array, A and B peptides, and the peptides directly mediating the behavior derive from a common ancestral gene.

VI. Cloning Genes Expressed in Individual Neurons: The R15 Peptide

The egg-laying peptide provides an example of the relationship between genes expressed in a cluster of identified neurons and a specific behavior. In *Aplysia,* physiologic processes may be controlled by single identified neurons. The analysis of the pattern of gene expression in single neurons may therefore permit us to relate the function of individual neurons to the activity of specific genes. Linda Buck and Reuven Stein in my laboratory have recently developed procedures that permit the isolation of genes whose expression may be restricted to a single neuron. These procedures have enabled us to clone a gene expressed in a single neuron, R15, which regulates water balance in *Aplysia.*

The autonomously bursting neuron, R15 (Fig. 1), synthesizes a protein hormone that, by analogy with the antidiuretic hormone of vertebrates, may control the resorption of Na^+ (Kupfermann and Weiss, 1976). In hypotonic sea water, the animal gains water, which upsets its internal osmolality. Compensating for this effect, the hypotonic sea water is sensed by an organ called the osphradium, which acts via a cluster of sensory neurons to inhibit the burst firing of R15 (Jahan-

Parwar *et al.*, 1969; Stinnakre and Tauc, 1969). This may inhibit hormone release, diminish Na^+ resorption, and in this way restore water balance. What is the nature of the peptide released by R15? What is its target, and what are its physiologic effects? These questions may be addressed by cloning the gene encoding the R15 peptides, deducing its amino acid sequence, and ultimately synthesizing the peptide to determine its physiologic effect.

How does one isolate a gene whose expression may be restricted to a single neuron? The abdominal ganglion of *Aplysia* consists of about 4000 neurons. If a gene is expressed in a single neuron then its concentration in a population of ganglion mRNA will equal its concentration within the mRNA of a single cell divided by 4000. A moderately prevalent mRNA, present at a level of 1 in 1000 mRNAs of a given cell, will be present at a level of 1 in 4,000,000 in a population of ganglion mRNA. In practice, however, a number of large neurons (including R15) can be identified within the abdominal ganglion which occupies from 1 to 5% of the volume of the ganglia. mRNAs uniquely expressed within such cells would be present at a frequency of 1 in 100,000 in ganglion mRNA populations. Those considerations suggest that it should be technically feasible, using differential screening procedures, to isolate moderately prevalent RNAs expressed solely within a single large neuron from cDNA libraries.

To isolate the R15 peptide, we first constructed a library of cDNA clones from poly(A)$^+$ mRNA from the entire abdominal ganglion. This library, which consists of 1.3×10^6 independent clones, was constructed utilizing a highly efficient bacteriophage λgt10 cloning system developed by Huynh *et al.* (1984). The neuron R15 comprises about 1% of the mass of the abdominal ganglion. Analysis of the proteins synthesized in R15 suggests that the small water balance peptide comprises 5–10% of the cell protein. If the mRNA encoding this peptide also comprises 10% of the mRNA in R15, then 0.1% of the mRNA in the ganglion should encode this specific peptide. Thus, 1 out of 1000 clones within the library should contain peptide sequences. We screened 20,000 independent cDNA clones in duplicate with 2 highly radioactive cDNA probes, 1 prepared from the mRNA of R15, which should contain sequences for the peptide, and 1 prepared from the cholinergic neuron R2, which should not contain the sequence for the R15 peptide.

Both R2 and R15 are large cells, and sufficient cDNA for these experiments can be prepared from as few as 5 neurons. By comparing the hybridization of 20,000 individual clones with R15 and R2 cDNA, we were able to isolate 5 clones that reproducibly hybridize with cDNA from R15 but not R2. All 5 clones share identical sequences and presumably derive from the same mRNA. The largest of these clones approximates the size of the mRNA observed on Northern blots, suggesting that we have obtained a clone close to full length.

We have used these clones in RNA hybridization experiments to characterize the expression of this gene in other neurons within the abdominal ganglion and within the four remaining central ganglia. Hybridization was performed with RNA from neurons R15, R14, and R2, and collections of right and left upper quadrant peptidergic neurons. Hybridization with the R15 clone is only observed with RNA from neuron R15 (Fig. 5). Interestingly, this gene does appear to be expressed within several other ganglia but not in any nonneural tissue examined.

As a control, we have also isolated a cDNA clone that hybridizes strongly to RNA from the right upper quadrant neurons (R3–R8) as well as from neuron R14 but shows no hybridization to RNA from R2, R15, or the left upper quadrant cluster (Fig. 5). This clone is likely to encode the abundant set of low-molecular-weight cardioactive proteins shared by neurons R3–R14 (Scheller et al., 1983a).

The unique cell-specific pattern of expression of the R15 clone, together with its abundance in R15 mRNA populations, suggests that it encodes the major water balance peptide. However, this is not yet proved. The sequence of this peptide is unknown and antibodies are unavailable. We have therefore determined the complete nucleotide sequence of the cDNA clone. The deduced amino acid sequence reveals a presumptive set of low-molecular-weight peptides which could be derived by cleavages of a larger precursor at either single arginines or paired Lys-Arg residues. Interestingly, the RNA encoding this peptide appears to be processed differently in different neurons, generating distinct but overlapping sets of peptides from the same gene. If these peptides are indeed responsible for maintenance of water balance, then we have encountered a situation similar to that described for ELH in which multiple different but related peptides derive from a single pre-

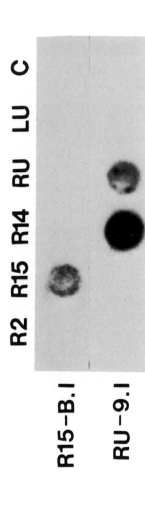

FIG. 5. Cell-specific expression of the R15 peptide gene. RNA was extracted from individual neurons including R2, R15, R3–R8 (RU), and L2, L3, L4, and L6 (LU neurons), dot blotted onto nitrocellulose, and hybridized with ³²P-labeled cloned cDNA encoding the R15 (R15−B.1) or R14 (RU−9.1) peptide.

cursor. The chemical synthesis of these peptides *in vitro* should now allow us to explore the functional properties of the individual peptides, their cellular targets, and the physiologic processes involved in water balance in *Aplysia*.

VII. The Development of the *Aplysia* Nervous System

The availability of cloned genes whose expression is restricted to specific neurons has allowed us to trace the developmental origin of these neurons and their ultimate fate in the adult nervous system. The analysis of specific gene expression in the nervous system poses problems analogous to those encountered in the study of early development. In each case, individual cells, or small groups of cells in a large population, are thought to express unique combinations of genes. How does one identify individual neurons expressing specific genes within developing embryos composed of several thousand to several million cells?

Linda McAllister, Richard Scheller, Eric Kandel and I have investigated the expression of the *ELH* gene family in the nervous system and peripheral organs of adult and developing *Aplysia* by means of *in situ* hybridization to mRNA along with immunocytochemical detection of the gene products (McAllister *et al.,* 1983). Using these techniques, we have been able to ask when during development the *ELH* genes are first expressed, and where the neurons expressing ELH originate? *Aplysia* is an annual organism which undergoes five developmental stages before reaching sexual maturity. The reproductive animal lays long egg strands containing approximately 10^6 fertilized ova packaged in egg cases which are composed of approximately 10 eggs. Egg laying initiates the first or embryonic phase of development which lasts about 10 days. The second, or larval phase, begins when the egg case ruptures, releasing the ciliated veliger larva. After 34 days, the larva stops swimming and enters the third or metamorphic stage. The organism settles on specific species of seaweed, which induces metamorphoses to the juvenile stage. In the 60 to 90 days of the fourth juvenile phase of development, the animal gradually grows into a fifth, much larger, sexually mature adult.

We have performed *in situ* hybridization experiments together with immunocytochemical experiments on sections of the developing organism from the formation of the veliger larva, through metamorphosis, to the adult. The central ganglia are already present in primitive form in the veliger larva, although no bag cells are apparent. At this early stage, we detected cells producing ELH or related peptides in a proliferative zone of epidermal cells lining the body wall long before the bag cells were present. *In situ* hybridization to sections of the veliger larva reveals an array of hybridizing cells distributed throughout the entire length of the inner surface of the body wall, with one particularly dense cluster of cells expressing ELH-related mRNA along the body cavity close to the head ganglia (Fig. 6). During this early stage in development, this proliferative ectoderm of the body wall is the major site of cells expressing the *ELH* genes, although occasional positive cells are observed within the central nervous system as well.

ELH-positive cells continue to accumulate in this proliferative zone throughout development. After metamorphosis, small clusters of these cells can be seen extending into the body cavity along what appear to be fibrous connective tissue strands. These strands connect the inner surface of the body wall with the central ganglia and appear to serve as pathways for neurons migrating from the proliferative ectoderm to the central nervous system. One particularly clear example is shown in Fig. 6, in which two strongly hybridizing cells are observed on a connective tissue fiber that has attached to the pleural–abdominal connective. The cells then leave the fiber tracts and appear to migrate along neural connectives to their appropriate location within the central nervous system.

What are the consequences of this migratory mode of development? In all animals the brain develops as a specialization of the skin, the ectoderm of the body surface. Depending upon the organism and the particular source, development may proceed *in situ* at or near the locus of proliferation or may involve a neuroproliferative zone and ultimate migration into the ganglion. One important advantage of a migratory mode of development may allow one proliferative zone to seed diverse segments of the nervous system with ELH-producing cells. However, earlier studies demonstrated ELH gene expression only in the bag cell cluster. If this migratory mode of development does indeed disperse ELH-expressing neurons, we would expect a more extensive distribution of ELH cells throughout the major ganglia.

Using immunofluorescence, Arlene Chiu and Felix Strumwasser at

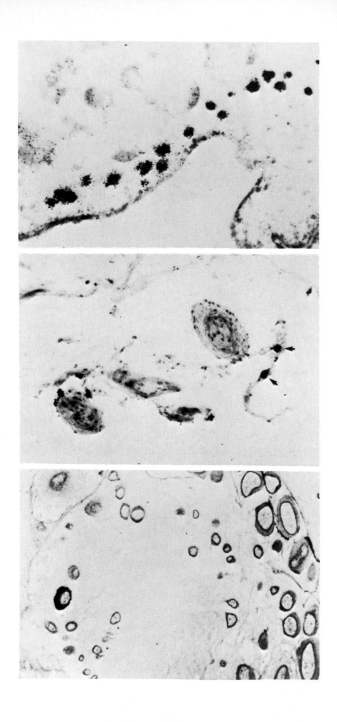

the California Institute of Technology (1981) have shown that occasional neurons outside the bag cell clusters express ELH. To systematically identify all of the cells that constitute the network of ELH-producing neurons, we have performed *in situ* hybridization and immunofluorescence on whole mounts and tissue sections of the total central nervous system. These exeriments reveal an extensive network of large and invariant cells producing both ELH, RNA, and protein in four of the five major ganglia of the central nervous system. Two cells expressing ELH in the pleural ganglion are clearly identified by *in situ* hybridization and immunocytochemistry as shown in Fig. 6.

Our study therefore suggests that cell division followed by migration allows one proliferative zone to seed diverse segments of the nervous system (the bag cells as well as the rest of the central ganglia) with ELH-producing cells. The function of the ELH-producing neurons outside of the bag cell cluster is unknown. It is possible that the pattern of gene expression in these various ELH-producing cells may differ depending upon location. A clone of identical ELH-producing cells arising in a single proliferative zone may therefore diversify during the migration process itself or in response to different environments in which the cells ultimately reside.

Finally, we may ask why, early in development the bag cell precursors express in abundance a gene product whose function is thought to be required only in the sexually mature adult. Perhaps migrating cells require specific gene products encoded with the ELH polyprotein for pathfinding and other developmental purposes. In this manner specific neurotransmitters or neurohormones may play different roles in different stages of development: an early role in guiding developmental pro-

---

FIG. 6. The detection of ELH neurons during development and in the adult ganglia. Upper panel: *in situ* hybridization through a section of the body wall of an organism 10 days postmetamorphosis. ELH cells are observed along the length of the body wall. (×175.) Middle panel: *in situ* hybridization to a transverse section through a developing pleural abdominal connective showing fibers containing ELH-positive cells migrating from the body wall to the connective where they migrate to their definitive locations within the ganglia. (×129.) Bottom panel: *in situ* hybridization to a section through the pleural ganglia showing a high density of grains in the cytoplasm of a single neuron. (×129.)

cesses and a later role in dictating the program of specific behaviors in the adult.

VIII. DISCUSSION

The behavioral potential of an organism is to a large extent encoded within the synaptic network connecting nerve cells. Specific neurons or sets of neurons are called into play by point-to-point contact at synapses mediated by classical neurotransmitter substances such as acetylcholine, norepinephrine or serotonin. The basic network is presumably organized by the expression of an invariant program during development and during critical periods early in the life of the organism. The recent discovery that neurons may use a variety of peptides to communicate with one another suggests that the number of possible chemical transmitters is far greater than previously assumed. Neuroactive peptides are released from nerve terminals in a fashion analogous to classical transmitters and, in some cases, both types of transmitter have been found to coexist in the same cell or even the same vesicle (Potter *et al.*, 1981). In contrast to classical neurotransmitters, peptides are largely synthesized on ribosomes in the cell body. They are then transported to nerve terminals where they may traverse a synapse, act locally by diffusing within the vicinity to neighboring neurons, or they may act at a distance (Jan and Jan, 1983). The fact that certain neurons release peptides and other neurons and target tissues have receptors for these peptides, superimposes an additional communication and decision-making network upon the network of conventional synaptic transmission.

Several neuroactive peptides are synthesized outside of the nervous system but function in the brain as neurotransmitters and neurohormones (Patzelt *et al.*, 1979; Noyes *et al.*, 1979; Breslow, 1979; Krieger, 1983). The significance of this tissue representation is often to coordinate other physiological events with behavior. For instance, upon injection, the octapeptide angiotensin II elicits a behavior in vertebrates completely analogous to spontaneous drinking. This peptide also increases secretion of aldosterone from the adrenal cortex and vasopressin from the posterior lobe of the pituitary gland. These hormones act on the kidneys to cause reabsorption of sodium and water from the urine (Fitzsimons, 1980). The combined effect serves to rehydrate the organism and illustrates a fundamental principle, the simultaneous coordination of physiologic changes with behavioral events to effect a common end.

The organization of the gene encoding the ELH precursor illustrates in molecular detail several properties of neuroactive peptides. The ELH gene encodes a precursor polyprotein. The N-terminus commences with a signal peptide which serves to attach the nascent chain to the rough endoplasmic reticulum (Blobel and Dobberstein, 1975). The growing peptide traverses the membrane into the lumen of the endoplasmic reticulum where posttranslational modification and transport to the Golgi occurs. In the Golgi, the peptides are partially processed and packaged into vesicles. The ELH precursor contains 10 pairs of basic residues which may serve as cleavage sites for a specific endopeptidase. Although the exact pathway of processing is unknown, four small peptides encoded in this precursor have been identified *in vivo*: ELH, α and β BCF, and acidic peptide. Three of these peptides have defined neuroactive properties either exciting or inhibiting the activity of specific neurons within the abdominal ganglion. Thus, at least four discrete peptides are cleaved from a single polyprotein which still contains the potential to release several additional peptides. A similar structure characterizes the proopiomelanocortin molecule along with the precursors for the two endorphins, dynorphin and proenkephalin, the arginine–vasopressin precursor, and the calcitonin precursor (Herbert *et al.*, 1981; Kakidani *et al.*, 1982; Land *et al.*, 1982; Craig *et al.*, 1982; Amara *et al.*, 1982).

Many neuroactive peptides characterized thus far therefore appear to be synthesized and cleaved from a large polyprotein composed of several peptide sequences. It is reasonable to ask what properties are inherent in such a synthetic pathway and how these properties may be particularly suited to the function of neuropeptides. First, the synthesis of polyproteins provides a simple mechanism of coordinate control; several different peptides may be simultaneously expressed under the control of a single promoter element and a single translational initiator. This coordination may extend beyond protein synthesis to the actual release of a set of peptides from a single vesicle. Thus, small peptides cleaved from a single precursor may be physically contained in the same vesicle until they are released by an action potential. Thus, this mechanism assures not only coordinate synthesis but coordinate release of companion peptides.

The coordinate expression of specific genes, each with their own independent promoter, is frequently observed in the eukaryotic chromosome. This presumably results from common regulatory elements present within independent promoters of a coordinated gene set or from the physical linkage of these genes within a domain which imparts common regulatory information to each member of the domain. This mechanism of coordinate control is quite distinct from that employed in the generation of neuropeptides.

The ''polyprotein'' pathway is more reminiscent of coordinate control mechanisms in prokaryotes in which a single polycistronic mRNA encodes several different proteins, each flanked by a ribosome binding site and bounded by independent start and stop codons. A polyprotein is similarly generated from a single RNA transcript but the punctuation employed at the level of translation in a polycistronic mRNA is replaced by posttranslational punctuation resulting in specific cleavages in a mature protein. Furthermore, the polyprotein and polycistronic RNA pathways may share common evolutionary origins since the cleavage site in polyproteins consists of Lys and Arg, two amino acids whose codons can mutate to both start and stop codons by single base changes.

A second property inherent in polyproteins is the ability to generate large numbers of different combinations of peptides by merely altering the pathway of processing. Thus, the ELH precursor protein contains 10 potential cleavage sites. If we consider that the probability of cleavage may differ in different cell types or in the same cell in response to different stimuli, then at the extreme the number of unique combinations may be as high as 2^{10}. The possibilities with the egg-laying peptides are even greater since these peptides are encoded by a small family of genes in which each member has diverged to generate new peptides. One particularly clear example involves the proopiomelanocortin precursor (POMC) which undergoes alternative processing pathways in the anterior and intermediate lobes of the pituitary to generate different peptides from a single precursor (Mains *et al.*, 1977; Roberts and Herbert, 1977a,b).

Thus, the combination of peptides released will depend on the specificity of proteolytic processing of a single polypeptide precursor. The specificity of processing may be inherent in the cleavage enzymes themselves or in modifying enzymes which alter the structure of precursor protein. Whatever the mechanism, it is apparent that a single precursor or family of precursors may release several different combinations of small neuroactive peptides. The purpose of this diversity might be to activate different patterns of behavior by modulating the activity of different combinations of neurons or target organs. This concept of combinational sets of neuropeptides, each derived from a single gene or family of genes, greatly expands the informational potential of the genome.

A third property inherent in the polyprotein pathway is a temporal flexibility which affords the cell the opportunity to determine when a given peptide is to be generated and how long it will remain active. The requirement for posttranscriptional cleavages to generate active neuropeptides provides for temporal control distinct from the initial transcription and translation event to generate the precursor molecule. The complement of peptides expressed may be altered in response to new stimuli by altering the processing pathway without the requirement for transcription of new peptide genes.

The polyprotein has also built punctuation signals into the sequence which may govern the stability of the active peptide. Cleavage at the sequence . . . -X-Gly-Lys-Arg frequently results in proteolysis and transamidation, generating a peptide, . . . -X-NH$_2$ with an amidated C-terminus. Cleavage and subsequent amidation in response to this signal occurs in several peptides, including arginine–vasopressin and POMC. A blocked C-terminus is likely to confer enhanced stability upon these peptides. Thus, peptides may retain a free or blocked C-terminus; the signals dictating C-terminal amidation reside within the polyprotein sequence itself. A general pattern is beginning to emerge from the analysis of the specific peptides involved in egg laying. ELH, as well as A and B peptides, which act as neurohormones as well as neurotransmitters, are consistently amidated. α and β BCF are thought to act solely as neurotransmitters and retain a free C-terminus. The pattern of amidation therefore is consistent with the functional requirements of the individual peptides. Peptides which act for long periods of time over long distances maintain a Gly-Lys-Arg at a C-terminal cleavage site. The resulting amidation presumably affords enhanced stability and therefore a longer duration of action. Peptides which act locally as a neurotransmitter are not amidated and are likely to be degraded more rapidly, a property frequently desired of neurotransmitter substances.

It is also worth noting that the size of the peptides in the egg-laying pathway also seems to correlate with functional requirements. Thus, small peptides such as the pentapeptide β BCF, incapable of folding into compact structures, are also likely to be more rapidly degraded. These peptides also act locally as neurotransmitters and are not amidated. The longer peptides, such as the 36-amino acid ELH, which can adopt stabilizing tertiary structures, are frequently amidated and are therefore better suited to protracted action at a distance.

Finally, the interspersion of active peptide sequences in the midst of nonfunctional protein sequence affords the evolutionary potential to expand a coordinate set of peptides without interrupting the preexisting set. If the intervening amino acids between two peptide sequences are indeed functionally inert, then they provide a repository for evolutionary changes which can create additional active peptides. In this manner, base changes within this intervening protein sequence may create new processing sites. Alternatively, sequences with their own preexisting cleavage sites may be inserted in this region. Internal duplications within a precursor also provide a mechanism to test new peptide possibilities without destroying the old. The ELH precursor contains a 240-bp stretch not present in the homologous precursor expressed in the atrial gland. This small insertion encodes three candidate peptides, one of which appears to have arisen from a small internal duplication. In this manner, the number of peptides expressed by this precursor has expanded without altering the ability of the polyprotein to express active ELH.

The term ''intervening amino acid sequence'' to describe the amino acids between active peptide sequence was chosen to emphasize the functional similarities between polyprotein processing and the mechanisms of RNA processing. First, both mechanisms provide a means for the coordinate synthesis of several different proteins encoded in a single transcription unit under the control of a single promoter. RNA transcripts with multiple introns and alternative splicing pathways may generate several different proteins from a single transcription unit.

The ability of a cell to alter these RNA processing events in different cells, or at different times in development, again provides an opportunity to generate unique combinations of proteins, each perhaps satisfying different functional requirements. Polyproteins maintain a similar flexibility in the choice of processing pathways as illustrated by proopiomelanocortin, which generates different peptides in different pituitary cell types. This mechanism therefore permits changes in the pattern of specific gene expression without changes in transcription.

Finally, introns provide evolutionary flexibility, which allows the creation and testing of new proteins or combinations of proteins at a far greater rate than in a contiguously colinear gene. This flexbility in both RNA and protein processing schemes is largely due to the presence of "intervening sequences" with no apparent function which may serve as repositories for evolutionary change. Thus, the numerous advantages inherent in an RNA cleavage–ligation mechanism are similarly inherent in a polyprotein cleavage mechanism but occur on different substrates at different stages in the process of gene expression.

Peptides as Mediators of Behavioral Units

Elementary behavioral responses can be broadly classified into two overlapping categories: reflex patterns and fixed action patterns. Fixed action patterns characteristically involve a stereotypic array of behavioral elements which together serve a common function. The behavioral array is thought to be generated by a "central nervous system program" in an "all-or-none" fashion such that the individual elements in the array either occur together in a coordinated sequence or do not occur at all. The characteristic form of such behaviors is often not modified by experience nor are additional patterns readily developed (Lorenz, 1965; Kandel, 1976). Thus, each animal inherits a repertory of fixed action patterns characteristic of the species.

The events of egg laying in Aplysia comprise a classical neuroendocrine fixed action pattern. During egg laying, a stereotyped behavioral array is apparent, involving a cessation of walking and eating, increased respiratory pumping, head waving, and egg deposition. How are these behaviors functionally related? Following the emergence of the egg string, the animal grabs the string in its mouth and covers it with mucus to deposit it on a stationary surface. Moving its head back and forth, it lays the string in an irregular pile. These seemingly unrelated behaviors thus serve to bring forth the fertilized eggs and maximize the potential for development.

How are the individual events within this repertory coordinately initiated? The entire array of behaviors can be elicited by excitation of the bag cells. ELH alone, however, cannot account for all of the effects of a bag cell discharge on the neurons of the abdominal ganglion, nor can it elicit the full array, indicating that additional factors produced by the bag cell are essential in mediating the array (Mackey and Carew, personal communication). Our data on the structure of the ELH gene suggest an obvious mechanism which provides for the coordinate pattern of behaviors associated with egg laying. The ELH gene expresses a polyprotein precursor which contains ELH along with several additional neuropeptides. It is therefore tempting to assume that the behavioral repertory is mediated by a small set of neuropeptides all encoded by a single gene, expressed in a single polyprotein, cleaved and stored together facilitating their coordinate release. Thus, a single genetic unit may encode the information dictating a single fixed action pattern.

Further, the individual behaviors may be ascribed to individual peptides or groups of peptides. Different combinations of overlapping peptides could then give rise to different behavioral patterns with overlapping elements. Feeding behavior in *Aplysia,* for example, represents a second fixed act which involves head waving. Common peptides may elicit this activity in both feeding and egg laying in association with other different peptides to generate these two distinct fixed action patterns. In this manner, more complex behaviors may be assembled by combining simple units of behavior, each mediated by one or a small number of neuropeptides.

REFERENCES

Arch, S. (1972). *J. Gen. Physiol.* **60,** 102–119.

Amara, S. G., Jonas, V., Rosenfeld, M. G., Ong, E. S., and Evans, R. M. (1982). *Nature (London)* **298,** 240–244.

Blobel, G., and Dobberstein, B. (1975). *J. Cell Biol.* **67,** 835–851.

Branton, W. D., Mayeri, E., Brownell, P., and Simon, S. (1978a). *Nature (London)* **274,** 70–72.

Branton, W. D., Arch, S., Smock, T., and Mayeri, E. (1978b). *Proc. Natl. Acad. Sci. U.S.A.* **75,** 5732–5736.

Breslow, E. (1979). *Annu. Rev. Biochem.* **48,** 251–274.

Chiu, A. Y., Hunkapiller, M. W., Heller, E., Stuart, D. K., Hood, L. E., and Strumwasser, F. (1979). *Proc. Natl. Acad. Sci. U.S.A.* **76,** 6656–6660.

Chui, A. Y., and Strumwasser, F. (1981). *J. Neurosci.* **1,** 812.

Coggeshall, R. E., Yaksta, B. A., and Swartz, F. J. (1971). *Chromosoma* **32,** 205–212.

Craig, R. K., Hall, L., Edbrooke, M. R., Allison, J., and MacIntyre, I. (1982). *Nature (London)* **295,** 345–347.

Darwin, C. (1871). "The Descent of Man and Selection in Relation to Sex." Murray, London.

Dudek, F. E., and Tobe, S. S. (1979). *Gen Comp. Endocrinol.* **36,** 618–627.

Fitzsimons, J. T. (1980). *In* "Peptides: Integrators of Cell and Tissue Function" (F. E. Bloom, ed.), pp. 99–106. Raven, New York.

Frazier, W. T., Kandel, E. R., Kupfermann, I., Waziri, R., and Coggeshall, R. E. (1967). *J. Neurophysiol.* **30**, 1288–1351.

Heller, E., Kaczmarek, L. K., Hunkapiller, M. W., Hood, L. E., and Strumwasser, F. (1980). *Proc. Natl. Acad. Sci. U.S.A.* **77**, 2328-2332.

Herbert, E., Birnberg, N., Lissitsky, J. -C., Civelli, O., and Uhler, M. (1981). *Neurosci. Comment.* **1**, 16–27.

Huynh, T., Young, R., and Davis R. (1984). *In* "Practical Approaches in Biochemistry" (D. Grover, ed.). IRL Press, Oxford.

Jahan-Parwar, B., Smith, M., and Von Baumgarten, R. (1969). *Am. J. Physiol.* **216**, 1246.

Jan, Y. N., and Jan, L. Y. (1983). *Trends Neurosci.* **6**(8), 320–325.

Kakidani, H., Furutani, Y., Takahashi, H., Noda, M., Morimoto, Y., Hirose, T., Asai, M., Inayama, S., Nakanishi, S., and Numa, S. (1982). *Nature (London)* **298**, 245–249.

Kandel, E. R. (1976). "Cellular Basis of Behavior." Freeman, San Francisco.

Kandel, E. R. (1979). "Behavioral Biology of *Aplysia*." Freeman, San Francisco.

Krieger, D. T. (1983). *Science* **222**, 975–985.

Kupfermann, I. (1970). *J. Neurophysiol.* **33**, 877–881.

Kupfermann, I., and Weiss, K. R. (1976). *J. Gen. Physiol.* **67**, 113.

Land, H., Schutz, G., Schmak, H., and Richter, D. (1982). *Nature (London)* **295**, 299–303.

Lasek, R. J., and Dower, W. J. (1971). *Science* **172**, 278–280.

Loh, Y. P., Sarne, Y., and Gainer, H. (1975). *J. Comp. Physiol.* **100**, 283–295.

Lorenz, K. (1965). "Evolution and Modification of Behavior." Univ. of Chicago Press, Chicago.

McAllister, L. B., Scheller, R. H., Kandel, E. R., and Axel, R. (1983). *Science* **222**, 800–808.

Mains, R. E., Eipper, B. A., and Ling, N. (1977). *Proc. Natl. Acad. Sci. U.S.A.* **74**, 3014–3018.

Mayeri, E., and B. Rothman. (1982). *In* "Neurosecretion–Molecules, Cells and Systems" (D. S. Farner and K. Lederis, eds.), pp. 307–318. Plenum, New York.

Mayeri, E., Brownell, P., Branton, W. D., and Simon, S. B. (1979a). *J. Neurophysiol.* **42**, 1165–1184.

Mayeri, E., Brownell, P., and Branton, W. D. (1979b). *J. Neurophysiol.* **42**, 1185–1197.

Noyes, B., Meuerech, M., Stein, R., and Agarwal, K. (1979). *Proc. Natl. Acad. Sci. U.S.A.* **76**, 1770–1774.

Patzelt, C., Tager, H. S., Carroll, R. J., and Steiner, D. F. (1979). *Nature (London)* **282**, 260–266.

Potter, D. D., Furshpan, E. J., and Landers, S. C. (1981). *Neurosci. Commun.* **1**, 1–9.

Roberts, J. L., and Herbert, E. (1977a). *Proc. Natl. Acad. Sci. U.S.A.* **74**, 4826–4830.

Roberts, J. L., and Herbert, E. (1977b). *Proc. Natl. Acad. Sci. U.S.A.* **74**, 5300–5304.

Rothman, B. S., Weir, G., and Dudek, F. E. (1982). *Science* **197**, 490–493.

Rothman, B. S., Mayeri, E., Brown, R. O., Yuan, P. M., and Shively, J. E. (1983). *Proc. Natl. Acad. Sci. U.S.A.* **80**, 5753–5758.

Scheller, R. H., Jackson, J. F., McAllister, L. B., Schwartz, J. H., Kandel, E. R., and Axel, R. (1982). *Cell* **28,** 707–719.

Scheller, R. H., Jackson, J. F., McAllister, L. B., Rothman, B. S., Mayeri, E., and Axel, R. (1983a). *Cell* **32,** 7–22.

Scheller, R. H., Rothman, B. S., and Mayeri, E. (1983b). *Trends Neurosci.* **6**(8) 340–345.

Stinnakre, J., and Tauc, L. (1969). *J. Exp. Biol.* **51,** 347.

Stuart, D. K., and Strumwasser, F. (1980). *J. Neurophysiol.* **43,** 399–519.

THE HUMAN T-CELL CIRCUIT—BIOLOGIC AND CLINICAL IMPLICATIONS*

STUART F. SCHLOSSMAN

Division of Tumor Immunology
Dana-Farber Cancer Institute, and
Harvard Medical School
Boston, Massachusetts

I. Introduction

O NE of the central problems in modern immunobiology is the mechanism by which T lymphocytes recognize antigen and carry out their functional program. Given the crucial role of T cells in host defenses, autoimmunity, immunodeficiency, and tumor immunity, it is not surprising that considerable attention has been given to investigation of the human immune response in recent years. Studies of the human T-cell response have been facilitated by developments in five areas: first, methods for the characterization and identification of human T-lymphocyte surface antigens utilizing monoclonal antibodies; second, new techniques for the isolation of highly purified subclasses of human T lymphocytes dependent on cell surface markers; third, *in vitro* methods to discriminate functional properties and interactions of the isolated subsets of T lymphocytes; fourth, techniques for the cloning of human T cells; and lastly, the ability to correlate normal and abnormal functional properties of T-lymphocyte subpopulations *in vitro* with *in vivo* disorders of the immune response. In this article, I will describe studies undertaken mainly by myself and colleagues which have dealt primarily with the differentiative and functional program of T lymphocytes. These studies show that during differentiation, T cells diverge into functionally distinct subsets, programmed for specific antigen recognition and for their respective effector and regulatory functions which can be defined by unique cell surface glycoprotein antigens (Schlossman,

*Lecture delivered October 20, 1983.

31

1972; Chess and Schlossman, 1977; Reinherz and Schlossman, 1980a,b).

II. Differentiation of T Lymphocytes

A thymic micro environment appears necessary for the orderly differentiation and development of specificity of T cells in all species tested. It appears that among hematopoietic stem cells in the bone marrow, prothymocytes exist which migrate to the thymus gland, where they are processed, become functionally competent, and are exported into the peripheral lymphoid compartment. Moreover, profound changes in cell surface antigens mark the stages of T-cell ontogeny.

In man, the earliest lymphoid cells within the thymus lack mature T-cell antigens but bear antigens shared by bone marrow cells of several lineages (Reinherz *et al.*, 1980a). This population is presumed to be representative of the prethymic stem cell and accounts for approximately 10% of thymic lymphocytes. Moreover, this population of cells is reactive with two monoclonal antibodies, anti-T9 and anti-T10 (early) (Fig. 1). Although these two antibodies are not specific for T cells

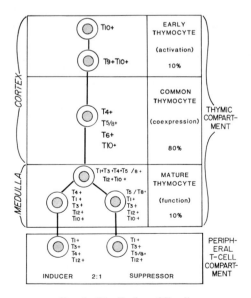

Fig. 1. Distribution of T cells.

(since they react with normal, activated, and malignant cells of non-T lineages), they are useful in providing an understanding of antigenic changes that occur during T-cell ontogeny. In fact, T9 has been reported by a number of laboratories to be the transferrin receptor. With maturation, thymocytes lose T9, retain T10, and acquire a thymocyte-distinct antigen defined by anti-T6 (the TL and HTL homolog). Concurrently, these cells express antigens defined by anti-T4 and anti-T5/8 (common). The $T4^+$, $T5^+/T8^+$, $T6^+$, and $T10^+$ thymocytes account for approximately 70% of the total thymic population. Early and common thymocytes are primarily cortical in location. Mature thymocytes, in contrast, are primarily located in the medulla and account for approximately 10% of the total thymic population. With further maturation, thymocytes lose the T6 antigen, acquire and fully express T1, T3, and T12 antigens, and segregate into $T4^+$ and $T8^+$ subsets (mature). Immunological competence is acquired with the development of the T3-associated 90-kDa heterodimer (T-cell antigen receptor) (Meuer *et al.*, 1983a; Umiel *et al.*, 1982), but is not fully expressed until the thymic lymphocytes are exported. While the majority of cortical cells are T3 negative, small numbers of common thymocytes can be identified which are both T3 and peanut agglutinin (PNA) positive. It is believed that these are the earliest cells in the maturational pathway to acquire function. The majority of functional cells within the thymus are found in the medulla. Outside the thymus the resting ($T1^+$, $T3^+$, $T12^+$, $T4^+$) and ($T1^+$, $T3^+$, $T12^+$, $T8^+$) subsets lack T10 and represent the circulating inducer (helper) and suppressor populations, respectively. In addition, it should be noted that the sheep erythrocyte receptor defined by anti-T11 is expressed on all thymocytes as well as peripheral blood T cells (Reinherz and Schlossman, 1982).

Unlike the majority of the thymocytes which are faintly reactive with anti-T1, anti-T3 and anti-T12 circulating peripheral T cells are strongly reactive. The T4 antigen is expressed on approximately 55–65% of peripheral T cells, and the T8 antigen is present on 20–30%. These two subsets correspond to TH_2- helper and TH_2+ cytotoxic/supressor cells, respectively (Evans *et al.*, 1978a; Reinherz and Schlossman, 1979). Moreover, unlike common thymocytes, T4 and T5/T8 antigens are expressed on mutually exclusive subsets of mature T cells. The distribution of these surface glycoproteins and their molecular weights are indicated in Table I.

TABLE I

MONOCLONAL ANTIBODIES TO HUMAN T-CELL SURFACE ANTIGENS

Monoclonal antibodies	Cell surface expression (% reactivity with antibodies)			Approximate molecular weights of antigens	
	Thymocytes	T cells	Non-T cells	Nonreduced	Reduced
Anti-T1	10	100	0	69K	69K
Anti-T3	10	100	0	20/25K	20/25K
Anti-T12	10	100	0	120K	—
Anti-T4 A, B, C	75	60	0	62K	62K
Anti-T5	80	25	0	76K	30K + 32K
Anti-T8 A, B, C	80	30	0	76K	30K + 32K
Anti-T6	70	0	0	49K	49K
Anti-T9	10	0	0	190K	94K
Anti-T10	95	5	10	37K	45K
Anti-T11	100	100	5	55K	55K
Anti-TQ1	5	50	10	—	—
Anti-Ti (clonotypic)	0	0	0	90K	49–51/43K

III. The T-Cell Receptor and Its
Functional Program

Given the existence of two distinct subpopulations of perhipheral T cells and the multiplicity of functional responses effected by T lymphocytes, it was very important to determine whether an individual T cell possessed all these effector and regulatory functions or whether T cells within a subset were unique with respect to their functional repertoire. A series of functional studies on isolated subpopulations of peripheral T lymphocytes has demonstrated that the latter hypothesis is correct and that the specific program of T cells is linked to the expression of a particular cell surface molecule.

For example, only the T4$^+$ population responded to soluble antigen and in AMLR when separated cells were used (Romain *et al.*, 1984). In contrast, both subsets of cells show a maximal response to cell surface alloantigens (Reinherz *et al.*, 1979a, 1980b) (Table II). In additional studies, it was shown that both populations responded similarly to mitogens such as Con A. In contrast, the T4$^+$ population responds maximally to phytohemagglutinin (PHA), while the T8$^+$ subset showed a diminished response.

One of the major effector functions of human T lymphocytes is their capacity to become sensitized to major histocompatibility complex (MHC) antigens on target cells and to effect specific cell-mediated killing. It was found that the vast majority of the cytotoxic effector cell

TABLE II

Functional Properties of T-Cell Subsets *in Vitro*

Response	Stimulus/Specificity/Interaction	T4$^+$	T8$^+$
Proliferation	Soluble antigen	+	−
	Autologous MLR	+	−
	Alloantigens	+	+
	Mitogens	+	+
Cytotoxicity	Class I alloantigens	−	+
	Class II alloantigens	+	−
Regulation	T–T	↑	↓
	T–B	↑	↓
	T–M∅	↑	↓

were T8$^+$ when separated after allogeneic activation in mixed lymphocyte culture whereas only a minor component of cytotoxic effector function resided within the T4$^+$ population. In contrast, when TH2$^-$ or T4$^+$ cells were separated prior to mixed lymphocyte reaction (MLR), one saw significant T4 killing (Evans *et al.*, 1978a; Reinherz *et al.*, 1979a). Subsequent studies have analyzed this cytotoxic response at a clonal level where it has been shown that alloreactive cytotoxic T-cell clones (CTL) could be derived from either the T4$^+$ or T8$^+$ subpopulations. More importantly, the target cell antigens recognized by individual T4 and T8 subsets have been shown to be products of different genes of the major histocompatibility complex (Meuer *et al.*, 1982a). Specifically, allosensitized T4$^+$ T cells are preferentially directed at class II MHC antigens on target cells whereas T8$^+$ T cells are directed at class I MHC antigens. The association between surface phenotype of the CTL and the class of MHC molecules recognized suggested that these subset-restricted structures might themselves facilitate recognition of and/or binding to different target cell antigens. This view has been strengthened by the finding that certain monoclonal antibodies to the T4 or T8 glycoproteins selectively inhibit cytolytic effector function of T4$^+$ or T8$^+$ CTL clones, respectively. Subsequent studies have indicated that T3 in association with unique clonotypic structures (Ti) of 43–49 kDa define the specific T-cell receptor (Reinherz *et al.*, 1981a, 1982a; Meuer *et al.*, 1982b, 1983b). The T4 and T8 structures, in contrast, act as associative recognition elements for class II and I molecules, respectively. A model for the T-cell receptor and the structures involved in T-cell recognition is given in Fig. 2 (Reinherz *et al.*, 1983a).

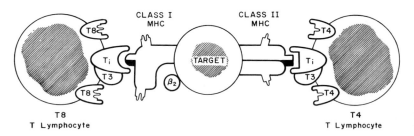

FIG. 2. Model of the human T-cell receptor.

In this model, each T lymphocyte displays on its surface two types of recognition units for antigen. The major recognition unit for antigen in association with MHC appears to be the T3–Ti complex which functions as the specific T-cell antigen receptor. In the case of allogeneic CTLs, the T3–Ti complex recognizes a polymorphic portion of the MHC molecule itself. With soluble antigen, in contrast, the T3–Ti complex appears to recognize soluble antigen in the context of MHC. The second recognition unit utilizes the T4 and T8 structures as associative recognition units for class II and I molecules, respectively. Cells bearing T4 and T8 have a clear but not necessarily absolute preference for their respective MHC antigens. It should be noted that the number of T3–Ti molecules is comparable on both resting T cells and CTL clones (30,000–40,000 molecules per cell) whereas the densities of T4 and T8 are increased 3-fold on activated cytotoxic clones (118/175,000 binding sites per cell) over that seen on the resting T lymphocytes (30,000–60,000 molecules per cell) (Meuer *et al.*, 1983a). The appearance of additional associative recognition structures, i.e., T4 and T8, may facilitate binding and provide one possible reason for their critical involvement in specific effector cell functions. Antibodies to T4 and T8 antigen clearly block the functions of T cells bearing these antigens whereas antibodies to MHC antigens block the target cells. Thus, both MHC antigens and T4 and T8 appear to play an important role in T-cell function and antigen recognition. Nevertheless, it should be stressed that the structures critical to specific antigen recognition and T-cell activation relate to the T3–Ti complex. Triggering of the T3–Ti complex with either anti-clonotypic antibody attached to beads, by allogeneic cells, or by antigen presented on the appropriate macrophages leads to a series of distinctive cellular events resulting in clonal amplification and specific effector functions (Meucr *et al.*, 1983c) (Fig. 3). Anti-T4 or T8 on beads, in contrast, did not trigger the cell. Following T3–Ti triggering, the receptor is modulated and evidence exists for both shedding and internalization. The T cell now develops a series of specific activation antigens including the appearance of the IL-2 receptor. IL-2 is critical for T-cell growth whereas the precise function of many of these activation structures such as Ia, T9, T10, J2, etc., is still poorly understood. Following triggering, the density of the associative recognition structures T4 and T8 increases three- to fourfold but the number of antigen receptors defined by T3–Ti remains unchanged. Part of the

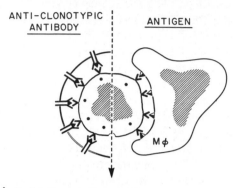

ANTI-CLONOTYPIC
ANTIBODY

ANTIGEN

Mφ

1. Modulation of the receptor
2. Activation
    a) activation structures
    b) increased growth factor receptors
    c) increased associative recognition
        structures
    d) lymphokine release
3. Clonal expansion

FIG. 3. Consequences of T3–Ti triggering.

enhanced clonal proliferative response to alloantigens or antigens plus self-MHC is both the development of IL-2 receptors and the endogenous secretion of IL-2, suggesting that the T cell can function as well via an autocrine pathway. Clonal expansion with the generation of T cells capable of producing lymphokines, regulating other cells, and fulfilling specific effector programs is the ultimate outcome of these specific events associated with receptor triggering.

One of the most challenging enigmas of immunology has been the nature of the T-cell receptor, its genetic organization, and distinction from immunoglobulin structure and function. Despite the extraordinary specificity of the T cell and its derivation with the B lymphocytes from a common hematopoietic progenitor, most data support the notion that the T-cell receptor and its membrane organization is distinct from known immunoglobulin structures and genes (Schlossman *et al.,* 1969; Schlossman and Yaron, 1970). In the last 2 years, we have concentrated our efforts in the isolation and identification of molecules from cloned

T-cell lines which serve as component parts of the antigen–receptor complex. Comparable results have now been obtained in a number of laboratories and it is fair to say that the enigma of the T-cell receptor will shortly be resolved at a molecular genetic level. Monoclonal antibodies directed at the unique Ti clonotypic structures have proven invaluable for the characterization of the T-cell receptor. Clonotypic specific antibodies have been prepared and each appears to recognize a 90-kDa molecule consisting of a 49- to 51-kDa alpha (α) and a 43-kDa beta (β) subunit (Reinherz et al., 1983b; Acuto et al., 1983a,b). These disulfide-linked heterodimers were found to be noncovalently associated in the membrane with T3. Unlike the monomorphic 20–25 kDa T3 molecule, the Ti structures on various T-cell clones, even when derived from the same donor, are immunologically and biochemically distinct. Anticlonotypic antibodies are non-cross-reactive and the Ti molecules defined have differing isoelectric points and distinct peptide maps following partial proteolytic cleavage. Moreover, in contrast to the anti-T3 antibodies which inhibited antigen recognition by all T lymphocytes, anti-clonotypic antibody selectively abrogated antigen-specific functions of only the specific clone to which it had been generated. These data implied that within the T3–Ti molecular complex, Ti contained the variable regions of the T-cell receptor. Further studies indicated that the α and β chains of the Ti complex bear no precursor–product relationship to one another but share common peptides with α and β chains from other Ti molecules isolated from genetically unrelated individuals (Acuto et al., 1983a). Thus, the Ti structures have variable and constant regions analogous to immunoglobulin light and heavy chains. Yet again, it should be noted that these Ti molecules are distinct from immunoglobulin molecules. The extent of homology with immunoglobulins is likely to be relatively low. Nevertheless, this intriguing question should be resolved shortly with precise molecular probes.

IV. REGULATORY SUBSETS OF T CELLS

Perhaps the most important difference between major T-cell subsets was their differential regulatory effects on the immune response (Evans et al., 1978; Chess and Schlossman, 1977; Reinherz and Schlossman, 1980b). The T4$^+$ cells were shown to provide inducer (helper) functions in T–T, T–B, and T–macrophage interactions. Although T4$^+$

cells are in general not cytotoxic when separated from an unfractionated population after allogeneic stimulation, they are required for optimal development of the T8$^+$ cytotoxic effector cell (Reinherz et al., 1979a, 1980b). Comparable results were obtained in earlier studies which showed that the Th$_2$$^+$ T-cell population defined by rabbit heteroantisera contained the cytotoxic effector cell whereas the TH$_2$$^-$ population contained the helper cell for development of cytotoxicity (Evans et al., 1978). Thus, the T4$^+$ T cells provided an inducer function in T–T interactions. Only the T4$^+$ T-cell subset provided the signals necessary to help autologous B cells proliferate and differentiate into immunoglobulin (Ig)-secreting cells. In contrast, the T8$^+$ T cells did not induce B cells to proliferate or differentiate. The role of the T4$^+$ cell in B-cell Ig production was described in both pokeweed mitogen (PWM)-stimulated and antigen-stimulated systems (Reinherz et al., 1980c; Morimoto et al., 1981a).

Prior studies demonstrated that antigen-triggered T cells produced helper factors including lymphocyte mitogenic factors, macrophage-activating factors, and T-cell replacing factor. In earlier studies, it was found that only the T4$^+$ subset made these nonspecific helper factors (Reinherz et al., 1980d). The T-cell subset restriction of these factors in man further stresses the importance of this T-cell subset for the induction of the human immune response. It should be emphasized, however, that other factors including IL-2 and γ-interferon can be derived from either subset, depending on the stimulus triggering the response (Meuer et al., 1982c).

The above findings helped assign an inducer role to the T4$^+$ population in T–T, T–B, and T–macrophage interactions. Moreover, they provided additional evidence that a secondary proliferative response to soluble antigen is almost entirely restricted to the inducer population. The regulatory effects of the T4$^+$ population do not appear limited to cells of lymphoid lineage. Since it is known that antigen-stimulated T lymphocytes produce factors which modulate erythroid stem cell production in vitro, it is probable that the T4$^+$ population of lymphocytes is important in some aspects of myeloid and erythroid differentiation. Similarly, osteoclast-activating factor and soluble factors inducing fibroblast proliferation and collagen synthesis have been shown to be derived from antigen-stimulated T lymphocytes. These findings suggest a much broader biological role for the T4$^+$ inducer population in man.

In contrast, the T8$^+$ subset contains a mature population of cells with cytotoxic and suppressor function but not inducer function (Reinherz *et al.*, 1980b). Following activation with Con A, T8$^+$ cells suppressed autologous T cells responding in mixed lymphocyte culture (MLC). In addition, this same T8$^+$ population suppressed B-cell Ig production. It should be emphasized at this point that although both T4$^+$ and T8$^+$ subpopulations proliferated equally well to mitogenic stimulation by Con A only the T8$^+$ population became suppressive. These results support the view that the T4$^+$ and T8$^+$ subpopulations have spearate programs for their respective helper and suppressor functions. Moreover, these programs are independent of their capacity to discriminate and react to nonspecific polyclonal mitogens or antigens. Further, these results suggest that the programming of the specific cell function is linked to the expression of a particular cell surface phenotype and that such programming occurs before cell activation.

Heterogeneity within the T-cell lineage does not stop at the level of the two major T-cell subsets, T4$^+$ and T8$^+$. Other studies have provided additional evidence to support the existence of subpopulations within the T4$^+$ subset (Morimoto *et al.*, 1981b, 1983). It was shown, for example, that approximately 40% of T4$^+$ T cells and 10% of T8$^+$ cells reacted with an antibody found in the serum of patients with active juvenile rheumatoid arthritis (JRA). These T4$^+$JRA$^+$ cells are required to induce the T8$^+$ subset to mediate suppression of B-cell Ig secretion. Thus, T4$^+$JRA$^+$ T cells appear to be the inducer cells of suppression while T4$^+$JRA$^-$ cells are the T inducers of help. Comparable results were obtained with a monoclonal antibody previously as TQ1 (Reinherz *et al.*, 1982b; Morimoto *et al.*, 1982a). The T4$^+$TQ1$^-$JRA$^-$ cells preferentially function to activate the immunologic system whereas the T4$^+$TQ1$^+$JRA$^+$ cell induces T8 to suppress and down regulate the immune system (Fig. 4). This model is at best a minimal one since it is already known that the T8 population can be divided into multiple populations including presuppressors, antigen-specific suppressors, and suppressor effectors which are definable in antigen-specific systems by cell surface phenotypes and sensitivity to irradiation.

V. Clinical Disorders of T Lymphocytes

In this article, we have produced evidence to support the theory that it is possible to detect T-lymphocyte subpopulations with unique biolog-

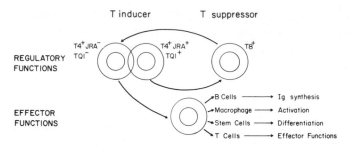

FIG. 4. Regulatory and effector functions of T inducer and T suppressor cells.

ical functions on the basis of their cell surface antigenic components. The application of this technology to human immunodiagnosis is still in its infancy. It is now possible to define the heterogeneity of T-cell malignancies; diseases of T-cell maturation and/or premature release; diseases associated with loss of T cells; diseases associated with imbalances of T-cell subset-restricted functions; and diseases associated with activation of T-cell subsets. In the following section, I will superficially review some of these areas.

Since immunological functions are acquired only at the latest stage of intrathymic ontogeny, premature release of immunologically incompetent cells or aberrations of T-cell maturation resulting in blocked differentiation could lead to immunodeficiency. The development of probes that make it possible to define points along the differentiative pathway has helped in the understanding of the heterogeneity of some of the congenital immunodeficiencies. For example, it has become evident that patients with severe combined immunodeficiency may have thymocytes blocked in differentiation either at early ($T10^+$ or $T9^+T10^+$) later stages of thymic differentiation where they have acquired mature T-cell antigens but still coexpress T4 and T8 ($T3^+T4^+T8^+T11^+T6^-$) (Reinherz and Schlossman, 1980b). It is only the latter patients who respond in MLR. These patients can now be readily distinguished from other patients with other immunologic defects. For example, major immunologic abnormalities result from alterations in mature T-cell subsets. Some patients with acquired agammaglobulinemia lack the $T4^+$ population and/or possess a T-cell population incapable of triggering B-cell synthesis of immunoglobulin (Reinherz *et al.*, 1981b,c). These specialized circumstances can be discriminated from the majority of patients with agammaglobulinemia, who have B-cell abnormalities but possess normal T cells. The presence of excessive numbers of suppressor cells also results in severe immunodeficiency. For example, in a small number of patients with acquired agammaglobulinemia, activated suppressor cells which express Ia were responsible for suppressing autologous B-cell production of immunoglobulin (Reinherz, 1979b). Increased numbers of activated suppressor cells have also been seen after viral infections including those caused by Epstein–Barr virus and cytomegalovirus (Reinherz and Schlossman, 1980f). In infectious mononucleosis, the self-limited increase in suppressor cells may account for transient immunologic hyporesponsiveness, but in patients with chronic graft-vs-host disease, persistent circulating suppressor cells cause prolonged immunologic incompetence (Reinherz et al., 1979c). More recently the syndrome of acquired immunodeficiency (AIDS) associated with tumors and susceptibility to opportunistic infections has also been shown to have characteristic T-cell abnormalities. These patients have marked evidence of immunoincompetence and demonstrate a reversed T4/T8 ratio, decreased T4 cells, a relative increase in T8 cells, and evidence of polyclonal activation of B cells (Wallace et al., 1982). Antigen-specific suppressor cells may also result in human disorders. Patients with lepromatous leprosy appear to have a $T5^+/T8^+$ population that can be specifically activated by lepromin (Mehra et al., 1980). In this case, activation of $T5^+/T8$ T cells is antigen specific; nevertheless, these activated suppressor cells may cause generalized immunosuppression. Presumably, the anergy seen in tuberculosis, systemic fungal infections, and protozoan infections may result from similiar mechanisms. Finally, it should be noted that an imbalance in the inducer/suppressor cell ratio is itself sufficient to result in diminished immunoglobulin production *in vitro* and agammaglobulinemia *in vivo*. A relative increase in suppressor cells is a common finding in patients with acquired agammaglobulinemia and circulating B cells. In this regard, it should be emphasized that T4/T8 ratios are an approximation of regulatory homeostasis since both the T4 and T8 populations are comprised of minor subsets of cells, each with unique functional programs. Thus, the loss of the $T4^+JRA^+TQ1^+$ cell could reverse the T4/T8 ratio, but the relative increase in suppressor cells may be functionally ineffective since they could not be activated.

Similar consequences could occur with loss of minor suppressor populations, i.e., a loss of suppression with minimal changes in the ratio. Despite these limitations, the overall T4/T8 ratio has been of considerable clinical utility as a first approximation of immune homeostasis.

Circulating activated T4$^+$ cells appear to result in different immunopathological abnormalities including the formation of autoantibodies directed at red cells, white cells, and platelets. Activated helper cells have been demonstrated in patients with a variety of autoimmune diseases including sarcoid, scleroderma, Sjogren's syndrome, etc. (Morim oto *et al.*, 1982b). Not only is there an increase in T4$^+$ cells, but these activated T lymphocytes, unlike resting lymphocytes, express Ia-like (HLA-D related) antigens (Evans *et al.*, 1978b; Reinherz *et al.*, 1979d). The presence of activated T lymphocytes in human disease is not uncommon. Whether activated T4$^+$ T cells themselves account for hyperglobulinemia, lymphocytosis, dermal infiltration, granuloma formation, or tissue damage is still not proved. Nevertheless, the demonstration that T4$^+$ CTLs are specific for class II molecules provides a mechanism for tissue damage. Such cytotoxic cells could conceivably damage a variety of cells bearing class II antigens including endothelial cells.

It is obvious that defects in immunoregulation could result from either a loss or decrease in the T5$^+$/T8 population. Loss of the T5$^+$/T8 T cells results in unopposed inducer functions and development of unregulated cytotoxic T4 cells. In patients with acute graft-vs-host disease, in which activated helper cells have been demonstrated, there is also a loss of suppressor cells. A similar loss of T5$^+$/T8 cells has been seen in naturally occurring autoimmune diseases including systemic lupus erythematosus, hemolytic anemia, multiple sclerosis, severe atopic eczema, hyper-IgE syndrome, and inflammatory bowel disease (Reinherz *et al.*, 1980g; Morimoto *et al.*, 1980a; Geha *et al.*, 1981). Moreover, the loss of the T5$^+$/T8 population may correlate temporally with the severity of clinical disease. The "immunologic" heterogeneity of these diverse clinical entities as well as the precise mechanism by which one population is lost or another activated are still not clear. There is evidence from patients with lupus that autoantibodies are present in the serum and directed at the T8 and other populations (Morimoto *et al.*, 1980b). Autoantibodies may selectively eliminate the suppressor population or modulate its functional properties. Similarly, in studies of patients with juvenile rheumatoid arthritis, the loss of suppressor cell function correlates with increased B-cell Ig secretion, the presence of autoantibodies to a $T4^+$ subset which induces suppressor cell function, and increased disease activity (Morimoto *et al.*, 1981b). The latter $T4^+JRA^+TQ1^+$ subset induces suppressor cells (T8) to down regulate the immune response. The absence of this population is functionally equivalent to the loss of suppression. Considerable heterogeneity of these autoimmune diseases could result from the loss of one or another major or minor regulatory population.

VI. Human T-Cell Malignant Diseases

The ability to define cell surface antigens that appear at specific stages of T-cell differentiation has, in addition, allowed for the orderly dissection of T-cell malignant processes in human beings. In fact, these T-cell diseases reflect the same degree of heterogeneity and maturation as is seen in normal T-cell ontogeny (Reinherz and Schlossman, 1981). For example, the tumor cells in most cases of acute T-cell lymphoblastic leukemia arise from an early thymocyte or prothymocyte compartment, whereas in only 20% of cases the cells are derived from a common thymocyte compartment and, therefore, bear the T6 antigen. To date, T-cell leukemias that arise from the most mature thymic compartment and express the T3 antigen are less common. Since normal thymocytes have not acquired mature T-cell functions at either the level of the early or common thymocytes, it is not surprising that the vast majority of acute lymphoblastic leukemia T cells in human beings have no demonstrable function.

The tumor populations from patients with T-cell chronic lymphocytic leukemia, Sezary syndrome, mycosis fungoides, and adult T-cell leukemias (ATL) of Japan are derived from the mature T-cell compartment and bear the T3 antigen (Reinherz and Schlossman, 1981; Shimoyama *et al.*, 1982). Therefore, as expected, some of these tumor cells display helper or suppressor functions. In this regard, all tumor populations from patients with Sezary syndrome and adult T-cell leukemias of Japan bear the $T3^+T4^+$ phenotype and may demonstrate a functional program associated with the inducer phenotype. This program may include induction of help or suppression. The finding that ATL in Japan, which is known to be $HTLV^+$, are all $T4^+$ suggests a possible receptor for the virus on this particular subset of cells. Similarly, T-cell chronic lymphocytic leukemia (T-CLL) populations have mature inducer or suppressor phenotypes. It would appear that the frequency of subset derivation of mature T-cell neoplasms corresponds to that expected from the normal ratio of inducer:suppressor cells (i.e., 2–3:1). The implications as to prognosis or oncogenic mechanisms are still poorly understood. Nevertheless, these tumors have proved invaluable for the study of T-cell differentiation since they faithfully reflect normal stages of differentiation.

VII. Immunotherapy by Selective T-Cell Subset Manipulation

The ability to dissect normal lymphoid differentiation and define the biology of T lymphocytes in health and disease has allowed for an understanding of many disorders of the human immune response. To date, the T-cell antibodies have proved useful in the diagnosis of autoimmune, immunodeficiency, and malignant diseases. It is anticipated that the heterogeneity of T lymphocytes and the functional program of yet to be defined minor populations of cells will provide newer and more exciting diagnostic criteria in the years to come.

Given the potency and specificity of many of the monoclonal antibodies when compared to conventional heteroantisera, it is not surprising that many monoclonal antibodies have already been utilized in the treatment of malignant diseases and for renal and bone marrow transplantation. Indeed, anti-T12, an antibody which does not activate human T cell, has proved itself to be extremely effective in preventing renal graft rejection in patients who have failed to respond to conventional immunosuppressive agents (Kirkman et al., 1983). To date, a number of patients with graft rejection have been treated and the results utilizing this approach are very promising. Moreover, what was unthinkable in recent years is now being readily accomplished, i.e., it is now possible to transplant bone marrow across the major histocompatibility complex. Anti-T12 has been utilized to successfully eliminate donor T lymphocytes from marrow transplants (Reinherz et al., 1982c). The removal of donor T lymphocytes has prevented graft-vs-host disease in the recipient and has allowed for the establishment of a normal immune response in patients who heretofore could not be transplanted because they lacked suitable donors. Lastly, many of the cell surface glycoproteins on human T lymphocytes including T3, Ti clonotypic structures, T4, T8, and activation antigens exert a functional role in antigen recognition, cell–cell interactions, and cellular migration. Thus, the antibodies themselves may serve as important probes to regulate the immune response by blocking the T-cell receptor, inhibiting T-cell migration or cellular interactions. One would anticipate in the years to come that these antibodies either alone or in combination with pharmacologic or toxic agents will provide major therapeutic agents for the treatment of multiple human diseases.

ACKNOWLEDGMENTS

This work was supported by National Institutes of Health Grant #AI12069.

REFERENCES

Acuto, O., Hussey, R. E., Fitzgerald, K. A., Protentis, J. P., Meuer, S. C., Schlossman, S. F., and Reinherz, E. L. (1983a). *Cell* **34**, 717.

Acuto, O., Meuer, S. C., Hodgdon, J. C., Schlossman, S. F., and Reinherz, E. L. (1983b). *J. Exp. Med.* **158**, 1368.

Chess, L., and Schlossman, S. F. (1977). *Adv. Immunol.* **25**, 213.

Evans, R. L., Lazaraus, H., Penta, A. C., and Schlossman, S. F. (1978a). *J. Immunol.* **120**, 1423.

Evans, R. L., Faldetta, T. J., Humphreys, R. E., Pratt, D. M., Yunis, E. J., and Schlossman, S. F. (1978b). *J. Exp. Med.* **148**, 1440.

Geha, R. S., Reinherz, E. L., Leung, D., McKee, K. T., Schlossman, S. F., and Rosen, F. S. (1981). *J. Clin. Invest.* **68**, 783.

Kirkman, R. L., Araujo, J. L., Busch, G. J., Carpenter, C. B., Milford, E. L., Schlossman, S. F., Strom, T. B., and Tilney, N. L. (1983). *Transplantation* **36**, 620.

Mehra, V., Mason, L. H., Rothman, W., Reinherz, E. L., Schlossman, S. F., and Bloom, B. R. (1980). *J. Immunol.* **125**, 1183.

Meuer, S. C., Schlossman, S. F., and Reinherz, E. L. (1982a). *Proc. Natl. Acad. Sci. U.S.A.* **79**, 4395.

Meuer, S. C., Hussey, R. E., Hodgdon, J. C., Hercend, T., Schlossman, S. F., and Reinherz, E. L. (1982b). *Science* **218**, 471.

Meuer, S. C., Hussey, R. E., Penta, A. C., Fitzgerald, K. A., Stadler, B. M., Schlossman, S. F., and Reinherz, E. L. (1982c). *J. Immunol.* **129**, 1076.

Meuer, S. C., Acuto, O., Hussey, R. E., Hodgdon, J. C., Fitzgerald, K. A., Schlossman, S. F., and Reinherz, E. L. (1983a). *Nature (London)* **303**, 803.

Meuer, S. C., Fitzgerald, K. A., Hussey, R. E., Hodgon, J. C., Schlossman, S. F., and Reinherz, E. L. (1983b). *J. Exp. Med.* **157**, 705.

Meuer, S. C., Hodgdon, J. C., Hussey, R. E., Protentis, J. P., Schlossman, S. F., and Reinherz, E. L. (1983c). *J. Exp. Med.* **158**, 988.

Morimoto, C., Reinherz, E. L., Steinberg, A. D., Schur, P. H., Mills, J. A., and Schlossman, S. F. (1980a). *J. Clin. Invest.* **66,** 1171.

Morimoto, C., Reinherz, E. L., Abe, T., Homma, M., and Schlossman, S. F. (1980b). *Clin. Immunol. Immunopathol.* **16,** 474.

Morimoto, C., Reinherz, E. L., and Schlossman, S. F. (1981a). *J. Immunol.* **127,** 69.

Morimoto, C., Reinherz, E. L., Borel, Y., Mantzourais, E., Steinberg, A. D., and Schlossman, S. F. (1981b). *J. Clin. Invest.* **67,** 753.

Morimoto, C., Distaso, J. A., Borel, Y., Schlossman, S. F., and Reinherz, E. L. (1982a). *J. Immunol.* **128,** 1645.

Morimoto, C., Reinherz, E. L., Nadler, L. M., Distaso, J. A. Steinberg, A. D., and Schlossman, S. F. (1982b). *Clin. Immunol. Immunopathol.* **22,** 270.

Morimoto, C., Reinherz, E. L., Borel, Y., and Schlossman, S. F. (1983). *J. Immunol.* **130,** 157.

Reinherz, E. L., and Schlossman, S. F. (1979). *J. Immunol.* **122,** 1335.

Reinherz, E. L., and Schlossman, S. F. (1980a). *Cell* **19,** 821.

Reinherz, E. L., and Schlossman, S. F. (1980b). *N. Engl. J. Med.* **303,** 370.

Reinherz, E. L., and Schlossman, S. F. (1981). *Cancer Res.* **41,** 4767.

Reinherz, E. L., and Schlossman, S. F. (1982). *In* "The Potential Role of T Subpopulation in Cancer Therapy" (A. Fefer, ed.), pp. 253–268. Raven, New York.

Reinherz, E. L., Kung, P. C., Goldstein, G., and Schlossman, S. F. (1979a). *Proc. Natl. Acad. Sci. U.S.A.* **76,** 4061.

Reinherz, E. L., Rubinstein, A. J., Geha, R. S., Strelkauskas, A. J., Rosen, F. S., and Schlossman, S. F. (1979b). *N. Engl. J. Med.* **301,** 1018.

Reinherz, E. L., Parkman, R., Rappeport, J., Rosen, F. S., and Schlossman, S. F. (1979c). *N. Engl. J. Med.* **300,** 1061.

Reinherz, E. L., Kung, P. C., Pesando, J. M., Ritz, J., Goldstein, G., and Schlossman, S. F. (1979d). *J. Exp. Med.* **150,** 1472.

Reinherz, E. L., Kung, P. C., Goldstein, G., Levey, R. H., and Schlossman, S. F. (1980a). *Proc. Natl. Acad. Sci. U.S.A.* **77,** 1588.

Reinherz, E. L., Kung, P. C., Goldstein, G., and Schlossman, S. F. (1980b). *J. Immunol.* **124,** 1301.

Reinherz, E. L., Morimoto, C., Penta, A. C., and Schlossman, S. F. (1980c). *Eur. J. Immunol.* **10,** 570.

Reinherz, E. L., Kung, P. C., Breard, J. M., Goldstein, G., and Schlossman, S. F. (1980d). *J. Immunol.* **124,** 1883.

Reinherz, E. L., Schlossman, S. F., and Rosen, F. S. (1980e). Primary Immunodeficiencies. *INSERM Symp., 16th,* pp. 109–117.

Reinherz, E. L., O'Brien, C., Rosenthal, P., and Schlossman, S. F. (1980f). *J. Immunol.* **125,** 1269.

Reinherz, E. L., Weiner, H. L., Hauser, S. L., Cohen, J. A., Distaso, J. A., and Schlossman, S. F. (1980g). *N. Engl. J. Med.* **303,** 125.

Reinherz, E. L., Hussey, R. E., Fitzgerald, K., Snow, P., Terhorst, C., and Schlossman, S. F. (1981a). *Nature (London)* **294,** 168.

Reinherz, E. L., Cooper, M. D., Schlossman, S. F., and Rosen, F. S. (1981b). *J. Clin. Invest.* **68,** 699.

Reinherz, E. L., Geha, R., Wohl, M., Morimoto, C., Rosen, F. S., and Schlossman S. F. (1981c). *N. Engl. J. Med.* **304,** 811.

Reinherz, E. L., Meuer, S., Fitzgerald, K. A., Hussey, R. E., Levine, H., and Schlossman, S. F. (1982a). *Cell* **30,** 735.

Reinherz, E. L., Morimoto, C., Fitzgerald, K. A., Hussey, R. E., Daley, J. F., and Schlossman, S. F. (1982b). *J. Immunol.* **128,** 463.

Reinherz, E. L., Geha, R., Rappeport, J. M., Wilson, M., Penta, A. C., Hussey, R. E., Fitzgerald, K. A., Daley, J. F., Levine, H., Rosen, F. S., and Schlossman, S. F. (1982c). *Proc. Natl. Acad. Sci. U.S.A.* **79,** 6047.

Reinherz, E. L., Meuer, S. C., and Schlossman, S. F. (1983a). *Immunol. Today* **4,** 5; *Immunol. Rev.* **74,** 83.

Reinherz, E. L., Meuer, S. C., Fitzgerald, K. A., Hussey, R. E., Hodgdon, J. C., Acuto, O., and Schlossman, S. F. (1983b). *Proc. Natl. Acad. Sci.* **80,** 4104.

Romain, P. L., Morimoto, C., Daley, J. F., Palley, L. S., Reinherz, E. L., and Schlossman, S. F. (1984). *Clin. Immunol. Immunopathol.* **30,** 117.

Schlossman, S. F. (1972). *Transplant. Rev.* **10,** 97.

Schlossman, S. F., and Yaron, A. (1970). *Ann. N.Y. Acad. Sci.* **169,** 108.

Schlossman, S. F., Herman, J., and Yaron, A. (1969). *J. Exp. Med.* **130,** 1031.

Shimoyama, M., Tobinai, K., Hirose, M., and Minato, K. (1982). *Gann Monogr. Cancer Res.* (28), 23.

Umiel, T., Daley, J. F., Bhan, A. K., Levey, R. H., Schlossman, S. F., and Reinherz, E. L. (1982). *J. Immunol.* **129,** 1054.

Wallace, J. I., Coral, F. S., Rimm, I. J., Lane, H., Levine, H., Reinherz, E. L., Schlossman, S. F., and Sonnabend, J. (1982). *Lancet* **I,** 908.

SUPEROXIDE DISMUTASES: REGULARITIES AND IRREGULARITIES*

IRWIN FRIDOVICH

Department of Biochemistry
Duke University Medical Center
Durham, North Carolina

I. Introduction

A. *Oxygen: Benign and Malign*

O$_N$ the one hand O_2 provides enormous advantages and on the other it imposes a universal toxicity. This toxicity is importantly due to the intermediates of oxygen reduction, i.e., O_2^-, H_2O_2, and OH·. Any organism that avails itself of the benefits of oxygen needs to maintain an elaborate system of defenses against these intermediates. We now concern ourselves with the superoxide dismutases which, by catalytically scavenging O_2^-, provide a defense against it and against any reactive radical species which can be derived from it.

B. *Superoxide Dismutation: Spontaneous and Enzymatic*

There is compelling evidence that superoxide dismutases are essential components of the biological defense against oxygen toxicity. Yet because the dismutation of O_2^- is a rapid spontaneous process, it is not immediately evident why enzymes should be needed to catalyze this reaction. At pH 7.8, in water, the rate constant for the spontaneous dismutation is $8 \times 10^4\ M^{-1}\ sec^{-1}$. However, this reaction is second order in O_2^- and its first half-life therefore an inverse function of the initial concentration of O_2^-. At $1 \times 10^{-4}\ M\ O_2^-$ the first half-life would be ~ 0.05 seconds, whereas at $1 \times 10^{-10}\ M\ O_2^-$ it would be 14 hours.

*Lecture delivered November 17, 1983.

51

The reaction between O_2^- and the superoxide dismutases is first order in O_2^-, and the half-life would be independent of the concentration of O_2^-. Given a tissue concentration of nearly 1×10^{-5} M superoxide dismutase and a steady state concentration of O_2^- of 1×10^{-11} M, we estimate that the enzyme-catalyzed dismutation would be 10^6-fold faster than the spontaneous process because the likelihood of collision of an O_2^- with the enzyme is 10^6-fold greater than the likelihood of collision with another O_2^-. In addition, the rate constant for the reaction of O_2^- with the enzyme is 2×10^9 M^{-1} sec^{-1}, which is 10^4-fold faster than the spontaneous reaction. Considering both of these factors, we see that the enzymatic process eliminates O_2^- 10^{10}-fold faster than would the spontaneous process under conditions likely to apply *in vivo*.

C. Multiple Defenses

The dismutation of O_2^- produces H_2O_2, which is also a threat to the life of cells. There are catalases and peroxidases dedicated to the elimination of H_2O_2. The defensive team is thus composed of superoxide dismutases, to lower the steady state level of O_2^-, and catalases plus peroxidases to do the same for H_2O_2. These enzymes are also mutually protective when both O_2^- and H_2O_2 are being made. O_2^- inactivates catalase by converting the resting ferric enzyme to the poorly active ferro-oxy (compound III), and also by converting the perferryl intermediate (compound I) to the inactive ferryl state (compound II) (1). O_2^- also inhibits heme-containing peroxidases by conversion to compound III. Superoxide dismutases prevent these inactivations. On the other hand, H_2O_2 inactivates two of the three known types of superoxide dismutases (2–4). Catalases or peroxidases prevent this. Superoxide dismutases plus catalases and peroxidases thus constitute a mutually supportive defensive team acting to speed the conversion of the dangerous superoxide and hydrogen peroxide to water.

II. SOURCES OF O_2^-

A. Spontaneous Oxidations

The univalent pathway is the most facile route for the reduction of O_2. This is explained by the spin restriction (5). Seen in this light, autoxidations should usually generate O_2^-, and they do. Among the autoxidations relevant to biology and which have been shown to produce O_2^-, we find those of hemoglobin (6), myoglobin (7), reduced cytochrome c (8), reduced ferredoxins (9), leukoflavins (10), tetrahydropterins (11), catecholamines (12,13), and polyhydric phenols (14). Such autoxidations are sometimes chain reactions in which O_2^- can serve as initiator and as chain propagator. Such chain reactions are strongly inhibited by superoxide dismutase and this inhibition has been used as the basis for convenient assays for these enzymes (12–14).

B. Enzymes Producing O_2^-

Xanthine oxidase, aldehyde oxidase, dihydro-orotic dehydrogenase, and a variety of flavin dehydrogenases, all produce some O_2^- during their catalytic cycles. The best known of these is the milk xanthine oxidase (15), in which the partition of electron outflow between the univalent and divalent routes of dioxygen reduction depends upon pH, pO_2, and substrate concentration (16), which has been explained in terms of the extent of steady state reduction of the enzyme during catalysis (17). The respiratory burst exhibited by activated granulocytes appears due to a membrane-associated NADPH oxidase that reduces dioxygen to O_2^- (18).

C. Organelles

Mitochondria, chloroplasts, microsomes, and nuclei have been shown to generate O_2^-. This is often due to autoxidation of reduced components of electron transport assemblies and is easily demonstrated after the endogenous superoxide dismutase has been washed away. Particles prepared from mitochondria (19–21) and from chloroplasts (22) have been shown to produce O_2^-. Some of the O_2^- made by intact mitochondria can be detected in the suspending medium (23). Liver microsomes, acting on NADPH, have been shown to produce O_2^- by trapping the O_2^- with lactoperoxidase (24), by reduction of succinylated cytochrome c (25), and by spin trapping and EPR detection (26,27). Hepatic nuclei have also been shown to release O_2^- (28).

D. Intact Cells

O_2^- made within cells should not escape into the suspending medium, because of scavenging by intracellular superoxide dismutase. When O_2^- production by suspensions of intact cells is reported (29), one must suspect that it was actually made in the medium by autoxidation of reducing agents escaping from the cells. Thus, methyl viologen augments extracellular O_2^- production by suspensions of *Escherichia coli* and this was due to release of the reduced viologen, followed by its autoxidation in the medium (30). Phagocytic cells, such as human neutrophils (31), do secrete large amounts of O_2^-, when activated, due to the action of a membrane-associated NADPH oxidase.

It is apparent that there are numerous sources of O_2^- in any given aerobic cell. However, granulocytes excepted, we know neither the specific major source of O_2^- in any cell type, nor the precise amount of that O_2^- production. The ubiquity of superoxide dismutases (SODs) within aerobic cells hinders such measurements. In an attempt to gain such information an inhibitory antibody was used to suppress the SOD activity in extracts of *Streptococcus faecalis*. It was then possible to show that in such extracts fortified with NADH, 17% of the total electron flow to dioxygen was associated with O_2^- production (32). The rate of production in mammalian liver has been estimated to be 24 nmol O_2^- min^{-1} g^{-1}, and the intramitochondrial steady state concentration of this radical to be $\sim 1 \times 10^{-11} M$ (33).

III. Effects of O_2^-

A. Direct Effects

O_2^- is not indiscriminately reactive. Indeed, its failure to react rapidly with a few amino acids and citric cycle intermediates (34) has led a small number of investigators to the opinion that it is innocuous (35,36). This is a curious conclusion which ignores the many reports of cell death due to increased production of O_2^- and preventable by elevated levels of superoxide dismutase. Information concerning the possible chemical basis of the observed toxic effects of O_2^- is beginning to accumulate.

NADH in free solution does not react rapidly with O_2^-, but, when

NADH is bound to lactic dehydrogenase, it reacts with O_2^- at a rate of $3.6 \times 10^4\ M^{-1}\ sec^{-1}$. Since the oxidation of NADH by O_2^- yields an NAD· radical, which can then reduce O_2 to O_2^-, a free radical chain reaction occurs (37). Lactic dehydrogenase thus gives the appearance of catalyzing the chain oxidation of NADH by O_2^-. This illustrates the profound effect of microenvironment upon the reactions of O_2^-. Other compounds that have been shown to react with O_2^- include epinephrine (38), 6-hydroxydopamine (13), catechols (39), pamoate (40), bile pigments (41), oxyhemoglobin (42), hydroxyl amines (43), phenylhydrazine (44), lipid peroxides (45), α-tocopherol (46), and the 1,2-dihydroxyethylthiamine-pyrophosphate intermediate of the trans-ketolase reaction (47).

B. Effects of O_2^- Mediated by HO_2·

O_2^- is the conjugate base of HO_2·, whose pK_a is 4.8 in water. HO_2· is a stronger oxidant than is O_2^-. The ionization of HO_2· involves charge separation and is facilitated by high dielectric constant. Consequently, the pK_a of HO_2· is elevated as dielectric constant is lowered. The movement of O_2^- from water into the low dielectric environments of lipid micelles, membranes, or the interior of globular proteins, would be accompanied by its conversion to HO_2·. In addition the pH adjacent to polyanionic surfaces is lower than that of the bulk solvent. The pH in the Gouy–Chapman–Stern layer adjacent to phospholipid membranes can be 3 pH units below that of the surrounding water and entry of O_2^- into this layer would result in protonation. The reactivity of HO_2· could contribute importantly to that of O_2^- in biological systems. HO_2· has been shown to react with linoleate and with arachidonate at a rate of approximately $300\ M^{-1}\ sec^{-1}$ (48). A compendium of rate constants for reactions of O_2^- and HO_2· is available (49).

C. Effects of O_2^- Due to Basicity

The dismutation of O_2^- to $H_2O_2 + O_2$ is strongly favored and it consumes protons. O_2^-, in a nonprotic solvent, therefore behaves like a very powerful base. It can, by proton abstraction, generate carbanions that then react rapidly with O_2. Many of the oxidations in nonprotic solvents, which have attributed to O_2^-, appear to proceed by this proton abstraction pathway (50). This may have relevance to restricted low dielectric microenvironments within cells.

D. Effects of O_2^- Mediated by $OH\cdot$

O_2^- gives rise to H_2O_2 by the dismutation process, and O_2^- plus H_2O_2 can then generate $OH\cdot$. This process was first noticed with an enzymatic source of O_2^- plus H_2O_2 (51). This process was called the Haber–Weiss reaction, because Haber and Weiss had earlier proposed the reduction of H_2O_2, to $OH^- + OH\cdot$, by O_2^-. Other investigators, too numerous to list here, have since documented the production of $OH\cdot$ from $O_2^- + H_2O_2$. Much of this literature has been reviewed (52).

The role of iron complexes as catalysts of this process, at first overlooked because iron was present as an impurity of the reagents used, was finally appreciated (53), and a biological form of iron (lactoferrin) was reported to be a very effective catalyst (54). An analogous process, catalyzed by bound copper, has been noted (55). Antibiotics, such as Saframycins (56) and Rifamycin SV (57), have been shown to produce $OH\cdot$ by this Haber–Weiss process. Since O_2^- functions as a reductant for iron in the Haber–Weiss reaction it has been argued that it would be unable to compete in this process with other reductants such as thiols. The O_2^--dependent production of $OH\cdot$ from H_2O_2 has, however, recently been demonstrated in the presence of thiols (58).

$OH\cdot$ can be generated from O_2^- plus H_2O_2, but we are left wondering about the biological relevance of this process. There are indications that it may occur within living systems. Chloroplast lamellae, when illuminated, appear to produce $OH\cdot$ from O_2^- plus H_2O_2 (59). Alloxan, by reduction to dialuric acid followed by reoxidation, can increase intracellular production of O_2^- and H_2O_2. The diabetogenic action of alloxan is lessened by scavengers of $OH\cdot$ (60) and of O_2^- (61). The toxic effects of alloxan on isolated Islets of Langerhans (62,63) and on cultured fibroblasts (64) are similarly affected. Alloxan increases lipid peroxidation in vitamin E-deficient rats. Mannitol, often used as a scavenger of $OH\cdot$ in enzymatic systems, protected (65). Liver microsomes exhibit an alcohol-oxidizing activity that appears to be due to $OH\cdot$, derived from O_2^- plus H_2O_2 (66,67). Suspensions of neutrophils, producing large amounts of O_2^-, have also been shown to generate $OH\cdot$ (68,69). These observations lead to the conclusion that O_2^- plus H_2O_2

can generate OH·, or something very much like OH·, *in vivo,* as well as *in vitro.*

E. O_2^- Toxicity without the Haber–Weiss Reaction

Streptococcus sanguis was studied because it can grow without iron and is facultative. When grown aerobically, it accumulates millimolar levels of H_2O_2 in the medium. It makes superoxide dismutase containing manganese, and contains 50- to 100-fold more of this enzyme when grown aerobically than when grown anaerobically. Extracts of *S. sanguis* contain an NADH–quinone reductase that mediates O_2^- and H_2O_2 production from quinones, such as plumbagin. Plumbagin increased the oxygen consumption by *S. sanguis* and imposed an oxygen-dependent toxicity, which was diminished by high intracellular levels of superoxide dismutase (70).

Dimethylsulfoxide (DMSO) freely permeates these cells and was used as an indicating scavenger for OH·. Aerobic cells of *S. sanguis* generated OH·, in the presence of plumbagin, but this could be prevented by superoxide dismutase or by catalase, added to the medium. OH· production was therefore extracellular. Moreover, 0.5 *M* DMSO did not protect against the oxygen-dependent toxicity of plumbagin (70). It follows that in *S. sanguis* increased rates of O_2^- production, caused by plumbagin, exerted a toxicity that was not mediated by OH·.

IV. SUPEROXIDE DISMUTASES

A. Distribution of Isozymes

Three types of superoxide dismutases, all of which efficiently catalyze the same reaction and which fall into two families, have thus far been discovered. The common selection pressure of oxygenation, imposed by photosynthesis upon a varied anaerobic biota, facilitated the parallel evolution of superoxide dismutases. The iron-containing (FeS-OD) and the manganese-containing (MnSOD) enzymes are characteristically found in prokaryotes and are closely related, as shown by amino acid sequence homology. The copper and zinc-containing superoxide dismutases (CuZnSOD) are usually found in eukaryotes and appear to have been independently evolved (71). The distribution of these enzymes must reflect a fascinating story of evolutionary events, but it has proved difficult to unravel.

FeSOD and MnSOD are found in bacteria and a survey indicated some species with MnSOD, some with FeSOD, and others which contained both (32). Eukaryotes contain CuZnSOD in the cytosol and MnSOD in the matrix of mitochondria. This was shown with yeast (72), plants (73), chicken liver (74), and rat liver (75). The similarity between the mitochondrial and the prokaryotic MnSODs supports the endosymbiotic origin of these organelles (76). Yet, in human and in baboon liver, MnSOD is found in the cytosol as well as in mitochondria (77).

Anomalies in this overall pattern of distribution have yet to be fully explained. Thus, the CuZnSOD is usually found in the cytosol of eukaryotes. Yet it was noted in a bacterium (78), which lives as a symbiont in the light organ of the ponyfish and which appears to have obtained this enzyme by gene transfer from the host fish (79). Not so readily explained is the CuZnSOD found in the free-living bacterium *Caulobacter crescentus* (80). FeSODs, usually found only in prokaryotes, also occur in a few plants, specifically water lilies, mustards, and ginko trees (81). Since only these, among over 40 families of plants examined, contained FeSOD, gene transfers may again have been the root cause.

B. Aerotolerant Organisms Lacking Superoxide Dismutase

Lactobacillus plantarum (82), *Mycoplasma pneumoniae* (83), and a disseminating strain of *Neisseria* (84) have been found to lack this enzyme. For the case of *L. plantarum* an explanation for this apparent anomaly is in hand. These bacteria grow best in Mn-rich media and accumulate this metal to an intracellular concentration of approximately 25 mM. Mn(II) can catalyze the dismutation of O_2^-. It is a much less efficient catalyst than superoxide dismutase, but given the high concentration of Mn(II) available in these cells, it suffices. Depression of intracellular Mn(II), by growth in manganese-deficient medium, causes loss of oxygen tolerance and enhanced sensitivity toward the oxygen-dependent toxicity of quinones. Surveys of numerous Lactobacilli revealed some with superoxide dismutase and some with high Mn(II), but none with both. Mn(II) thus serves as a functional replacement for superoxide dismutase and, in organisms that ordinarily live in Mn-rich decaying plant material, this seems a sensible substitution (85–87).

C. Catalytic Mechanism

O_2^- is unstable with respect to O_2 plus H_2O_2 and goes over to these products by dismutation. We need to consider three dismutation reactions (88). These are

$$HO_2 \cdot + HO_2 \cdot \quad \rightarrow \quad H_2O_2 + O_2, \quad k_2 = 7.6 \times 10^5 \ M^{-1} \ sec^{-1} \quad (1)$$
$$HO_2 \cdot + O_2^- + H^+ \quad \rightarrow \quad H_2O_2 + O_2, \quad k_2 = 8.8 \times 10^7 \ M^{-1} \ sec^{-1} \quad (2)$$
$$O_2^+ + O_2^+ \ 2H^+ \quad \rightarrow \quad H_2O_2 + O_2, \quad K_2 < 0.3 \ M^{-1} \ sec^{-1} \quad (3)$$

The spontaneous dismutation will therefore be most rapid at pH 4.8 and the rate will diminish by a factor of 10 for each unit increase in pH above 4.8. The simplest mechanism for catalysis of reaction 3 would utilize a metal cation, which could mediate the electron transfer between one O_2^- and the next and in the second half-reaction yield a peroxo complex which could protonate as the complex dissociated.

In the superoxide dismutases the active site metal does undergo cycles of reduction and reoxidation as it mediates electron transfer between the reactants. Thus,

$$E - Me^n + O_2^- \quad \rightarrow \quad E - Me^{n-1} + O_2 \quad (4)$$
$$E - Me^{n-1} + O_2^- \quad \rightarrow \quad E - Me^n - O_2^{2-} \quad (5)$$
$$E - Me^n - O_2^{2-} \quad \xrightarrow{H^+} \quad E - Me^n + HO_2^- \xrightarrow{H^+} \quad H_2O_2 \quad (6)$$

The superoxide dismutases are very efficient catalysts and operate at a rate of $\sim 2 \times 10^9 \ M^{-1} \ sec^{-1}$ at 25°C. This is close to the diffusion limit. The energy of activation is 26.9 kJ/M, which is 1.5 times greater than that expected for a purely diffusion-controlled reaction (89).

Since the active site metal represents less than 1% of the surface area of SOD, Koppenol wondered how it was possible to achieve rates close to the diffusion limit. He (90) proposed a virtual electrostatic funnel based upon a net negative charge on the protein, combined with a cluster of positive charges at the active site. This would minimize unproductive collisions with the protein, while favoring collisions with the active site region. In the case of the bovine erythrocyte CuZnSOD enough structural information is in hand to know that these features are present (91,92). Increasing ionic strength decreased the activity of the

CuZnSOD and acylation of lysine residues inverted this response to ionic strength (93). These results indicate that lysine residues do provide electrostatic facilitation for the reaction of the enzyme with O_2^-. There is an arginine residue in the active site crevice, close to the copper. Modification of this arginine with α,β-diketones markedly reduces catalytic activity (94,95), yet does not alter the response of the enzyme to ionic strength (93). It seems possible that this arginine provides for ion pairing and hence for stabilization of the O_2^- as it leaves the bulk solvent and enters the lower dielectric environment of the active site cleft.

V. FUNCTIONS OF SUPEROXIDE DISMUTASES

A. Specificity

Given that superoxide dismutases catalyze a reaction which occurs quite rapidly even in the absence of catalysis and that free Cu(II) can catalyze the dismutation of O_2^-, the question of specificity is a serious one. The CuZnSOD, MnSOD, and FeSOD were obtained by isolation from diverse biological sources solely on the basis of activity. Electrophoresis on polyacrylamide gels, followed by activity staining, indicates that the materials isolated exhibit the same mobility as the active components of the crude extracts. Moreover, all of the bands of activity seen in the crude extracts can often be accounted for in terms of the isolated superoxide dismutases. It follows that these enzymes are the only significant catalysts of O_2^- dismutation in the cell types examined. Free metals, low-molecular-weight metal complexes, and the plethora of other metalloproteins present in cell extracts do not contribute detectably to the superoxide dismutase activity of these extracts. Certain lactobacilli, discussed above (85–87), are exceptions in that they utilize very high intracellular levels of Mn(II) as a functional replacement for superoxide dismutase. All of this information indicates a high degree of specificity of SOD for O_2^-, and the pulse radiolysis data thus far available support this idea (96,97).

B. Induction of Superoxide Dismutase in Bacteria

Control of the biosynthesis of enzymes by their substrates, or by products uniquely derived from these substrates, provides cells with important economies. Microorganisms, which must be able to accommodate to a variety of growth conditions, make good use of this mechanism so that they will not waste cell substance and energy producing particular enzymes, except when they are needed. Superoxide dismutase synthesis is controlled in this way, and induction of superoxide dismutase by increased intracellular fluxes of O_2^- has been seen in *Streptococcus faecalis* (98), *Photobacter leiognathi* (78), *Escherichia coli* (99,100), *Listeria monocytogenes* (101), *Vibrio eltor* (102), *Bacterioides fragilis* (103), *Rhizobium japonicum* (104), *Salmonella typhimurium* (105), *Selenomonas ruminantium* (106), and *Streptococcus sanguis* (70).

In most cases these inductions were brought about by increased exposure to oxygen, but inductions can be caused at fixed pO_2 by conditions which increased the intracellular production of O_2^-. In *E. coli*, growth based upon fermentation of glucose depresses superoxide dismutase, whereas dependence upon a respiratory energy supply elevates this enzyme (107). When grown in a glucose-limited chemostat, *E. coli* exhibits greater respiration and higher supcroxide dismutase at increased growth rates (108). Redox-active compounds, such as methyl viologen or quinones, which divert intracellular electron flow from the cytochrome pathway to an O_2^--producing pathway, markedly increased cyanide-resistant respiration and superoxide dismutase in *E. coli* (109–111).

In the case of *E. coli*, which contains both MnSOD and FeSOD, the FeSOD is constitutive and is made even under anaerobic conditions, when O_2^- production is not possible (99). In contrast, the MnSOD is not made anaerobically and is inducible by O_2^-. Anaerobically grown *E. coli* contain only FeSOD, whereas cells induced by growth at high pO_2 or in the presence of methyl viologen or quinones contain a high level of MnSOD, in addition to FeSOD (99). In a facultative organism this is a sensible arrangement in that the FeSOD provides a constant standby defense against oxygen toxicity, while the MnSOD allows fine tuning of the defense to match the level of the threat.

C. Inductions of Superoxide Dismutase in Eukaryotes

Increases in superoxide dismutase content in response to increased pO_2 or intracellular O_2^- production have been seen with yeast (112), potato slices (113), endothelial cells (114), and rat lung (115,116). The sea anemone *Anthopleura elegantissima* contains more superoxide dismutase when exposed to the oxygen generated by the symbiotic alga *Symbiodinium microadriaticum,* than when not so exposed (117). These inductions are clearly related to enhanced O_2^- production and are easily comprehended. Less obvious is the induction of superoxide dismutase in poplar leaves by SO_2 (118). SO_2 hydrates and ionizes to sulfite, which can be oxidized by a free radical chain pathway initiated by O_2^-. The lethality of SO_2 could thus be exacerbated by O_2^- and therefore minimized by superoxide dismutase. The induction of this enzyme by SO_2 could signify that O_2^- production is augmented in the presence of sulfite or that a sulfite radical, produced by interaction of O_2^- with sulfite, is a powerful inducer of superoxide dismutase biosynthesis.

D. Protections by Superoxide Dismutase

Elevation of intracellular superoxide dismutase in bacteria has been seen to impart resistance against the toxicity of oxygen and against the oxygen-dependent toxicities of streptonigrin, methyl viologen, plumbagin, pyocyanine, and related substances (98, 99, 103, 107, 108, 110, 111, 119, 120). This correlation held true in several organisms and when induction was achieved by several different strategies. Induction of superoxide dismutase, with parallel acqusition of enhanced tolerance toward oxygen toxicity, has also been seen in yeast (112), rat lung (115,121), and *Oscillatoria limnetica* (122).

Superoxide dismutase added to the medium has been seen to protect bacteria and bacteriophage against the lethality of an extracellular source of O_2^- (30,123–125) and to enhance the oxygen resistance of *Campylobacter fetus* (126). Mammalian 3T3 cells, in culture, were similarly protected against the damaging effect of an enzymatic source of O_2^- (127). Application of a source of O_2^- to the hamster cheek pouch initiates a physiological cascade resulting in leucocyte margination and vascular leakage, and superoxide dismutase prevented these deleterious effects (128). Near ultraviolet irradiation of coliphage T7 in the presence of H_2O_2 caused a loss of infectivity that could be prevented by superoxide dismutase (129). There are reports of protection against ionizing radiation (130–138). Chromosomal aberrations seen in autoimmune diseases (139), in some strains of inbred mice (140), and induced by phorbol ester in cultured 3T3 cells (141), are also diminished by superoxide dismutase.

Alloxan, a diabetogenic agent, is capable of O_2^- production via cyclical reduction to dialuric acid and autoxidation back to alloxan. Enhanced production of O_2^- and H_2O_2 could lead to OH· production, and if OH· were the proximal damaging agent then a scavenger of OH·, such as ethanol, might protect. Ethanol was shown to protect against the diabetogenic action of alloxan (13). When a series of OH· scavengers were tested in mice their abilities to mitigate the effects of alloxan paralleled their rates of reaction with OH· (60). When alloxan was applied to isolated mouse islets, superoxide dismutase, catalase, or OH· scavengers were seen to protect (62). These results were repeated and extended by the observation that a chelating agent, capable of preventing the iron-catalyzed production of OH· from O_2^- plus H_2O_2, also prevented the damaging action of alloxan on islets (63). Superoxide dismutase, coupled to polyethylene glycol to extend its circulating lifetime, prevented the diabetogenic effect of alloxan on mice (61). This protective effect has been observed repeatedly (64, 142–144).

We may conclude that O_2^- is the substrate for the superoxide dismutases *in vivo* as well as *in vitro*, and that a wide variety of deleterious effects, which are mediated by O_2^-, can be diminished or eliminated by superoxide dismutase.

VI. O_2^-, Inflammation and Reperfusion Injury

A. Inflammation

Injected superoxide dismutase has been seen to exert an antiinflammatory effect. Much of this literature has been reviewed (114, 145). The mechanism of this effect appears to be multifactorial. Thus, the O_2^- secreted by activated neutrophils can cause tissue injury which can be prevented by superoxide dismutase placed into the extracellular compartment (146–148). In addition, O_2^- acts upon a component of normal plasma and converts it into a potent neutrophil chemotaxin (149, 150). The latter effect provides for a self-amplification of the inflammatory response, which will persist as long as the neutrophils arriving at the site of inflammation continue to encounter an activating stimulus, such as opsonized bacteria. When bovine CuZnSOD is injected into a rat its circulating half-life is approximately 6 minutes and its rapid clearance from the extracellular compartment limits its antiinflammatory effect. Coupling the enzyme with ficoll extends its circulatory lifetime, without compromising its activity, and thus multiplies its anti-inflammatory effect (151). A similar effect has been achieved by coupling the enzyme to a homologous serum albumin (152) and to polyethylene glycol (153).

Inflammation of the lung was caused by inspiration of xanthine oxidase plus xanthine, which acts as a source of O_2^-. This caused acute lung damage which was prevented by superoxide dismutase, but not by catalase (154). Similar results were obtained in an inflammation caused by the reverse passive Arthus reaction (155).

B. Reperfusion Injury

Temporary interruption of blood flow to a tissue results in damage. It has been assumed that this damage occurs during the period of hypoxia and is due to depletion of ATP. Another possibility is that the deleterious effects actually occur during reperfusion and are due to free radical generation (156). Imagine an accumulation of reduced substances during hypoxia, such that reperfusion and reoxygenation resulted in a burst of free radical production. Several reports now lend substance to this proposal. Injected superoxide dismutase has been seen to diminish infarct size and creatine kinase depletion in rats subject to left coronary artery ligation (157,158). Myocardial infarction has been shown to result in complement activation with the release of C5A which in turn activates neutrophils, causing them to become adherent and to release O_2^- and H_2O_2. In an *in vitro* model, plasma from animals suffering myocardial infarction damaged endothelial cells in culture and this was prevented by superoxide dismutase and catalase (159).

The mechanism of reperfusion injury has been elegantly studied in the feline intestine and the role of O_2^- confirmed (160–162). Thus, superoxide dismutase protected against the increased capillary permeability and the mucosal lesions imposed by 3 hours of ischemia. Pretreatment of the animals with allopurinol, to inhibit xanthine oxidase, also protected. It thus appears that intestinal hypoxia is accompanied by conversion of the xanthine dehydrogenase to xanthine oxidase with concomitant degradation of ATP to hypoxanthine. Reperfusion then allows the xanthine oxidase to oxidize the accumulated hypoxanthine with production of O_2^- and H_2O_2 (16).

VII. Concluding Remarks

Limitations of time and space have precluded an exhaustive survey of the large and rapidly growing literature of the superoxide radical and the superoxide dismutases. It is clear, from the limited data cited, that O_2^- is a commonly encountered intermediate of oxygen reduction in both biotic and abiotic systems and that this free radical constitutes a threat to the chemical integrity of living cells. This threat may arise from the intrinsic and relatively selective reactivity of O_2^-, or by way of its protonation to the more strongly oxidizing $HO_2\cdot$, or it may be due to generation of the vastly reactive $OH\cdot$ by the iron-catalyzed Haber–Weiss process. Indeed, all of these modalities, plus others yet to be discovered, are probably germane to the deleterious actions of O_2^- in cells. Whatever the mechanism, some defense is essential and in the great majority of organisms it is provided by the superoxide dismutases, which catalytically scavenge O_2^-.

References

1. Kono, Y., and Fridovich, I. (1982). Superoxide radical inhibits catalase. *J. Biol. Chem.* **257**, 5751–5754.
2. Beauchamp, C. O., and Fridovich, I. (1973). Isozymes of superoxide dismutase from wheat germ. *Biochim. Biophys. Acta* **317**, 50–64.
3. Bray, R. C., Cockle, S. A., Fielden, E. M., Roberts, P. B., Rotilio, G., and Calabrese, L. (1974). Reduction and inactivation of superoxide dismutase by hydrogen peroxide. *Biochem. J.* **139**, 43–48.
4. Asada, K., Yoshikawa, K., Takahashi, M.-A., Maeda, Y., and Enmanji, K. (1975). Superoxide dismutase from a blue-green alga, *Plectonema boryanum. J. Biol. Chem.* **250**, 2801–2807.
5. Taube, H. (1965). Mechanisms of oxidation with oxygen. *J. Gen. Physiol.* **49**, 29–50.
6. Misra, H. P., and Fridovich, I. (1972). The generation of superoxide radical during the autoxidation of hemoglobin. *J. Biol. Chem.* **247**, 6960–6962.
7. Gotoh, T., and Shikama, K. (1976). Generation of the superoxide radical during the autoxidation of oxymyoglobin. *J. Biochem.* **80**, 397–399.
8. Cassell, R. H., and Fridovich, I. (1975). Role of superoxide radical in the autoxidation of cytochrome *c. Biochemistry* **14**, 1866–1869.

9. Misra, H. P., and Fridovich, I. (1971). The generation of superoxide radical during the autoxidation of ferredoxins. *J. Biol. Chem.* **246**, 6886–6890.

10. Ballou, D., Palmer, G., and Massey, V. (1969). Direct demonstration of superoxide anion production during the oxidation of reduced flavin and its catalytic decomposition by erythrocuprein. *Biochem. Biophys. Res. Commun.* **36**, 898–904.

11. Nishikimi, M. (1975). Generation of superoxide anion in the reaction of tetrahydropterins with molecular oxygen. *Arch. Biochem. Biophys.* **166**, 273–279.

12. Misra, H. P., and Fridovich, I. (1972). The role of superoxide anion in the autoxidation of epinephrine and a simple assay for superoxide dismutases. *J. Biol. Chem.* **247**, 3170–3175.

13. Cohen, G., and Heikkila, R. (1974). The generation of hydrogen peroxide, superoxide radical and hydroxyl radical by 6-hydroxydopamine, dialuric acid and related cytotoxic agents. *J. Biol. Chem.* **249**, 2447–2452.

14. Marklund, S., and Marklund, G. (1974). Involvement of the superoxide anion radical in the autoxidation of pyrogallol and a convenient assay for superoxide dismutase. *Eur. J. Biochem.* **47**, 469–474.

15. McCord, J. M., and Fridovich, I. (1968). The reduction of cytochrome c by milk xanthine oxidase. *J. Biol. Chem.* **243**, 5753–5760.

16. Fridovich, I. (1972). Quantitative aspects of the production of superoxide anion radical by xanthine oxidase. *J. Biol. Chem.* **245**, 4053–4057.

17. Porras, A. G., Olson, J. S., and Palmer, G. (1981). The reaction of reduced xanthine oxidase with oxygen. Kinetics of peroxide and superoxide formation. *J. Biol. Chem.* **256**, 9096–9103.

18. Babior, B. M., and Peters, W. A. (1981). The superoxide-producing enzyme of human neutrophils: Further properties. *J. Biol. Chem.* **256**, 2321–2323.

19. Loschen, G., Azzi, A., Richler, C., and Flohé, L. (1974). Superoxide radicals as precursors of mitochondrial hydrogen peroxide. *FEBS Lett.* **42**, 68–72.

20. Boveris, A. (1977). Mitochondrial production of superoxide radical and hydrogen peroxide. *Adv. Exp. Med. Biol.* **78**, 67–82.

21. Turrens, J. F., and Boveris, A. (1980). Generation of superoxide anion by the NADH dehydrogenase of bovine heart mitochondria. *Biochem. J.* **191**, 421–427.

22. Asada, K., and Kiso, K. (1973). Initiation of aerobic oxidation of sulfite by illuminated spinach chloroplasts. *Eur. J. Biochem.* **33**, 253–257.

23. Nohl, H., and Hegner, D. (1978). Do mitochondria produce superoxide, *in vivo*? *Eur. J. Biocehm.* **82**, 563–567.

24. Debey, P., and Balny, C. (1973). Production of superoxide ions in rat liver microsomes. *Biochimie* **55**, 329–332.

25. Kuthan, H., Tsuji, H., Graf, H., Ullrich, V., Werringloer, J., and Estabrook, R. W. (1978). Generation of superoxide anion as a source of hydrogen peroxide in a reconstituted monooxygenase system. *FEBS Lett.* **91**, 343–345.

26. Rosen, G. M., and Rauckman, E. J. (1981). Spin trapping of free radicals during hepatic microsomal lipid peroxidation. *Proc. Natl. Acad. Sci. U.S.A.* **78**, 7346–7349.

27. Rosen, G. M., Finkelstein, E., and Rauckman, E. J. (1982). A method for the

detection of superoxide in biological systems. *Arch. Biochem. Biophys.* **215**, 367–378.

28. Patton, S. E., Rosen, G. M., and Rauckman, E. J. (1980). Superoxide production by purified hamster hepatic nuclei. *Mol. Pharmacol.* **18**, 588–593.

29. Shvinka, J. E., Toma, M. K., Galinina, N. I., and Skards, I. V. (1979). Production of superoxide radicals during bacterial respiration. *J. Gen. Microbiol.* **113**, 377–382.

30. Hassan, H. M., and Fridovich, I. (1979). Paraquat and *Escherichia coli*. Mechanism of production of extracellular superoxide radical. *J. Biol. Chem.* **254**, 10846–10852.

31. Babior, B. M. (1979). Oxygen-dependent microbial killing by phagocytes, Parts I and II. *N. Engl. J. Med.* **298**, 659–668, 721–725.

32. Britton, L., Malinowski, D. P., and Fridovich, I. (1979). Superoxide dismutase and oxygen metabolism in *Streptococcus faecalis* and comparisons with other organisms. *J. Bacteriol.* **134**, 229–236.

33. Chance, B., Sies, H., and Boveris, A. (1979). Hydroperoxide metabolism in mammalian organs. *Physiol. Rev.* **59**, 527–605.

34. Bielski, B. H. J., and Richter, H. W. (1977). A study of superoxide radical chemistry by stopped-flow radiolysis and radiation-induced oxygen consumption. *J. Am. Chem. Soc.* **99**, 3019–3023.

35. Fee, J. A. (1980). Is superoxide toxic? *Dev. Biochem.* **11B**, 41–48.

36. Sawyer, D. T., and Valentine, J. S. (1981). How super is superoxide? *Acc. Chem. Res.* **14**, 393–400.

37. Bielski, B. H. J., and Chan, P. C. (1975). Kinetic study by pulse radiolysis of the lactate dehydrogenase-catalyzed chain oxidation of nicotinamide adenine dinucleotide by $HO_2 \cdot$ and O_2^- radicals. *J. Biol. Chem.* **250**, 318–321.

38. McCord, J. M., and Fridovich, I. (1969). Superoxide dismutase: An enzymic function for erythrocuprein (hemocuprein). *J. Biol. Chem.* **244**, 6049–6055.

39. Greenstock, C. L., and Miller, R. W. (1975). The oxidation of Tiron by superoxide anion. Kinetics of the reaction in aqueous solution and in chloroplasts. *Biochim. Biophys. Acta* **396**, 11–16.

40. Hassan, H. M., Dougherty, H., and Fridovich, I. (1980). Inhibitors of superoxide dismutase. A cautionary tale. *Arch. Biochem. Biophys.* **199**, 349–354.

41. Robertson, P., Jr., and Fridovich, I. (1982). A reaction of the superoxide radical with tetrapyrroles. *Arch. Biochem. Biophys.* **213**, 353–357.

42. Lynch, R. E., Lee, G. R., and Cartwright, G. E. (1976). Inhibition by superoxide dismutase of methemoglobin formation from oxyhemoglobin. *J. Biol. Chem.* **251**, 1015–1019.

43. Elstner, E. F., and Heupel, A. (1976). Inhibition of nitrite formation from hydroxyl ammonium chloride: A simple assay for superoxide dismutase. *Anal. Biochem.* **70**, 616–620.

44. Misra, H. P., and Fridovich, I. (1976). The oxidation of phenylhydrazine: Superoxide and mechanism. *Biochemistry* **14**, 681–687.

45. Sutherland, M. W., and Gebicki, J. M. (1982). A reaction between the superoxide

free radical and lipid hydroperoxide in sodium linoleate micelles. *Arch. Biochem. Biophys.* **214**, 1–11.

46. Nishikimi, M., Yamada, H., and Yagi, K. (1980). Oxidation by superoxide of tocopherols dispersed in aqueous media with deoxycholate. *Biochim. Biophys. Acta* **627**, 101–108.

47. Asami, S., and Akazawa, T. (1977). Enzymic formation of glycollate in chromatium. Role of superoxide radical in a transketolase-type mechanism. *Biochemistry* **16**, 2202–2207.

48. Gebicki, J. M., and Bielski, B. H. J. (1981). Comparison of the capacities of the perhydroxyl radical and the superoxide radicals to initiate chain oxidation of linoleic acid. *J. Am. Chem. Soc.* **103**, 7020–7022.

49. Ross, F., and Ross, A. B. (1977). Selected specific rates of reactions of transients from water in aqueous solution. III. Hydroxyl radical and perhydroxyl radical and their radical anions. U.S. Natl. Stand. Ref. Data Ser., Natl. Bur. Stand., Publ. 59, GPO, Washington DC.

50. Nanni, E. J., Stallings, M. D., and Sawyer, D. T. (1980). Does superoxide ion oxidize catechol, α-tocopherol and ascorbic acid by direct electron transfer. *J. Am. Chem. Soc.* **102**, 4481–4485.

51. Beauchamp, C., and Fridovich, I. (1970). A mechanism for the production of ethylene from methional: The generation of hydroxyl radical by xanthine oxidase. *J. Biol. Chem.* **254**, 4641–4646.

52. Fridovich, I. (1981). Superoxide radical and superoxide dismutase. *In* "Oxygen and Living Processes" (D. L. Gilbert, ed.), pp. 250–272. Springer-Verlag, Berlin and New York.

53. McCord, J. M., and Day, E. D., Jr. (1978). Superoxide-dependent production of hydroxyl radical catalyzed by the iron–EDTA complex. *FEBS Lett.* **86**, 139–142.

54. Ambruso, D. R., and Johnson, R. B. (1981). Lactoferrin enhances hydroxyl radical production by human neutrophils, neutrophil particulate fractions, and an enzymatic generating system. *J. Clin. Invest.* **67**, 352–360.

55. Samuni, A., Chevion, M., and Czapski, G. (1981). Unusual copper-induced sensitization of the biological damage due to superoxide radicals. *J. Biol. Chem.* **256**, 12632–12635.

56. Lown, J. W., Joshua, A. V., and Lee, J. S. (1982). Molecular mechanisms of binding and single strand scission of deoxyribonucleic acid by the antitumor antibiotics saframycins A and C. *Biochemistry* **21**, 419–428.

57. Kono, Y., and Sugiura, Y. (1982). Electron spin resonance studies on the oxidation of rifamycins catalyzed by metal ions. *J. Biochem.* **91**, 397–401.

58. Rowley, D. A., and Halliwell, B. (1982). Superoxide-dependent formation of hydroxyl radicals in the presence of thiol compounds. *FEBS Lett.* **138**, 33–36.

59. Elstner, E. F., and Konze, J. R. (1974). Light-dependent ethylene production by isolated chloroplasts. *FEBS Lett.* **45**, 18–21.

60. Heikkila, R. E., Winston, B., Cohen, G., and Barden, H. (1976). Alloxan-induced diabetes. Evidence for hydroxyl radical as a cytotoxic intermediate. *Biochem. Pharmacol.* **25**, 1085–1092.

61. Grandkvist, K., Marklund, S., and Taljedal, I-B. (1981). Superoxide dismutase is a prophylactic against alloxan diabetes. *Nature (London)* **294,** 158–160.
62. Grandkvist, K., Marklund, S., Sehlin, J., and Taljedal, I. B. (1979). Superoxide dismutase, catalase, and scavengers of hydroxyl radical protect against the toxic action of alloxan on pancreatic islet cells *in vitro. Biochem. J.* **182,** 17–25.
63. Fischer, L. J., and Hamburger, S. A. (1980). Inhibition of alloxan action in isolated pancreatic islets by superoxide dismutase, catalase and a metal chelator. *Diabetes* **29,** 213–216.
64. Ishibashi, F., and Howard, B. V. (1981). Alloxan and hydrogen peroxide action on glucose metabolism in cultured fibroblasts. Generation of oxygen-containing free radicals as a mechanism of alloxan action. *J. Biol. Chem.* **256,** 12134–12139.
65. Dillard, C. J., Kunert, K. J., and Tappel, A. L. (1982). Effects of vitamin E, ascorbic acid and mannitol on alloxan-induced lipid peroxidation in rats. *Arch. Biochem. Biophys.* **216,** 204–212.
66. Cederbaum, A. I., Dicker, E., and Cohen, G. (1978). Effect of hydroxyl radical scavengers on microsomal oxidation of alcohols and on associated microsomal reactions. *Biochemistry* **17,** 3058–3064.
67. Cederbaum, A. I., and Cohen, G. (1980). Oxidative demethylation of *tert*-butyl alcohol by rat liver microsomes. *Biochem. Biophys. Res. Commun.* **97,** 730–736.
68. Repine, J. E., Eaton, J. A., Anders, M. W., Hoidal, J. R., and Fox, R. B. (1979). Generation of hydroxyl radical by chemicals, enzymes and human phagocytes: An improved detection system using the anti-inflammatory agent-dimethyl sulfoxide. *J. Clin. Invest.* **64,** 1642–1651.
69. Sagone, A. L., Decker, M. A., Wells, R. M., and DiMocko, C. (1980). A new method for the detection of hydroxyl radical production by phagocytic cells. *Biochim. Biophys. Acta* **628,** 90–97.
70. DiGuiseppi, J., and Fridovich, I. (1982). Oxygen toxicity in *Streptococcus sanguis:* The relative importance of superoxide and hydroxyl radicals. *J. Biol. Chem.* **257,** 4046–4051.
71. Walker, J. E., Auffret, A. D., Brock, C. J., and Steinman, H. M. (1980). Structural comparisons of superoxide dismutases. *Dev. Biochem.* **11A,** 212–222.
72. Ravindranath, S. D., and Fridovich, I. (1975). Isolation and characterization of a manganese-containing superoxide dismutase from yeast. *J. Biol. Chem.* **250,** 6107–6112.
73. Baum, J. A., and Scandalios, J. G. (1981). Isolation and characterization of the cytosolic and mitochondrial superoxide dismutases of maize. *Arch. Biochem. Biophys.* **206,** 249–264.
74. Weisiger, R. A., and Fridovich, I. (1973). Superoxide dismutase: Organelle specificity. *J. Biol. Chem.* **248,** 3583–3592.
75. Peeters-Joris, C., Vandervoorde, A. M., and Baudhuin, P. (1973). Intracellular localization of superoxide dismutase in rat liver. *Arch. Int. Physiol. Biochem.* **81,** 981.
76. Steinman, H. M., and Hill, R. L. (1973). Sequence homologies among bacterial and mitochondrial superoxide dismutases. *Proc. Natl. Acad. Sci. U.S.A.* **70,** 3725–3729.

77. McCord, J. M., Boyle, J. A., Day, E. D., Jr., Rizzolo, L. J., and Salin, M. L. (1977). A manganese-containing superoxide dismutase from human liver. *In* "Superoxide and Superoxide Dismutases" (A. M. Michelson, J. M. McCord, and I. Fridovich, eds.), pp. 129–138. Academic Press, New York.

78. Puget, K., and Michelson, A. M. (1974). Isolation of a new copper-containing superoxide dismutase. Bacteriocuprein. *Biochem. Biophys. Res. Commun.* **58,** 830–838.

79. Martin, J. P. Jr., and Fridovich, I. (1981). Evidence for a natural gene transfer from the ponyfish to its bioluminescent bacterial symbiont *Photobacter leiognathi:* The close relationship between bacteriocuprein and the copper–zinc superoxide dismutase of teleost fishes. *J. Biol. Chem.* **256,** 6080–6089.

80. Steinman, H. M. (1982). Copper–zinc superoxide dismutase from *Caulobacter crescentus* CB15, a novel bacteriocuprein form of the enzyme. *J. Biol. Chem.* **257,** 10283–10293.

81. Bridges, S. M., and Salin, M. L. (1981). Distribution of iron-containing superoxide dismutases in vascular plants. *Plant Physiol.* **68,** 275–278.

82. McCord, J. M., Keele, B. B., Jr., and Fridovich, I. (1971). An enzyme-based theory of obligate anaerobiosis: The physiological function of superoxide dismutase. *Proc. Natl. Acad. Sci. U.S.A.* **68,** 1024–1027.

83. Lynch, R. E., and Cole, B. C. (1980). *Mycoplasma pneumoniae:* A prokaryote which consumes oxygen and generates superoxide but which lacks superoxide dismutase. *Biochem. Biophys. Res. Commun.* **96,** 98–105.

84. Norrod, P. (1979). Superoxide dismutase of *Neisseria gonorrhoeae. Abstr. Annu. Meet. Am. Soc. Microbiol,* p. 43.

85. Archibald, F. S., and Fridovich, I. (1981). Defenses against oxygen toxicity in *Lactobacillus plantarum. J. Bacteriol.* **145,** 442–451.

86. Archibald, F. S., and Fridovich, I. (1981). Manganese, superoxide dismutase and oxygen tolerance in some lactic acid bacteria. *J. Bacteriol.* **146,** 928–936.

87. Archibald, F. S., and Fridovich, I. (1982). The scavenging of superoxide radical by manganous complexes, *in vitro. Arch. Biochem. Biophys.* **214,** 452–463.

88. Bielski, B. H. J., and Allen, A. O. (1977). Mechanism of the disproportionation of superoxide radicals. *J. Phys. Chem.* **81,** 1048–1050.

89. Takahashi, M. A., and Asada, K. (1982). A flash-photometric method for determination of reactivity of superoxide: Application to superoxide dismutase assay. *J. Biochem.* **91,** 889–896.

90. Koppenol, W. H. (1981). The physiological role of the charge distribution on superoxide dismutase. *In* "Oxygen and Oxy-Radicals in Chemistry and Biology" (M. A. J. Rodgers and E. L. Powers, eds.), pp. 671–674. Academic Press, New York.

91. Richardson, J. S., Thomas, K. A., Rubin, B. H., and Richardson, D. C. (1975). Crystal structure of bovine Cu, Zn superoxide dismutase at 3 Å resolution: Chain tracing and metal ligands. *Proc. Natl. Acad. Sci. U.S.A.* **72,** 1349–1363.

92. Getzoff, E. D., Tainer, J. A., Weiner, P. K., Kollman, P. A., Richardson, J. S., and Richardson, D. C. (1983). Nature **306,** 287–290.

93. Cudd, A., and Fridovich, I. (1982). Electrostatic interactions in the reaction mecha-

nism of bovine erythrocyte superoxide dismutase. *J. Biol. Chem.* **257,** 11443–11447.

94. Malinowski, D. P., and Fridovich, I. (1979). Chemical modification of arginine at the active site of bovine erythrocyte superoxide dismutase. *Biochemistry* **18,** 5909–5917.

95. Borders, C. L., and Johansen, J. T. (1980). Identification of arginine 143 as the essential arginyl residue in yeast copper, zinc superoxide dismutase by use of a chromophoric arginine reagent. *Biochem. Biophys. Res. Commun.* **96,** 1071–1078.

96. Wardman, P. (1979). Specificity of superoxide dismutase in catalyzing redox reactions: A pulse radiolysis study. *Stud. Phys. Theor. Chem.* **6,** 189–196.

97. O'Neill, P., and Fielden, E. M. (1980). Pulse radiolysis investigation of the interaction of bovine superoxide dismutase with organic free radicals. *Dev. Biochem.* **11A,** 357–363.

98. Gregory, E. M., and Fridovich, I. (1973). The induction of superoxide dismutase by molecular oxygen. *J. Bacteriol.* **114,** 543–548.

99. Hassan, H. M., and Fridovich, I. (1977). Enzymatic defenses against the toxicity of oxygen and of streptonigrin in *Escherichia coli* K12. *J. Bacteriol.* **129,** 1574–1583.

100. Yano, K., and Nishie, H. (1978). Superoxide dismutase (E.C. 1.15.1.1) in facultatively anaerobic bacteria. Enzyme levels in relation to growth conditions. *J. Gen. Appl. Microbiol.* **24,** 333–340.

101. Welch, D. F., Sword, C. P., Brehm, S., and Dusanic, C. (1979). Relationship between superoxide dismutase and pathogenic mechanisms of listeria monocytogenes. *Infect. Immun.* **23,** 863–872.

102. Ghosh, S., and Chatterjee, G. C. (1979). Superoxide dismutase activity in *Vibrio eltor* in relation to oxygen toxicity and the bacteriocidal action of nitrofurantoin. *J. Gen. Appl. Microbiol.* **25,** 367–374.

103. Privalle, C. T., and Gregory, E. M. (1979). Superoxide dismutase and oxygen lethality in *Bacterioides fragilis. J. Bacteriol.* **138,** 139–145.

104. Stowers, M. D., and Elkan, G. H. (1981). An inducible iron-containing superoxide dismutase in *Rhizobium japonicum. Can. J. Microbiol.* **27,** 1202–1208.

105. Moody, C. S., and Hassan, H. M. (1982). Mutagenicity of oxygen free radicals. *Proc. Natl. Acad. Sci. U.S.A.* **79,** 2855–2859.

106. Samah, O. A., and Wimpenny, J. W. T. (1982). Some effect of oxygen on the phyisology of *Selenomonas ruminantium* WPL 151/1 grown in continuous culture. *J. Gen. Microbiol.* **128,** 355–360.

107. Hassan, H. M., and Fridovich, I. (1977). Regulation of superoxide dismutase synthesis in *Escherichia coli:* Glucose effect. *J. Bacteriol.* **132,** 505–510.

108. Hassan, H. M., and Fridovich, I. (1977). Physiological function of superoxide dismutase in glucose-limited chemostat cultures of *Escherichia coli. J. Bacteriol.* **130,** 805–811.

109. Hassan, H. M., and Fridovich, I. (1977). Regulation of the synthesis of superoxide dismutase in *Escherichia coli.* Induction by methyl viologen. *J. Biol. Chem.* **252,** 7667–7672.

110. Hassan, H. M., and Fridovich, I. (1978). Superoxide radical and the oxygen en-

hancement of the toxicity of paraquat in *Escherichia coli*. *J. Biol. Chem.* **253**, 8143–8148.

111. Hassan, H. M., and Fridovich, I. (1979). Intracellular production of superoxide radical and of hydrogen peroxide by redox active compounds. *Arch. Biochem. Biophys.* **196**, 385–395.

112. Gregory, E. M., Goscin, S. A., and Fridovich, I. (1974). Superoxide and oxygen toxicity in a eukaryote. *J. Bacteriol.* **117**, 456–460.

113. Boveris, A., Sanchez, R. A., and Beconi, M. T. (1978). Antimycin and cyanide-resistant respiration and superoxide anion production in fresh and aged potato tuber mitochondria. *FEBS Lett.* **92**, 333–338.

114. Housset, B., and Junod, A. F. (1981). Enzyme response of cultured endothelial cells to hyperoxia. *Bull. Eur. Physiopathol. Respir.* **17** (Suppl.), 107–110.

115. Crapo, J. D., and Tierney, D. L. (1974). Superoxide dismutase and pulmonary oxygen toxicity. *Am. J. Physiol.* **226**, 1401–1407.

116. Stevens, J. B., and Autor, A. P. (1977). Induction of superoxide dismutase in neonatal rat lung. *J. Biol. Chem.* **252**, 3509–3514.

117. Dykens, J. A., and Shick, J. M. (1982). Oxygen production by endosymbiotic algae controls superoxide dismutase activity in their animal host. *Nature (London)* **297**, 579–580.

118. Tanaka, K., and Sugahara, K. (1980). Role of superoxide dismutase in defense against sulfur dioxide toxicity and an increase in superoxide dismutase activity with sulfur dioxide fumigation. *Plant Cell Physiol.* **21**, 601–612.

119. Gregory, E. M., and Fridovich, I. (1973). Oxygen toxicity and the superoxide dismutase. *J. Bacteriol.* **114**, 1193–1197.

120. Hassan, H. M., and Fridovich, I. (1980). Mechanism of the antibiotic action of pyocyanine. *J. Bacteriol.* **141**, 156–163.

121. Sjostrom, K., and Crapo, J. D. (1981). Adaptation to oxygen by pre-exposure to hypoxia: Enhanced activity of mangani-superoxide dismutase. *Clin. Respir. Physiol.* **17** (Suppl.), 111–116.

122. Friedberg, D., Fine, M., and Oren, A. (1979). Effect of oxygen on the cyanobacterium *Oscillatoria limnetica*. *Arch. Microbiol.* **123**, 311–313.

123. Lavelle, F., Michelson, A. M., and Dimitrejevic, L. (1973). Biological protection by superoxide dismutase. *Biochem. Biophys. Res. Commun.* **55**, 350–357.

124. Babior, B., Curnutte, J. T., and Kipnes, R. S. (1975). Biological defense mechanisms. Evidence for the participation of superoxide in bacterial killing by xanthine oxidase. *J. Lab. Clin. Med.* **85**, 235–244.

125. Kellogg, E. W., III, Yost, M. G., Barthakur, N., and Kreuger, A. P. (1979). Superoxide involvement in the bactericidal effects of negative air ions on *Staphylococcus albus*. *Nature (London)* **281**, 400–401.

126. Hoffman, P. S., George, H. A., Krieg, N. R., and Smibert, R. M. (1979). Studies of the microaerophilic nature of *Campylobacter* fetus subsp. jejuni. II. Role of exogenous superoxide and peroxide. *Can. J. Microbiol.* **25**, 8–16.

127. Cope, P. A., and Dawson, M. (1980). The effects of interactions between sodium ascorbate and superoxide radicals generated by hypoxanthine and xanthine oxidase in 3T3 cells. *Cell Biol. Int. Rep.* **4**, 748.

128. Del Maestro, R. F., Thaw, H. H., Björk, J., Planker, M., and Arfors, K. E. (1980). Free radicals as mediators of tissue injury. *Acta Physiol. Scand. Suppl.* **492,** 43–57.

129. Ahmad, S. I. (1981). Synergistic action of near ultraviolet radiation and hydrogen peroxide on the killing of coliphage T7: Possible role of superoxide radical. *Photobiochem. Photobiophys.* **2,** 173–180.

130. Michelson, A. M., and Buckingham, M. E. (1974). Effects of superoxide radicals on myoblast growth and differentiation. *Biochem. Biophys. Res. Commun.* **58,** 1079–1086.

131. Petkau, A., Kelly, K., Chelack, W. S., Pleskach, S. D., Barefoot, C., and Meeker, B. E. (1975). Radioprotection of bone marrow stem cells by superoxide dismutase. *Biochem. Biophys. Res. Commun.* **67,** 1167–1174.

132. Van Hemmen, J. J., and Meuling, W. J. A. (1975). Inactivation of biologically active DNA by γ-ray-induced superoxide radicals and their dismutation products singlet molecular oxygen and hydrogen peroxide. *Biochim. Biophys. Acta* **402,** 133–141.

133. Petkau, A., and Chelack, W. S. (1976). Radio-protective effect of superoxide dismutase on model phospholipid membranes. *Biochim. Biophys. Acta* **433,** 445–456.

134. Nordenson, I., Beckman, G., and Beckman, L. (1976). The effect of superoxide dismutase and catalase on radiation-induced chromosome breaks. *Hereditas* **82,** 125–126.

135. Petkau, A., Chelack, W. S., and Pleskach, S. D. (1976). Protection of post-irradiated mice by superoxide dismutase. *Int. J. Radiat. Biol.* **29,** 297–299.

136. Misra, H. P., and Fridovich, I. (1976). Superoxide dismutase and the oxygen enhancement of radiation lethality. *Arch. Biochem. Biophys.* **176,** 577–581.

137. Oberley, L. W., Lindgren, A. L., Baker, S. A., and Stevens, R. H. (1976). Superoxide ion as the cause of the oxygen effect. *Radiat. Res.* **68,** 320–328.

138. McLennon, G., Oberley, L. W., and Autor, A. P. (1980). The role of oxygen-derived free radicals in radiation-induced damage and death of nondividing eukaryotic cells. *Radiat. Res.* **84,** 122–132.

139. Emerit, I., and Michelson, A. M. (1980). Chromosome instability in human and murine autoimmune disease: Anticlastogenic effect of superoxide dismutase. *Acta Physiol. Scand. Suppl.* **492,** 59–65.

140. Emerit, I., Levy, A., and Michelson, A. M. (1981). Effect of superoxide dismutase on the chromosomal instability of New Zealand black mice. *Cytogenet. Cell Genet.* **30,** 65–69.

141. Nagasawa, H., and Little, J. B. (1981). Factors influencing the induction of sister chromatid exchanges in mammalian cells by 12-O-tetradecanoyl-phorbol-13-acetate. *Carcinogenesis* **2,** 601–607.

142. Mkhitaryan, V. G., and Gevorkyan, D. M. (1981). Effects of vitamin E, superoxide dismutase and zinc ions on the lipid peroxidation process in the alloxan diabetic rat. *Biol. Zh. Arm.* **34,** 783–788.

143. Uchigata, Y., Yamamoto, H., Kawamura, A., and Okamoto, H. (1982). Protection by superoxide dismutase, catalase and poly(ADP-ribose) synthetase inhibitors

against alloxan and streptozotocin-induced islet DNA breaks. *J. Biol. Chem.* **257**, 6084–6088.

144. McCord, J. M., and English, D. (1981). Superoxide dismutase, an anti-inflammatory drug. *In* "Enzymes as Drugs" (J. M. Holcenberg and J. Roberts, eds.), pp. 353–365. Wiley, New York.

145. Beckman, R., and Flohé, L. (1981). The pathogenic role of superoxide radicals in inflammation efficacy of exogenous superoxide dismutase. *Clin. Respir. Physiol.* **17** (Suppl.), 275–286.

146. McCord, J. M. (1974). Free radicals and inflammation: Protection of synovial fluid by superoxide dismutase. *Science* **185**, 529–531.

147. Sacks, T., Moldow, C. F., Craddock, P. R., Bowers, T. K., and Jacob, H. S. (1978). Oxygen radicals mediate endothelial cell damage by complement-stimulated granulocytes: An *in vitro* model of immune vascular damage. *J. Clin. Invest.* **61**, 1161–1167.

148. McCord, J. M., and Wong, K. (1979). Phagocyte-produced free radicals: Role in cytotoxicity and inflammation. *Proc. Int. Leukocyte Cult. Conf.* pp. 625–629.

149. Petrone, W. F., English, D. K., Wong, K., and McCord, J. M. (1980). Free radicals and inflammation: Superoxide-dependent activation of a neutrophil chemotactic factor in plasma. *Proc. Natl. Acad. Sci. U.S.A.* **77**, 1159–1163.

150. Perez, H. D., Weksler, B. B., and Goldstein, I. M. (1980). Generation of a chemotactic lipid from arachidonic acid by exposure to a superoxide-generating system. *Inflammation* **4**, 313–328.

151. McCord, J. M., Stokes, S. H., and Wong, K. (1979). Superoxide radical as a phagocyte-produced chemical mediator of inflammation. *Adv. Inflamm. Res.* **1**, 273–80.

152. Wang, K., Cleland, L. G., and Poznansky, M. J. (1980). Enhanced anti-inflammatory effect and reduced immunogenicity of bovine liver superoxide dismutase by conjugation with homologous albumin. *Agents Act.* **10**, 231–239.

153. Pyatak, P. S., Abuchowski, A., and Davis, F. F. (1980). Preparation of a polyethylene glycol: Superoxide dismutase adduct and an examination of its blood circulating life and antiinflammatory activity. *Res. Commun. Chem. Pathol. Pharmacol.* **29**, 113–127.

154. Johnson, K. J., Fantone, J. C., III, Kaplan, J., and Ward, P. (1981). *In vivo* damage to rat lungs by oxygen metabolites. *J. Clin. Invest.* **67**, 983–993.

155. McCormick, J. R., Harkin, M. M., Johnson, K. J., and Ward, P. A. (1981). The effect of superoxide dismutase on pulmonary and dermal inflammation. *Am. J. Pathol.* **102**, 55–61.

156. Fridovich, I. (1979). Hypoxia and oxygen toxicity. *Adv. Neurol.* **26**, 255–259.

157. Rao, P. S., Evans, R. G., Val-Mejias, J., Ayres, S. M., and Mueller, H. S. (1978). The role of superoxide dismutase in reducing CK depletion of infarcted myocardium in the rat. *Clin. Res.* **26**, 262A.

158. Bailie, M. B., and Jolly, S. R. (1982). Reduction of myocardial ischemic injury by superoxide dismutase plus catalase. *Fed. Proc., Fed. Am. Soc. Exp. Biol.* **41**, 1736.

159. Greenberg, C. S., Hammerschmidt, D. E., Craddock, P. R., Yamada, O., and Jacob, H. S. (1979). Atheroma cholesterol (CH) activates complement (C) and

aggregates PMNs: Possible role in myocardial infarct (MI) and in cholesterol embolization syndrome (ChES). *Clin. Res.* **27,** 509A.

160. Granger, D. N., Rutili, G., and McCord, J. M. (1981). Superoxide radicals in feline intestinal ischemia. *Gastroenterology* **81,** 22–29.

161. Parks, D. A., Bulkley, G. B., Granger, D. N., Hamilton, S. R., and McCord, J. M. (1982). Ischemia injury in the cat small intestine: Role of superoxide radicals. *Gastroenterology* **82,** 9–15.

162. Parks, D. A., Granger, D. N., and Bulkley, G. B. (1982). Superoxide radicals and mucosal lesions of the ischemic small intestine. *Fed. Proc., Fed. Am. Soc. Exp. Biol.* **41,** 1742.

MAPPING LOCAL FUNCTIONAL ACTIVITY BY MEASUREMENT OF LOCAL CEREBRAL GLUCOSE UTILIZATION IN THE CENTRAL NERVOUS SYSTEM OF ANIMALS AND MAN*

LOUIS SOKOLOFF

Laboratory of Cerebral Metabolism
National Institute of Mental Health
U.S. Public Health Service
Department of Health and Human Services
Bethesda, Maryland

I. Introduction

THE brain is a complex, heterogeneous organ composed of many anatomical and functional components with markedly different levels of functional activity that vary independently with time and function. Other tissues are generally far more homogeneous, with most of their cells functioning similarly and synchronously in response to a common stimulus or regulatory influence. The central nervous system, however, consists of innumerable subunits, each integrated into its own set of functional pathways and networks and subserving only one or a few of the many activities in which the nervous system participates. Understanding how the nervous system functions requires knowledge not only of the mechanisms of excitation and inhibition but even more so of their precise localization in the nervous system and the relationships of neural subunits to specific functions.

Historically, studies of the central nervous system have concentrated heavily on localization of function and mapping of pathways related to specific functions. These have been carried out neuroanatomically and histologically with staining and degeneration techniques, behaviorally

---

*Lecture delivered January 19, 1984.

[1]Abbreviations used in this article: DG, 2-deoxyglucose; DG6P, 2-deoxyglucose 6-phosphate; G6P, glucose 6-phosphate.

with ablation and stimulation techniques, electrophysiologically with electrical recording and evoked electrical responses, and histochemically with a variety of techniques, including fluorescent and immunofluorescent methods and autoradiography of orthograde and retrograde axoplasmic flow. Many of these conventional methods suffer from a sampling problem. They generally permit examination of only one potential pathway at a time, and only positive results are interpretable. Furthermore, the demonstration of a pathway reveals only a potential for function; it does not reveal its significance in normal function.

Tissues that do physical and/or chemical work, such as heart, kidney, and skeletal muscle, exhibit a close relationship between energy metabolism and the level of functional activity. The existence of a similar relationship in the tissues of the central nervous system has been more difficult to prove, partly because of uncertainty about the nature of the work associated with nervous functional activity, but mainly because of the difficulty in assessing the levels of functional and metabolic activities in the same functional component of the brain at the same time. Much of our present knowledge of cerebral energy metabolism *in vivo* has been obtained by means of the nitrous oxide technique of Kety and Schmidt (1948a) and its modifications (Scheinberg and Stead, 1949; Lassen and Munck, 1955; Eklöf *et al.,* 1973; Gjedde *et al.,* 1975), which measure the average rates of energy metabolism in the brain as a whole. These methods have demonstrated changes in cerebral metabolic rate in association with gross or diffuse alterations of cerebral function and/or structure, as, for example, those that occur during postnatal development, aging, senility, anesthesia, disorders of consciousness, and convulsive states (Kety, 1950, 1957; Lassen, 1959; Sokoloff, 1960, 1976). They have not detected changes in cerebral metabolic rate in a number of conditions with, perhaps, more subtle alterations in cerebral functional activity, for example, deep slow-wave sleep, performance of mental arithmetic, sedation and tranquilization, schizophrenia, and LSD-induced psychosis (Kety, 1950; Lassen, 1959; Sokoloff, 1969). It is possible that there are no changes in cerebral energy metabolism in these conditions. The apparent lack of change could also be explained by either a redistribution of local levels of functional and metabolic activity without significant change in the average of the brain as a whole or the restriction of altered metabolic activity to regions too small to be detected in measurements of the brain as a whole. What has clearly been needed is a method that measures the rates of energy metabolism in specific discrete regions of the brain in normal and altered states of functional activity.

In pursuit of this goal Kety and his associates (Landau *et al.*, 1955; Freygang and Sokoloff, 1958; Kety, 1960; Reivich *et al.*, 1969) developed a quantitative autoradiographic technique to measure the local tissue concentrations of chemically inert, diffusible, radioactive tracers which they used to determine the rates of blood flow simultaneously in all the structural components visible and identifiable in autoradiographs of serial sections of the brain. The application of this quantitative autoradiographic technique to the determination of local cerebral metabolic rate has proved to be more difficult because of the inherently greater complexity of the problem and the unsuitability of the labeled species of the normal substrates of cerebral energy metabolism, oxygen and glucose. The radioisotopes of oxygen have too short a physical half-life. Both oxygen and glucose are too rapidly converted to carbon dioxide, and CO_2 is too rapidly cleared from the cerebral tissues. Sacks (1957), for example, has found in man significant losses of $^{14}CO_2$ from the brain within 2 minutes after the onset of an intravenous infusion of [^{14}C]glucose, labeled either uniformly, in the C-1, C-2, or C-6 positions. These limitations of [^{14}C]glucose have been avoided by the use of 2-deoxy-D-[^{14}C]glucose, a labeled analog of glucose with special properties that make it particularly appropriate for this application (Sokoloff *et al.*, 1977). It is metabolized through part of the pathway of glucose metabolism at a definable rate relative to that of glucose. Unlike glucose, however, its product, [^{14}C]deoxyglucose 6-phosphate, is essentially trapped in the tissues, allowing the application of the quantitative autoradiographic technique. The use of radioactive 2-deoxyglucose to trace glucose utilization and the autoradiographic technique to achieve regional localization has recently led to the development of a method that measures the rates of glucose utilization simultaneously in all components of the central nervous system in the normal conscious state and during experimental physiological, pharmacological, and pathological conditions (Sokoloff *et al.*, 1977). Because the procedure is so designed that the concentrations of radioactivity in the tissues during autoradiography are more or less proportional to the rates of glucose utilization, the autoradiographs provide pictorial representations of the relative rates of glucose utilization in all the cerebral structures visualized. Numerous studies with this method have established that there is a close relationship between functional activity and energy metabolism in the central nervous system (Sokoloff, 1977; Plum *et al.*, 1976), and the method has become a potent new tool for mapping functional neural pathways on the basis of evoked metabolic responses.

II. Theory

The method is derived from a model based on the biochemical properties of 2-deoxyglucose (Fig. 1A) (Sokoloff *et al.*, 1977). 2-Deoxyglucose is transported bidirectionally between blood and brain by the same carrier that transports glucose across the blood–brain barrier (Bidder, 1968; Bachelard, 1971; Oldendorf, 1971). In the cerebral tissues it is phosphorylated by hexokinase to 2-deoxyglucose 6-phosphate (Sols and Crane, 1954). Deoxyglucose and glucose are, therefore, competitive substrates for both blood–brain transport and hexokinase-catalyzed phosphorylation. Unlike glucose 6-phosphate, however, which is

---

Fig. 1. (A) Diagrammatic representation of the theoretical model. C_i^* represents the total ^{14}C concentration in a single homogeneous tissue of the brain. C_P^* and C_P represent the concentrations of [^{14}C]deoxyglucose and glucose in the arterial plasma, respectively; C_E^* and C_E represent their respective concentrations in the tissue pools that serve as substrates for hexokinase. C_M^* represents the concentration of [^{14}C]deoxyglucose 6-phosphate in the tissue. The constants k_1^*, k_2^*, and k_3^* represent the rate constants for carrier-mediated transport of [^{14}C]deoxyglucose from plasma to tissue, for carrier-mediated transport back from tissue to plasma, and for phosphorylation by hexokinase, respectively. The constants k_1, k_2, and k_3 are the equivalent rate constants for glucose. [^{14}C]Deoxyglucose and glucose share and compete for the carrier that transports both between plasma and tissue and for hexokinase, which phosphorylates them to their respective hexose 6-phosphates. The dashed arrow represents the possibility of glucose 6-phosphate hydrolysis by glucose-6-phosphatase activity, if any. (From Sokoloff *et al.*, 1977; Sokoloff, 1978a.) (B) Operational equation of radioactive deoxyglucose method and its functional anatomy. T represents the time at the termination of the experimental period; λ equals the ratio of the distribution space of deoxyglucose in the tissue to that of glucose; Φ equals the fraction of glucose which, once phosphorylated, continues down the glycolytic pathway; and K_m^* and V_m^* and K_m and V_m represent the familiar Michaelis–Menten kinetic constants of hexokinase for deoxyglucose and glucose, respectively. The other symbols are the same as those defined in Fig. 1A. (From Sokoloff, 1978a.)

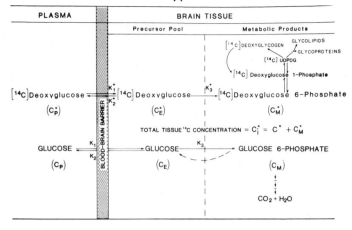

A

PLASMA	BRAIN TISSUE	
	Precursor Pool	Metabolic Products

B

Functional Anatomy of the Operational Equation of the

[¹⁴C] Deoxyglucose Method

General Equation for Measurement of Reaction Rates with Tracers:

$$\text{Rate of Reaction} = \frac{\text{Labeled Product Formed in Interval of Time, 0 to T}}{\left[\begin{array}{c}\text{Isotope Effect}\\\text{Correction Factor}\end{array}\right]\left[\begin{array}{c}\text{Integrated Specific Activity}\\\text{of Precursor}\end{array}\right]}$$

Operational Equation of [¹⁴C] Deoxyglucose Method:

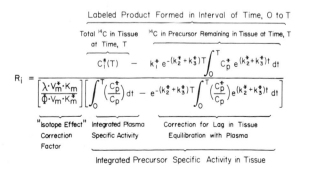

$$R_i = \frac{C_i^*(T) - k_1^* e^{-(k_2^*+k_3^*)T}\int_0^T C_p^* e^{(k_2^*+k_3^*)t}\,dt}{\left[\dfrac{\lambda \cdot V_m^* \cdot K_m}{\Phi \cdot V_m \cdot K_m^*}\right]\left[\displaystyle\int_0^T \left(\dfrac{C_p^*}{C_p}\right)dt - e^{-(k_2^*+k_3^*)T}\int_0^T \left(\dfrac{C_p^*}{C_p}\right)e^{(k_2^*+k_3^*)t}\,dt\right]}$$

Labeled Product Formed in Interval of Time, 0 to T

Total ¹⁴C in Tissue at Time, T   ¹⁴C in Precursor Remaining in Tissue at Time, T

"Isotope Effect" Correction Factor   Integrated Plasma Specific Activity   Correction for Lag in Tissue Equilibration with Plasma

Integrated Precursor Specific Activity in Tissue

metabolized further eventually to CO_2 and water and to a lesser degree via the hexosemonophosphate shunt, deoxyglucose 6-phosphate cannot be converted to fructose 6-phosphate and is not a substrate for glucose-6-phosphate dehydrogenase (Sols and Crane, 1954). There is very little glucose-6-phosphatase activity in brain (Hers, 1957) and even less deoxyglucose-6-phosphatase activity (Sokoloff *et al.*, 1977). Deoxyglucose 6-phosphate can be converted into deoxyglucose 1-phosphate and then into UDP-deoxyglucose and eventually into glycogen, glycolipids, and glycoproteins, but these reactions are slow and in mammalian tissues only a very small fraction of the deoxyglucose 6-phosphate formed proceeds to these products (Nelson *et al.*, 1984). In any case, these compounds are secondary, relatively stable products of deoxyglucose 6-phosphate, and all together represent the products of deoxyglucose phosphorylation. Deoxyglucose 6-phosphate and its derivatives, once formed, are, therefore, essentially trapped in the cerebral tissues, at least long enough for the duration of the measurement.

If the interval of time is kept short enough, for example, less than 1 hour, to allow the assumption of negligible loss of [^{14}C]DG6P from the tissues, then the quantity of [^{14}C]DG6P accumulated in any cerebral tissue at any given time following the introduction of [^{14}C]DG into the circulation is equal to the integral of the rate of [^{14}C]DG phosphorylation by hexokinase in that tissue during that interval of time. This integral is in turn related to the amount of glucose that has been phosphorylated over the same interval, depending on the time courses of the relative concentrations of [^{14}C]DG and glucose in the precursor pools and the Michaelis–Menten kinetic constants for hexokinase with respect to both [^{14}C]DG and glucose. With cerebral glucose consumption in a steady state, the amount of glucose phosphorylated during the interval of time equals the steady state flux of glucose through the hexokinase-catalyzed step times the duration of the interval, and the net rate of flux of glucose through this step equals the rate of glucose utilization.

These relationships can be mathematically defined and an operational equation derived if the following assumptions are made: (1) a steady state for glucose (i.e., constant plasma glucose concentration and constant rate of glucose consumption) throughout the period of the procedure; (2) homogeneous tissue compartment within which the concentrations of [^{14}C]DG and glucose are uniform and exchange directly with the plasma; and (3) tracer concentrations of [^{14}C]DG (i.e., molecular concentrations of free [^{14}C]DG essentially equal to zero). The operational equation which defines R_i, the rate of glucose consumption per unit mass of tissue, i, in terms of measurable variables is presented in Fig. 1B.

The rate constants are determined in a separate group of animals by a nonlinear, iterative process which provides the least-squares best fit of an equation which defines the time course of total tissue ^{14}C concentration in terms of the time, the history of the plasma concentration, and the rate constants to the experimentally determined time courses of tissue and plasma concentrations of ^{14}C (Sokoloff et al., 1977). The rate constants have thus far been completely determined only in normal conscious albino rats (Table I). Partial analyses indicate that the values are quite similar in the conscious monkey (Kennedy et al., 1978), dog (Duffy et al., 1982), and cat (M. Miyaoka, J. Magnes, C. Kennedy, and L. Sokoloff, unpublished data).

The λ, Φ, and the enzyme kinetic constants are grouped together to constitute a single, lumped constant (Fig. 1B). It can be shown mathematically that this lumped constant is equal to the asymptotic value of the product of the ratio of the cerebral extraction ratios of [^{14}C]DG and glucose and the ratio of the arterial blood to plasma-specific activities when the arterial plasma [^{14}C]DG concentration is maintained constant (Sokoloff et al., 1977). The lumped constant is also determined in a separate group of animals from arterial and cerebral venous blood samples drawn during a programmed intravenous infusion which produces and maintains a constant arterial plasma [^{14}C]DG concentration (Sokoloff et al., 1977). An example of such a determination in a conscious monkey is illustrated in Fig. 2. Thus far the lumped constant has been determined only in the albino rat, monkey, cat, dog, and sheep (Table II). The lumped constant appears to be characteristic of the species and does not appear to change significantly in a wide range of physiological conditions (Table II) (Sokoloff et al., 1977). It has been found to change in pathophysiological conditions, moderately in hyperglycemia (Schuier et al., 1981), markedly in hypoglycemia (Suda et al., 1981), and whenever the rate of glucose utilization becomes limited by glucose supply.

Despite its complex appearance, the operational equation is really nothing more than a general statement of the standard relationship by which rates of enzyme-catalyzed reactions are determined from mea-

TABLE I

VALUES OF RATE CONSTANTS IN THE NORMAL CONSCIOUS ALBINO RAT[a]

Structure	Rate constants (min^{-1}) $\pm$ standard error of estimates			Distribution volume (ml/g)	Half-life of Precursor pool (min)
	k_1^*	k_2^*	k_3^*	$k_1^*/(k_2^* + k_3^*)$	$\log_e 2/(k_2^* + k_3^*)$
Gray matter					
Visual cortex	0.189 ± 0.048	0.279 ± 0.176	0.063 ± 0.040	0.553	2.03
Auditory cortex	0.226 ± 0.068	0.241 ± 0.198	0.067 ± 0.057	0.734	2.25
Parietal cortex	0.194 ± 0.051	0.257 ± 0.175	0.062 ± 0.045	0.608	2.17
Sensory–motor cortex	0.193 ± 0.037	0.208 ± 0.112	0.049 ± 0.035	0.751	2.70
Thalamus	0.188 ± 0.045	0.218 ± 0.144	0.053 ± 0.043	0.694	2.56
Medial geniculate body	0.219 ± 0.055	0.259 ± 0.164	0.055 ± 0.040	0.697	2.21
Lateral geniculate body	0.172 ± 0.038	0.220 ± 0.134	0.055 ± 0.040	0.625	2.52
Hypothalamus	0.158 ± 0.032	0.226 ± 0.119	0.043 ± 0.032	0.587	2.58
Hippocampus	0.169 ± 0.043	0.260 ± 0.166	0.056 ± 0.040	0.535	2.19

Amygdala	0.149 ± 0.028	0.235 ± 0.109	0.032 ± 0.026	0.558	2.60
Caudate–putamen	0.176 ± 0.041	0.200 ± 0.140	0.061 ± 0.050	0.674	2.66
Superior colliculus	0.198 ± 0.054	0.240 ± 0.166	0.046 ± 0.042	0.692	2.42
Pontine gray matter	0.170 ± 0.040	0.246 ± 0.142	0.037 ± 0.033	0.601	2.45
Cerebellar cortex	0.225 ± 0.066	0.392 ± 0.229	0.059 ± 0.031	0.499	1.54
Cerebellar nucleus	0.207 ± 0.042	0.194 ± 0.111	0.038 ± 0.035	0.892	2.99
Mean	0.189 ±	0.245 ±	0.052 ±	0.647 ±	2.39 ±
± SEM	0.012	0.040	0.010	0.073	0.40
White matter					
Corpus callosum	0.085 ± 0.015	0.135 ± 0.075	0.019 ± 0.033	0.552	4.50
Genu of corpus callosum	0.076 ± 0.013	0.131 ± 0.075	0.019 ± 0.034	0.507	4.62
Internal capsule	0.077 ± 0.015	0.134 ± 0.085	0.023 ± 0.039	0.490	4.41
Mean	0.079 ±	0.133 ±	0.020 ±	0.156 ±	4.51 ±
± SEM	0.008	0.046	0.020	0.171	0.90

[a] From Sokoloff et al. (1977).

surements made with radioactive tracers (Fig. 1B). The numerator of the equation represents the amount of radioactive product formed in a given interval of time; it is equal to C_i^*, the combined concentrations of [^{14}C]DG and [^{14}C]DG6P in the tissue at time, T, measured by the quantitative autoradiographic technique, less a term that represents the free unmetabolized [^{14}C]DG still remaining in the tissue. The denominator represents the integrated specific activity of the precursor pool times a factor, the lumped constant, which is analogous to a correction factor for an isotope effect. The term with the exponential factor in the denominator takes into the account the lag in the equilibration of the tissue precursor pool with the plasma.

III. Experimental Procedure for Measurement of Local Cerebral Glucose Utilization

A. Theoretical Considerations in the Design of the Procedure

The operational equation of the method specifies the variables to be measured in order to determine R_i, the local rate of glucose consumption in the brain. The following variables are measured in each experi-

---

Fig. 2. Data obtained and their use in determination of the lumped constant and the combination of rate constants, $(k_2^* + k_3^*)$, in a representative experiment. (A) Time courses of arterial blood and plasma concentrations of [^{14}C]DG and glucose and cerebral venous blood concentrations of [^{14}C]DG and glucose during programmed intravenous infusion of [^{14}C]DG. (B) Arithmetic plot of the function derived from the variables in (A) and combined as indicated in the formula on the ordinate against time. This function declines exponentially, with a rate constant equal to $(k_2^* + k_3^*)$, until it reaches an asymptotic value equal to the lumped constant, 0.35, in this experiment (dashed line). (C) Semilogarithmic plot of the curve in (B) less the lumped constant, i.e., its asymptotic value. Solid circles represent actual values. This curve is analyzed into two components by a standard curve-peeling technique to yield the two straight lines representing the separate components. Open circles are points for the fast component, obtained by subtracting the values for the slow component from the solid circles. The rate constants for these two components represent the values of $(k_2^* + k_3^*)$ for two compartments; the fast and slow compartments are assumed to represent gray and white matter, respectively. In this experiment the values for $(k_2^* + k_3^*)$ were found to equal 0.462 (half-time = 1.5 minutes) and 0.154 (half-time = 4.5 minutes) in gray and white matter, respectively. (From Kennedy et al., 1978.)

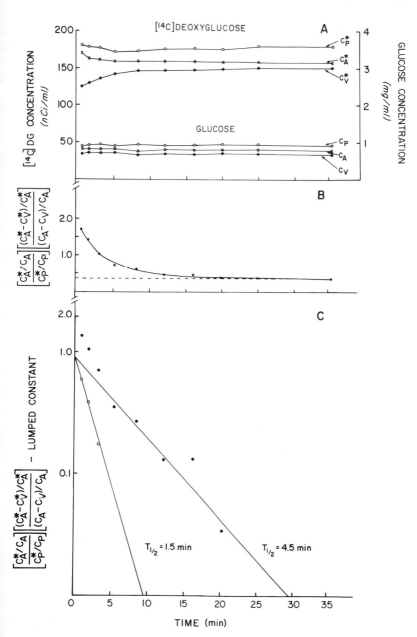

TABLE II

VALUES OF THE LUMPED CONSTANT IN SEVERAL SPECIES[a]

Animal	Number of animals	Mean ± SD	SEM
Albino rat			
Conscious	15	0.464 ± 0.099^b	± 0.026
Anesthetized	9	0.512 ± 0.118^b	± 0.039
Conscious (5% CO_2)	2	0.463 ± 0.122^b	± 0.086
Combined	26	0.481 ± 0.119	± 0.023
Rhesus monkey			
Conscious	7	0.344 ± 0.095	± 0.036
Cat			
Anesthetized	6	0.411 ± 0.013	± 0.005
Dog (Beagle puppy)			
Conscious	7	0.558 ± 0.082	± 0.031
Sheep			
Fetus	5	0.416 ± 0.031	± 0.014
Newborn	4	0.382 ± 0.024	± 0.012
Mean	9	0.400 ± 0.033	± 0.011

[a] Note: The values were obtained as follows: rat, Sokoloff et al. (1977); monkey, Kennedy et al. (1978); cat, M. Miyaoka, J. Magnes, C. Kennedy, M. Shinohara, and L. Sokoloff (unpublished data); dog, Duffy et al. (1982); sheep, Abrams et al. (1984).

[b] No statistically significant difference between normal conscious and anesthetized rats ($0.3 < p < 0.4$) and conscious rats breathing 5% CO_2 ($p > 0.9$).

ment: (1) the entire history of the arterial plasma [^{14}C]deoxyglucose concentration, C_P^*, from zero time to the time of killing, T; (2) the steady state arterial plasma glucose level, C_P, over the same interval; and (3) the local concentration of ^{14}C in the tissue at the time of killing, $C_i^*(T)$. The rate constants, k_1^*, k_2^*, and k_3^*, and the lumped constant, λ $V_m^* K_m / \Phi V_m K_m^*$, are not measured in each experiment; the values for these constants that are used are those determined separately in other groups of animals as described above and presented in Tables I and II.

The operational equation is generally applicable with all types of arterial plasma [^{14}C]DG concentration curves. Its configuration, however, suggests that a declining curve approaching zero by the time of killing is the choice to minimize certain potential errors. The quantitative autoradiographic technique measures only total ^{14}C concentration in the tissue and does not distinguish between [^{14}C]DG6P and [^{14}C]DG. It is, however, [^{14}C]DG6P concentration, and any further products derived from it, that must be known to determine glucose consumption. The total product concentration is calculated in the numerator of the operational equation, which equals the total tissue ^{14}C content, $C_i^*(T)$, minus the [^{14}C]DG concentration remaining in the tissue, estimated by the term containing the exponential factor and rate constants. In the denominator of the operational equation there is also a term containing an exponential factor and rate constants. Both these terms have the useful property of approaching zero with increasing time if C_P^* is also allowed to approach zero. The rate constants, k_1^*, k_2^*, and k_3^*, are not measured in the same animals in which local glucose consumption is being measured. It is conceivable that the rate constants in Table I are not equally applicable in all physiological, pharmacological, and pathological states. One possible solution is to determine the rate constants for each condition to be studied. An alternative solution, and the one chosen, is to administer the [^{14}C]DG as a single intravenous pulse at zero time and to allow sufficient time for the clearance of [^{14}C]DG from the plasma and the terms containing the rate constants to fall to levels too low to influence the final result. To wait until these terms reach zero is impractical because of the long time required and the risk of effects of the small but finite rate of loss of [^{14}C]DG6P from the tissues. A reasonable time interval is 45 minutes; by this time the plasma level has fallen to very low levels, and, on the basis of the values of $(k_2^* + k_3^*)$ in Table I, the exponential factors have declined through at least 10 half-lives, at least under physiological conditions (Fig. 3).

B. Experimental Protocol

The animals are prepared for the experiment by the insertion of polyethylene catheters in an artery and vein. Any convenient artery or vein can be used. In the rat the femoral or the tail arteries and veins have been found satisfactory. In the monkey and cat the femoral vessels are probably most convenient. The catheters are inserted under anesthesia, and anesthetic agents without long-lasting aftereffects should be used.

Light halothane anesthesia with or without supplementation with nitrous oxide has been found to be quite satisfactory. At least 2 hours are allowed for recovery from the surgery and anesthesia before initiation of the experiment.

The design of the experimental procedure for the measurement of local cerebral glucose utilization was based on the theoretical considerations discussed above. At zero time a pulse of 125 μCi (no more than 2.5 μmol) of [^{14}C]deoxyglucose per kilogram of body weight is administered to the animal via the venous catheter. Arterial sampling is initiated with the onset of the pulse, and timed 50- to 100-μl samples of arterial blood are collected consecutively as rapidly as possible during the early period so as not to miss the peak of the arterial curve. Arterial sampling is continued at less frequent intervals later in the experimental period but at sufficient frequency to define fully the arterial curve. The

---

FIG. 3. Graphical representation of the significant variables in the operational equation used to calculate local cerebral glucose utilization. (A) Time courses of [^{14}C]deoxyglucose concentrations in arterial plasma and in average gray and white matter and [^{14}C]deoxyglucose 6-phosphate concentrations in average gray and white matter following an intravenous pulse of 50 μCi of [^{14}C]deoxyglucose. The plasma curve is derived from measurements of plasma [^{14}C]deoxyglucose concentrations. The tissue [^{14}C]deoxyglucose concentrations were calculated from the plasma curve and the mean values of k_1^*, k_2^*, and k_3^* for gray and white matter in Table I according to the second term in the numerator of the operational equation. The [^{14}C]deoxyglucose 6-phosphate concentrations in the tissues were calculated from the mean values of k_3^* and the integral of the [^{14}C]deoxyglucose concentrations in the tissues. The arrows point to the concentrations of [^{14}C]deoxyglucose and [^{14}C]deoxyglucose 6-phosphate in the tissues at the time of killing; the autoradiographic technique measures the total ^{14}C content (i.e., the sum of these concentrations) at that time, which is equal to $C_i^*(T)$, the first term in the numerator of the operational equation. Note that at the time of killing, the total ^{14}C content represents mainly [^{14}C]deoxyglucose 6-phosphate concentration, especially in gray matter. (B) Time courses of ratios of [^{14}C]deoxyglucose to glucose concentrations (i.e., specific activities) in plasma and average gray and white matter. The curve for plasma was determined by division of the plasma curve in (A) by the plasma glucose concentrations. The curves for the tissues were calculated by the derivative of the function in the right set of brackets in the denominator of the operational equation. The integrals in (B) are the integrals of the specific activities with respect to time and represent the areas under the curves. The integrals under the tissue curves are equivalent to all of the denominator of the operational equation, except for the lumped constant. Note that by the time of killing, the integrals of the tissue curves approach equality with each other and with that of the plasma curve. (From Sokoloff et al., 1977.)

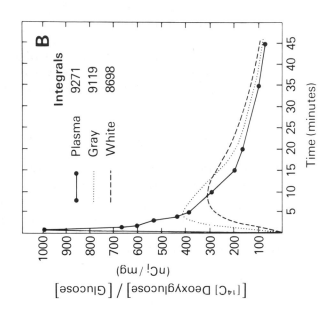

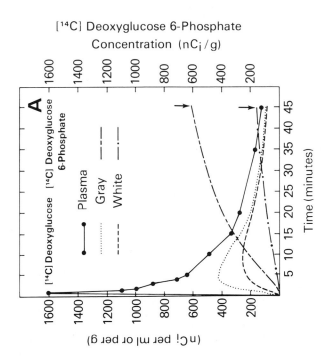

arterial blood samples are immediately centrifuged to separate the plasma, which is stored on ice until assayed for [^{14}C]DG by liquid scintillation counting and glucose concentrations by standard enzymatic methods. At approximately 45 minutes the animal is decapitated, the brain is removed and frozen in Freon XII or isopentane maintained between -50 and $-75°C$ with liquid nitrogen. When fully frozen, the brain is stored at $-70°C$ until sectioned and autoradiographed. The experimental period may be limited to 30 minutes. This is theoretically permissible and may sometimes be necessary for reasons of experimental expediency, but greater errors due to possible inaccuracies in the rate constants may result.

C. Autoradiographic Measurement of Tissue ^{14}C Concentration

The ^{14}C concentrations in localized regions of the brain are measured by a modification of the quantitative autoradiographic technique previously described (Reivich et al., 1969). The frozen brain is coated with chilled embedding medium (Lipshaw Manufacturing Co., Detroit, MI) and fixed to object holders appropriate to the microtome to be used. Brain sections, precisely 20 μm in thickness, are cut in a cryostat maintained at -21 to $-22°C$. The brain sections are picked up on glass cover slips, dried on a hot plate at 60°C for at least 5 minutes, and placed sequentially in an X-ray cassette. A set of [^{14}C]methylmethacrylate standards (Amersham Corp., Arlington Heights, IL), which include a blank and a series of progressively increasing ^{14}C concentrations, are also placed in the cassette. These standards must previously have been calibrated for their autoradiographic equivalence to the ^{14}C concentrations in brain sections, 20 μm in thickness, prepared as described above. The method of calibration has been previously described (Reivich et al., 1969).

Autoradiographs are prepared from these sections directly in the X-ray cassette with Kodak single-coated, blue-sensitive Medical X-ray Film, Type SB-5 (Eastman Kodak Co., Rochester, NY). The exposure time is generally 5–6 days with the doses used as described above, and the exposed films are developed according to the instructions supplied with the film. The SB-5 X-ray film is rapid but coarse grained. For finer grained autoradiographs and, therefore, better defined images with higher resolution, it is possible to use mammographic films, such as Du-Pont LoDose or Kodak MR-1 films, or fine grain panchromatic film, such as Kodak Plus-X, but the exposure times are 2–3 times longer. The autoradiographs provide a pictorial representation of the relative ^{14}C concentrations in the various cerebral structures and the plastic standards (Fig. 4). A calibration curve of the relationship between optical density and tissue ^{14}C concentration for each film is obtained by densitometric measurements of the portions of the film representing the various standards. The local tissue concentrations are then determined from the calibration curve and the optical densities of the film in the regions representing the cerebral structures of interest. Local cerebral glucose utilization is calculated from the local tissue concentrations of ^{14}C and the time courses of the plasma [^{14}C]DG and glucose concentrations according to the operational equation (Fig. 1B).

D. Theoretical and Practical Considerations

The design of the deoxyglucose method is based on an operational equation, derived by the mathematical analysis of a model of the biochemical behavior of [^{14}C]deoxyglucose and glucose in brain (Fig. 1). Although the model and its mathematical analysis are as rigorous and comprehensive as reasonably possible, it must be recognized that models almost always represent idealized situations and cannot possibly take into account all the known, let alone unknown, properties of a complex biological system. Several years have now passed since the introduction of the deoxyglucose method, and numerous applications of it have been made. The results of this experience generally establish the validity and worth of the method, but there are some potential problems in special situations which require further theoretical and practical considerations.

The main potential sources of error are the rate constants and the lumped constant. The problem with them is that they are not determined in the same animals and at the same time when local cerebral glucose utilization is being measured. They are measured in separate groups of comparable animals and then used subsequently in other animals in which glucose utilization is being measured. The part played by these constants in the method is defined by their role in the operational equation of the method (Fig. 1B).

1. Rate Constants

The rate constants, k_1^*, k_2^*, and k_3^*, for deoxyglucose have been fully determined for various cerebral tissues in the normal conscious albino

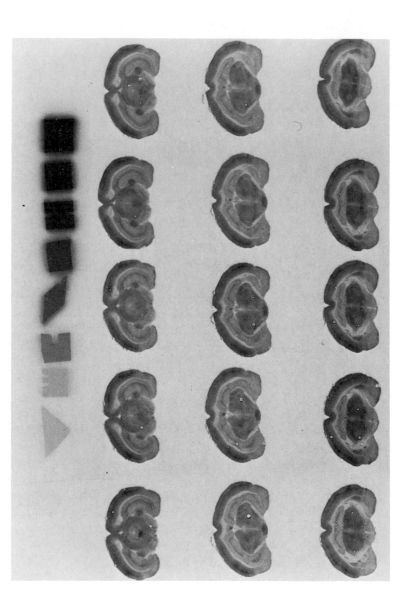

rat (Sokoloff *et al.*, 1977) (Table I), but they appear to be similar in other species. All the rate constants vary considerably from tissue to tissue, but the variation among gray structures and among white structures is considerably less than the differences between the two types of tissues (Table I). The rate constants, k_2^* and k_3^*, appear in the equation only as their sum, and $(k_2^* + k_3^*)$ is equal to the rate constant for the turnover of the free [^{14}C]deoxyglucose pool in the tissue. The half-life of the free [^{14}C]deoxyglucose pool can then be calculated by dividing $(k_2^* + k_3^*)$ into the natural logarithm of 2 and has been found to average 2.4 minutes in gray matter and 4.5 minutes in white matter in the normal conscious rat (Table I).

The rate constants vary not only from structure to structure but can be expected to vary with the condition. For example, k_1^* and k_2^* are influenced by both blood flow and transport of [^{14}C]deoxyglucose across the blood–brain barrier, and because of the competition for the transport carrier, the glucose concentrations in the plasma and tissue affect the transport of [^{14}C]deoxyglucose and, therefore, also k_1^* and k_2^*. The constant, k_3^*, is related to phosphorylation of [^{14}C]deoxyglucose and will certainly change when glucose utilization is altered. To minimize potential errors due to inaccuracies in the values of the rate constants used, it was decided to sacrifice time resolution for accuracy. If the [^{14}C]deoxyglucose is given as an intravenous pulse and sufficient time is allowed for the plasma to be cleared of the tracer, then the influence of the rate constants, and the functions that they represent, on the final result diminishes with increasing time until utlimately it becomes zero. This relationship is implicit in the structure of the operational equation (Fig. 1B); as C_P^* approaches zero, the terms containing the rate constants also approach zero with increasing time. The significance of this relationship is graphically illustrated in Fig. 5. From typical arterial plasma [^{14}C]dcoxyglucose and glucose concentration curves obtained in a normal conscious rat, the portion of the denominator of the operational equation underlined by the heavy bar was computed with a wide range of values for $(k_2^* + k_3^*)$ as a function of time. The values for $(k_2^* +$

FIG. 4. Autoradiograph of sections of conscious rat brain and of calibrated [^{14}C]methylmethacrylate standards used to quantify ^{14}C concentration in tissues. (From Sokoloff *et al.*, 1977.)

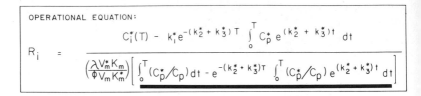

OPERATIONAL EQUATION:

$$R_i = \frac{C_i^*(T) - k_1^* e^{-(k_2^* + k_3^*)T} \int_0^T C_p^* e^{(k_2^* + k_3^*)t} \, dt}{\left(\dfrac{\lambda V_m^* K_m}{\phi V_m K_m^*}\right)\left[\int_0^T (C_p^*/C_p)\,dt - e^{-(k_2^* + k_3^*)T} \int_0^T (C_p^*/C_p)\, e^{(k_2^* + k_3^*)t}\, dt\right]}$$

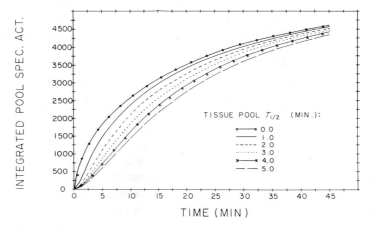

FIG. 5. Influence of time and rate constants, $(k_2^* + k_3^*)$, on integrated precursor pool specific activity in a normal conscious rat given an intravenous pulse of 50 μCi of [^{14}C]deoxyglucose at zero time. The time courses of the arterial plasma [^{14}C]deoxyglucose and glucose concentrations were measured following the pulse. The portion of the equation underlined, corresponding to integrated precursor pool specific activity, was computed as a function of time with different values of $(k_2^* + k_3^*)$, as indicated by their equivalent half-lives, calculated according to $T_{1/2} = 0.693/(k_2^* + k_3^*)$. (From Sokoloff, 1979.)

k_3^*) are presented as their equivalent half-lives caluclated as described above; the values of $(k_2^* + k_3^*)$ vary from infinite (i.e., $T_{1/2} = 0$ minutes) to 0.14 per minute (i.e., $T_{1/2} = 5$ minutes) and more than cover the range of values to be expected under physiological conditions. The portion of the equation underlined and computed represents the integral of the precursor pool specific activity in the tissue. The curves represent the time course of this function, one each for every value of $(k_2^* + k_3^*)$ examined. It can be seen that these curves are widely different at early times but converge with increasing time until at 45 minutes the differences over the entire range of $(k_2^* + k_3^*)$ equal only a small fraction of the value of the integral. These curves demonstrate that at short times enormous errors can occur if the values of the rate constants are not precisely known, but only negligible errors occur at 45 minutes, even over a wide range of rate constants of severalfold. In fact, it was precisely for this reason that [^{14}C]deoxyglucose rather than [^{14}C]glucose was selected as the tracer for glucose metabolism. The relationships are similar for glucose. Because the products of [^{14}C]glucose metabolism are so rapidly lost from the tissues, it is necessary to limit the experimental period to short times when enormous errors can occur if the rate constants are not precisely known for each individual structure. [^{14}C]Deoxyglucose permits the prolongation of the experimental period to times when inaccuracies in rate constants have little effect on the final result.

It should be noted, however, that in pathological conditions, such as severe ischemia or hyperglycemia, the rate constants may fall far below the range examined in Fig. 5. There is evidence, for example, that this occurs with hyperglycemia (Schuier, Dow-Edwards, Orzi, Namba, and Sokoloff, unpublished observations) and ischemia (Hawkins *et al.*, 1981). Also in conditions of markedly depressed cerebral glucose utilization and/or slow clearance of the [^{14}C]DG from the plasma, the second term in the numerator which contains the rate constants may not be much smaller than $C_i^*(T)$, the first term in the numerator. Inaccuracies in the rate constants may then produce considerable errors in the numerator. In such abnormal conditions it is necessary and feasible to redetermine the rate constants for the particular condition under study or else to prolong the experimental period and allow more time for the exponential terms to diminish further and then correct for the loss of [^{14}C]DG6P that would occur at later times (Sokoloff, 1982).

2. Lumped Constant

The lumped constant is composed of six separate constants. One of these, Φ, is a measure of the steady state hydrolysis of glucose 6-phosphate to free glucose and phosphate. Because in normal brain tissue there is little such phosphohydrolase activity (Hers, 1957), Φ is normally approximately equal to unity. The other components are arranged in three ratios: λ, which is the ratio of distribution spaces in the tissue for deoxyglucose and glucose; V_m^*/V_m; and K_m/K_m^*. Although each individual constant may vary from structure to structure and condition to condition, it is likely that the ratios tend to remain the same under normal physiological conditions. For reasons described in detail previously (Sokoloff *et al.*, 1977; Gjedde and Diemer, 1983), it is reasonable to believe that the lumped constant is the same throughout the brain and more or less characteristic of the species of animal under normal physiological conditions. Empirical experience thus far indicates that it is generally so, except in special pathophysiological states. The greatest experience has been accumulated in the albino rat. In this species the lumped constant for the brain as a whole has been determined under a variety of conditions (Sokoloff *et al.*, 1977). In the normal conscious rat the rates of local cerebral glucose utilization in the various structures of the brain, determined by the [^{14}C]deoxyglucose method with the single value of the lumped constant for the brain as a whole, correlates almost perfectly ($r = 0.96$) with local cerebral blood flow, measured by the [^{14}C]iodoantipyrine method, an entirely independent method (Sokoloff, 1978b). It is generally recognized that local blood flow is adjusted to local metabolic rate, but if the single value of the lumped constant did not apply to the individual structures studied, then errors in local glucose utilization would occur that might be expected to obscure the correlation. Also, the lumped constant has been directly determined in the albino rat in the normal conscious state, under barbiturate anesthesia, and during the inhalation of 5% CO_2; no significant differences were observed (Table II). The lumped constant does vary with the species of animal. It has now also been determined in the rhesus monkey (Kennedy *et al.*, 1978), cat (M. Miyaoka, J. Magnes, C. Kennedy, M. Shinohara, and L. Sokoloff, unpublished data), Beagle puppy (Duffy *et al.*, 1982), and sheep (Abrams *et al.*, 1984), and each species has a different value (Table II). The values for local rates of glucose utilization determined with these lumped constants in these species are very close to what might be expected from measurement of energy metabolism in the brain as a whole by other methods (Table III).

Although there is yet no experimental evidence of more than negligible changes in the lumped constant under physiological conditions, it certainly does change in pathophysiological states. In severe hypoglycemia there is a progressive and appreciable increase in the lumped constant when plasma glucose concentration falls below 70 mg% (Suda *et al.*, 1981), and in severe hyperglycemia there is a small decrease (Schuier *et al.*, 1981). Indeed, theoretically the lumped constant could be expected to change whenever there is an alteration in the balance between glucose supply to the tissue and the tissue's rate of glucose utilization. It is only when the rate of glucose utilization becomes limited by the supply, however, that a major change in the lumped constant occurs. Also, tissue damage may disrupt the normal cellular compartmentation, and there is no assurance that λ, the ratio of the distribution spaces for [^{14}C]deoxyglucose and glucose, is the same in damaged tissue as in normal tissue. In pathological states there may be release of lysosomal acid hydrolases that may hydrolyze glucose 6-phosphate and thus alter the value of Φ. It is necessary, therefore, to determine the lumped constant in each pathological or pathophysiological state.

3. Glucose-6-Phosphatase

Although relatively low, the activity of glucose-6-phosphatase in brain is not zero (Sokoloff, 1982). This enzyme is capable of hydrolyzing the product, [^{14}C]deoxyglucose 6-phosphate, back to free [^{14}C]deoxyglucose and thus cause loss of product. Fortunately, the product and enzyme are in separate cellular compartments. The [^{14}C]DG6P is formed in the cytosol and must be transported into the cisterns of the endoplasmic reticulum, where the glucose-6-phosphatase resides, before the hydrolysis can occur. This compartmentalization provides a period of time before the effects of glucose-6-phosphatase become significant. If the experimental period is kept within 45 minutes, then the influence of glucose-6-phosphatase is negligible and can be ignored (Sokoloff, 1982; Sokoloff *et al.*, 1977). If, however, it is necessary to extend the experimental period to longer intervals, as, for example, in studies in man with positron emission tomography (Phelps *et al.*, 1979), then it is necessary to account for the effects of glucose-6-phosphatase activity. This has been done by modifying slightly the original model to include a k_4^*, the rate constant for [^{14}C]DG6P hydrolysis by glucose-6-phosphatase, and deriving a modified operational equation that incorporates it (Huang *et al.*, 1980; Sokoloff, 1982).

E. Computerized Color-Coded Image Processing

The autoradiographs provide pictorial representations of only the relative concentrations of the isotope in the various tissues. Because of the use of a pulse followed by a long period before killing, the isotope is contained mainly in deoxyglucose 6-phosphate, which reflects the rate of glucose metabolism. The autoradiographs are, therefore, pictorial representations also of the relative but not the actual rates of glucose utilization in all the structures of the nervous system. The resolution of differences in relative rates is limited, however, by the ability of the human eye to recognize differences in shades of gray. Manual densitometric analysis permits the computation of actual rates of glucose utilization with a fair degree of resolution, but it generates enormous tables of data which fail to convey the tremendous heterogeneity of metabolic rates, even within anatomic structures, or the full information contained within the autoradiographs. Goochee *et al.* (1980) have developed a computerized image-processing system to analyze and transform the autoradiographs into color-coded maps of the distribution of the actual rates of glucose utilization exactly where they are located throughout the central nervous system. The autoradiographs are scanned automatically by a computer-controlled scanning microdensitometer. The optical density of each spot in the autoradiograph, from 25 to 100 μm as selected, is stored in a computer, converted to ^{14}C concentration on the basis of the optical densities of the calibrated ^{14}C plastic standards, and then converted to local rates of glucose utilization by solution of the operational equation of the method. Colors are assigned to narrow ranges of the rates of glucose utilization, and the autoradiographs are then displayed in a color TV monitor in color along with a calibrated color scale for identifying the rate of glucose utilization in each spot of the autoradiograph from its color. These color maps add a third dimension, the rate of glucose utilization encoded in a color scale, to the spatial dimensions already present on the autoradiographs.

III. Rates of Local Cerebral Glucose Utilization in the Normal Conscious State

The most extensive measurements of local cerebral glucose utilization have been carried out in the albino rat (Sokoloff *et al.*, 1977) and monkey (Kennedy *et al.*, 1978). These values are presented in Table III. The rates of local cerebral glucose utilization in the normal conscious rat vary widely throughout the brain. The values in white structures tend to group together and are always considerably below those of

TABLE III

REPRESENTATIVE VALUES FOR LOCAL CEREBRAL GLUCOSE UTILIZATION
IN THE NORMAL CONSCIOUS ALBINO RAT AND MONKEY
(μmol/100 g/min)[a]

Structure	Albino rat (10)[b]	Monkey (7)[c]
Gray matter		
Visual cortex	107 ± 6	59 ± 2
Auditory cortex	162 ± 5	79 ± 4
Parietal cortex	112 ± 5	47 ± 4
Sensory–motor cortex	120 ± 5	44 ± 3
Thalamus: lateral nucleus	116 ± 5	54 ± 2
Thalamus: ventral nucleus	109 ± 5	43 ± 2
Medial geniculate body	131 ± 5	65 ± 3
Lateral geniculate body	96 ± 5	39 ± 1
Hypothalamus	54 ± 2	25 ± 1
Mamillary body	121 ± 5	57 ± 3
Hippocampus	79 ± 3	39 ± 2
Amygdala	52 ± 2	25 ± 2
Caudate–putamen	110 ± 4	52 ± 3
Nucleus accumbens	82 ± 3	36 ± 2
Globus pallidus	58 ± 2	26 ± 2
Substantia nigra	58 ± 3	29 ± 2
Vestibular nucleus	128 ± 5	66 ± 3
Cochlear nucleus	113 ± 7	51 ± 3
Superior olivary nucleus	133 ± 7	63 ± 4
Inferior colliculus	197 ± 10	103 ± 6
Superior colliculus	95 ± 5	55 ± 4
Pontine gray matter	62 ± 3	28 ± 1
Cerebellar cortex	57 ± 2	31 ± 2
Cerebellar nuclei	100 ± 4	45 ± 2
White matter		
Corpus callosum	40 ± 2	11 ± 1
Internal capsule	33 ± 2	13 ± 1
Cerebellar white matter	37 ± 2	12 ± 1
Weighted average for whole brain		
	68 ± 3	36 ± 1

[a] *Note*: The values are the means ± standard errors from measurements
made in the number of animals indicated in parentheses.

[b] From Sokoloff *et al.* (1977).

[c] From Kennedy *et al.* (1978).

gray structures. The average value in gray matter is approximately three times that of white matter, but the individual values vary from approximately 50 to 200 μmol of glucose/100 g/min. The highest values are in the structures involved in auditory functions with the inferior colliculus clearly the most metabolically active structure in the brain.

The rates of local cerebral glucose utilization in the conscious monkey exhibit similar heterogeneity, but they are generally one-third to one-half the values in corresponding structures of the rat brain (Table III). The differences in rates in the rat and monkey brain are consistent with the different cellular packing densities in the brains of these two species.

The average glucose utilization of the brain as a whole, weighted for the relative sizes of the individual structures, can be determined by means of the computerized image-processing system (Goochee *et al.*, 1980). The values thus obtained (Table III) are very close to those obtained with other methods that measure directly the average in the brain as a whole.

IV. Effects of General Anesthesia

General anesthesia produced by thiopental reduces the rates of glucose utilization in all structures of the rat brain (Table IV) (Sokoloff *et al.*, 1977). The effects are not uniform, however. The greatest reductions occur in the gray structures, particularly those of the primary sensory pathways. The effects in white matter, though definitely present, are relatively small compared to those of gray matter. These results are in agreement with those of previous studies in which anesthesia has been found to decrease the cerebral metabolic rate of the brain as a whole (Kety, 1950; Lassen, 1959; Sokoloff, 1976).

V. Relation between Local Functional Activity and Energy Metabolism

The results of a variety of applications of the method demonstrate a clear relationship between local cerebral functional activity and glucose consumption in the components of the central nervous system. The most striking demonstrations of the close coupling between function and energy metabolism are seen with experimentally induced local altera-

TABLE IV

EFFECTS OF THIOPENTAL ANESTHESIA ON LOCAL CEREBRAL
GLUCOSE UTILIZATION IN THE RAT[a,b]

Structure	Local cerebral glucose utilization (μmol/100 g/min)		
	Control (6)[c]	Anesthetized (8)[c]	% Effect
Gray matter			
Visual cortex	111 ± 5	64 ± 3	− 42
Auditory cortex	157 ± 5	81 ± 3	− 48
Parietal cortex	107 ± 3	65 ± 2	− 39
Sensory–motor cortex	118 ± 3	67 ± 2	− 43
Lateral geniculate body	92 ± 2	53 ± 3	− 42
Medial geniculate body	126 ± 6	63 ± 3	− 50
Thalamus: lateral nucleus	108 ± 3	58 ± 2	− 46
Thalamus: ventral nucleus	98 ± 3	55 ± 1	− 44
Hypothalamus	63 ± 3	43 ± 2	− 32
Caudate–putamen	111 ± 4	72 ± 3	− 35
Hippocampus: Ammon's horn	79 ± 1	56 ± 1	− 29
Amygdala	56 ± 4	41 ± 2	− 27
Cochlear nucleus	124 ± 7	79 ± 5	− 36
Lateral lemniscus	114 ± 7	75 ± 4	− 34
Inferior colliculus	198 ± 7	131 ± 8	− 34
Superior olivary nucleus	141 ± 5	104 ± 7	− 26
Superior colliculus	99 ± 3	59 ± 3	− 40
Vestibular nucleus	133 ± 4	81 ± 4	− 39
Pontine gray matter	69 ± 3	46 ± 3	− 33
Cerebellar cortex	66 ± 2	44 ± 2	− 33
Cerebellar nucleus	106 ± 4	75 ± 4	− 29
White matter			
Corpus callosum	42 ± 2	30 ± 2	− 29
Genu of corpus callosum	35 ± 5	30 ± 2	− 14
Internal capsule	35 ± 2	29 ± 2	− 17
Cerebellar white matter	38 ± 2	29 ± 2	− 24

[a] From Sokoloff et al. (1977).

[b] Determined at 30 minutes following pulse of [^{14}C]deoxyglucose.

[c] The values are the means ± standard errors obtained in the number of animals indicated in parentheses. All the differences are statistically significant at the $p < 0.05$ level.

tions in functional activity that are restricted to a few specific areas in the brain. The effects on local glucose consumption are then so pronounced that they are not only observed in the quantitative results but can be visualized directly on the autoradiographs which are really pictorial representations of the relative rates of glucose utilization in the various structural components of the brain.

A. Effects of Increased Functional Activity

1. Effects of Sciatic Nerve Stimulation

Electrical stimulation of one sciatic nerve in the rat under barbiturate anesthesia causes pronounced increases in glucose consumption (i.e., increased optical density in the autoradiographs) in the ipsilateral dorsal horn of the lumbar spinal cord (Kennedy et al., 1975).

2. Effects of Experimental Focal Seizures

The local injection of penicillin into the hand–face area of the motor cortex of the Rhesus monkey has been shown to induce electrical discharges in the adjacent cortex and to result in recurrent focal seizures involving the face, arm, and hand on the contralateral side (Caveness, 1969). Such seizure activity causes selective increases in glucose consumption in areas of motor cortex adjacent to the penicillin locus and in small discrete regions of the putamen, globus pallidus, caudate nucleus, thalamus, and substantia nigra of the same side (Fig. 6) (Kennedy et al., 1975). Similar studies in the rat have led to comparable results and provided evidence on the basis of an evoked metabolic response of a "mirror" focus in the motor cortex contralateral to the penicillin-induced epileptogenic focus (Collins et al., 1976).

B. Effects of Decreased Functional Activity

Decrements in functional activity result in reduced rates of glucose utilization. These effects are particularly striking in the auditory and visual systems of the rat and the visual system of the monkey.

1. Effects of Auditory Occlusion

In the albino rat some of the highest rates of local cerebral glucose utilization are found in components of the auditory system, i.e., audito-

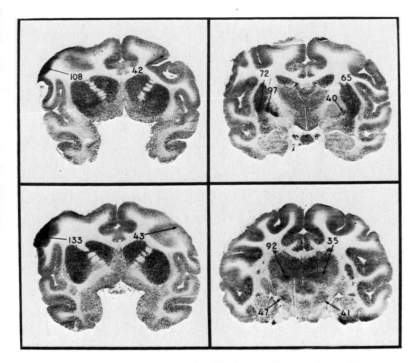

FIG. 6. Effects of focal seizures produced by local application of penicillin to motor cortex on local cerebral glucose utilization in the Rhesus monkey. The penicillin was applied to the hand and face area of the left motor cortex. The left side of the brain is on the left in each of the autoradiographs in the figure. The numbers are the rates of local cerebral glucose utilization in μmol/100 g tissue/min. Note the following: *upper left,* motor cortex in region of penicillin application and corresponding region of contralateral motor cortex; *lower left,* ipsilateral and contralateral motor cortical regions remote from area of penicillin applications; *upper right,* ipsilateral and contralateral putamen and globus pallidus; *lower right,* ipsilateral and contralateral thalamic nuclei and substantia nigra. (From Sokoloff, 1977.)

ry cortex, medial geniculate ganglion, inferior colliculus, lateral lemniscus, superior olive, and cochlear nucleus (Table III). Bilateral auditory deprivation by occlusion of both external auditory canals with wax markedly depresses the metabolic activity in all of these areas (Sokoloff, 1977). The reductions are symmetrical bilaterally and range from 35 to 60%. Unilateral auditory deprivation also depresses the glucose consumption of these structures but to a lesser degree, and some of the structures are asymmetrically affected. For example, the metabolic activity of the ipsilateral cochlear nucleus equals 75% of the activity of the contralateral nucleus. The lateral lemniscus, superior olive, and medial geniculate ganglion are slightly lower on the contralateral side, while the contralateral inferior colliculus is markedly lower in metabolic activity than the ipsilateral structure. These results demonstrate that there is some degree of lateralization and crossing of auditory pathways in the rat.

2. Visual Occlusion in the Rat

In the rat, the visual system is 80 to 85% crossed at the optic chiasma (Lashley, 1934; Montero and Guillery, 1968), and unilateral enucleation removes most of the visual input to the central visual structures of the contralateral side. In the conscious rat studied 2–24 hours after unilateral enucleation, there are marked decrements in glucose utilization in the contralateral superior colliculus, lateral geniculate ganglion, and visual cortex as compared to the ipsilateral side (Kennedy et al., 1975).

3. Visual Occlusion in the Monkey

In animals with binocular visual systems, such as the Rhesus monkey, there is only approximately 50% crossing of the visual pathways, and the structures of the visual system on each side of the brain receive equal inputs from both retinae. Although each retina projects more or less equally to both hemispheres, their projections remain segregated and terminate in six well-defined laminae in the lateral geniculate ganglia, three each for the ipsilateral and contralateral eyes (Hubel and Wiesel, 1968, 1972; Wiesel et al., 1974; Rakic, 1976). This segregation is preserved in the optic radiations which project the monocular representations of the two eyes for any segment of the visual field to adjacent regions of layer IV of the striate cortex (Hubel and Wiesel, 1968, 1972). The cells responding to the input of each monocular terminal zone are distributed transversely through the thickness of the striate cortex resulting in a mosaic of columns, 0.3–0.5 mm in width, alternately representing the monocular inputs of the two eyes. The nature and distribution of these ocular dominance columns have been previously characterized by electrophysiological techniques (Hubel and

Wiesel, 1968), Nauta degeneration methods (Hubel and Wiesel, 1972), and by autoradiographic visualization of axonal and transneuronal transport of [3H]proline- and [3H]fucose-labeled protein and/or glycoprotein (Wiesel et al., 1974; Rakic, 1976). Bilateral or unilateral visual deprivation, either by enucleation or by the insertion of opaque plastic disks, produces consistent changes in the pattern of distribution of the rates of glucose consumption, all clearly visible in the autoradiographs, that coincide closely with the changes in functional activity expected from known physiological and anatomical properties of the binocular visual system (Kennedy et al., 1976).

In animals with intact binocular vision no bilateral asymmetry is seen in the autoradiographs of the structures of the visual system (Figs. 7A, 8A). The lateral geniculate and oculomotor nuclei appear to be of fairly uniform density and essentially the same on both sides (Fig. 7A). The visual cortex is also the same on both sides (Fig. 8A), but throughout all of area 17 there is heterogenous density distributed in a characteristic laminar pattern. These observations indicate that in animals with binocular visual input the rates of glucose consumption in the visual pathways are essentially equal on both sides of the brain and relatively uniform in the oculomotor and lateral geniculate nuclei, but markedly different in the various layers of the striate cortex.

Autoradiographs from animals with both eyes occluded exhibit generally decreased labeling of all components of the visual system, but the bilateral symmetry is fully retained (Figs. 7B, 8B), and the density within each lateral geniculate body is for the most part fairly uniform (Fig. 7B). In the striate cortex, however, the marked differences in the densities of the various layers seen in the animals with intact bilateral vision (Fig. 8A) are virtually absent so that, except for a faint delineation of a band within layer IV, the concentration of the label is essentially homogenous throughout the striate cortex (Fig. 8B).

Autoradiographs from monkeys with only monocular input because of unilateral visual occlusion exhibit markedly different patterns from those described above. Both lateral geniculate bodies exhibit exactly inverse patterns of alternating dark and light bands corresponding to the known laminae representing the regions receiving the different inputs from the retinae of the intact and occluded eyes (Fig. 7C). Bilateral asymmetry is also seen in the oculomotor nuclear complex; a lower density is apparent in the nuclear complex contralateral to the occluded

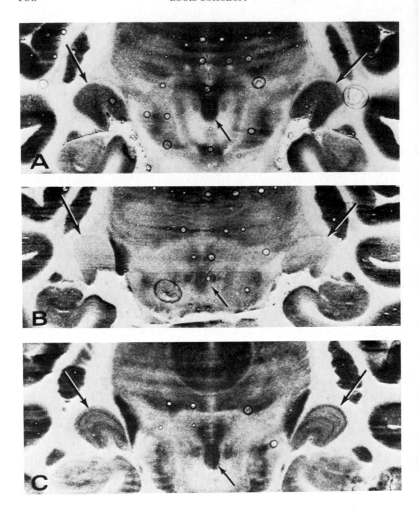

5.0 mm

Fig. 7. Autoradiography of coronal brain sections of monkey at the level of the lateral
geniculate bodies. Large arrows point to the lateral geniculate bodies; small arrows point
to oculomotor nuclear complex. (A) Animal with intact binocular vision. Note the bilateral symmetry and relative homogeneity of the lateral geniculate bodies and oculomtor
nuclei. (B) Animal with bilateral visual occlusion. Note the reduced relative densities, the
relative homogeneity, and the bilateral symmetry of the lateral geniculate bodies and

eye (Fig. 7C). In the striate cortex the pattern of distribution of the [^{14}C]DG6P appears to be a composite of the patterns seen in the animals with intact and bilaterally occluded visual input. The pattern found in the former regularly alternates with that of the latter in columns oriented perpendicularly to the cortical surface (Fig. 8C). The dimensions, arrangement, and distribution of these columns are identical to those of the ocular dominance columns described by Hubel and Wiesel (Hubel and Wiesel, 1968, 1972; Wiesel et al., 1974). These columns reflect the interdigitation of the representations of the two retinae in the visual cortex. Each element in the visual fields is represented by a pair of contiguous bands in the visual cortex, one for each of the two retinae or their portions that correspond to the given point in the visual fields. With symmetrical visual input bilaterally, the columns representing the two eyes are equally active and, therefore, not visualized in the autoradiographs (Fig. 8A). When one eye is blocked, however, only those columns representing the blocked eye become metabolically less active, and the autoradiographs then display the alternate bands of normal and depressed activities corresponding to the regions of visual cortical representation of the two eyes (Fig. 8C).

There can be seen in the autoradiographs from the animals with unilateral visual deprivation a pair of regions in the folded calcarine cortex that exhibit bilateral asymmetry (Fig. 8C). The ocular dominance columns are absent on both sides, but on the side contralateral to the occluded eye this region has the appearance of visual cortex from an animal with normal bilateral vision, and on the ipsilateral side this region looks like cortex from an animal with both eyes occluded (Fig. 8). These regions are the loci of the cortical representation of the blind spots of the visual fields and normally have only monocular input (Kennedy et al., 1975, 1976). The area of the optic disk in the nasal half of each retina cannot transmit to this region of the contralateral striate cortex which, therefore, receives its sole input from an area in the

oculomotor nuclei. (C) Animal with right eye occluded. The left side of the brain is on the left side of the photograph. Note the laminae and the inverse order of the dark and light bands in the two lateral geniculate bodies. Note also the lesser density of the oculomotor nuclear complex on the side contralateral to the occluded eye. (From Kennedy et al., 1976.)

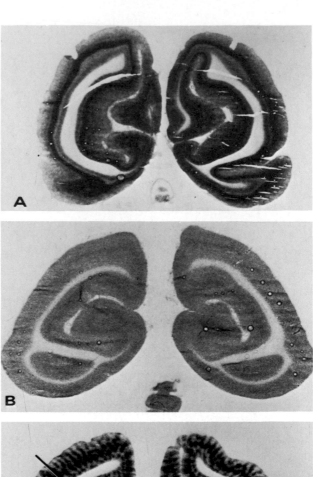

5.0 mm

temporal half of the ipsilateral retina. Occlusion of one eye deprives this region of the ipsilateral striate cortex of all input while the corresponding region of the contralateral striate cortex retains uninterrupted input from the intact eye. The metabolic reflection of this ipsilateral monocular input is seen in the autoradiograph in Fig. 8C.

The results of these studies with the [^{14}C]deoxyglucose method in the binocular visual system of the monkey represent the most dramatic demonstration of the close relationship between physiological changes in functional activity and the rate of energy metabolism in specific components of the central nervous system.

VI. Applications of the Deoxyglucose Method

The results of studies like those described above on the effects of experimentally induced focal alterations of functional activity on local glucose utilization have demonstrated a close coupling between local functional activity and energy metabolism in the central nervous system. The effects are often so pronounced that they can be visualized directly on the autoradiographs, which provide pictorial representations of the relative rates of glucose utilization throughout the brain. This technique of autoradiographic visualization of evoked metabolic responses offers a powerful tool to map functional neural pathways simul-

Fig. 8. Autoradiographs of coronal brain sections from Rhesus monkeys at the level of the striate cortex. (A) Animal with normal binocular vision. Note the laminar distribution of the density; the dark band corresponds to layer IV. (B) Animal with bilateral visual deprivation. Note the almost uniform and reduced relative density, especially the virtual disappearance of the dark band corresponding to layer IV. (C) Animal with right eye occluded. The half-brain on the left side of the photograph represents the left hemisphere contralateral to the occluded eye. Note the alternate dark and light striations, each approximately 0.3–0.4 mm in width, that represent the ocular dominance columns. These columns are most apparent in the dark band corresponding to layer IV, but extend through the entire thickness of the cortex. The arrows point to regions of bilateral asymmetry where the ocular dominance columns are absent. These are presumably areas with normally only monocular input. The one on the left, contralateral to occluded eye, has a continuous dark lamina corresponding to layer IV which is completely absent on the side ipsilateral to the occluded eye. These regions are believed to be the loci of the cortical representations of the blind spots. (From Kennedy et al., 1976.)

taneously in all anatomical components of the central nervous system, and extensive use has been made of it for this purpose (Plum *et al.*, 1976). The results have clearly demonstrated the effectiveness of metabolic responses, either positive or negative, in identifying regions of the central nervous system involved in specific functions.

The method has been used most extensively in qualitative studies in which regions of altered functional activity are identified by the change in their visual appearance relative to other regions in the autoradiographs. Such qualitative studies are effective only when the effects are lateralized to one side or when only a few discrete regions are affected; other regions serve as the controls. Quantitative comparisons cannot, however, be made for equivalent regions between two or more animals. To make quantitative comparisons between animals, the fully quantitative method must be used, which takes into account the various factors, particularly the plasma glucose level, that influence the magnitude of labeling of the tissues. The method must be used quantitatively when the experimental procedure produces systemic effects and alters metabolism in many regions of the brain.

A comprehensive review of the many qualitative and quantitative applications of the method is beyond the scope of this article. Only some of the many neurophysiological, neuroanatomical, pharmacological, and pathophysiological applications of the method will be briefly noted merely to illustrate the broad extent of its potential usefulness.

A. *Neurophysiological and Neuroanatomical Applications*

Many of the physiological applications of the [^{14}C]deoxyglucose method were in studies designed to test the method and to examine the relationship between local cerebral functional and metabolic activities. These applications have been described above. The most dramatic results have been obtained in the visual systems of the monkey and the rat. The method has, for example, been used to define the nature, conformation, and distribution of the ocular dominance columns in the striate cortex of the monkey (Fig. 8C) (Kennedy *et al.*, 1976). It has also been used to do the same for the orientation columns in the striate cortex of the monkey (Hubel *et al.*, 1978; Schoppmann and Stryker, 1981). A by-product of the studies of the ocular dominance columns was the identification of the loci of the visual cortical representation of the blind spots of the visual fields (Fig. 8C) (Kennedy *et al.*, 1976).

Tootell *et al.* (1982) have used the [^{14}C]deoxyglucose method very effectively to map the retinotopic organization of the primate striate cortex. Studies are in progress to map the pathways of higher visual functions beyond the striate cortex; the results thus far demonstrate extensive areas of involvement of the inferior temporal cortex in visual processing (Macko *et al.,* 1982). Des Rosiers *et al.* (1978) have used the method to demonstrate functional plasticity in the striate cortex of the infant monkey. The ocular dominance columns are already present on the first day of life, but if one eye is kept patched for 3 months, the columns representing the open eye broaden and completely take over the adjacent regions of cortex containing the columns for the eye that had been patched. Inasmuch as there is no longer any cortical representation for the patched eye, the animal becomes functionally blind in one eye. This phenomenon is almost certainly the basis for the cortical blindness or amblyopia that often occurs in children with uncorrected strabismus.

There have also been extensive studies of the visual system of the rat. This species has little if any binocular vison and, therefore, lacks the ocular dominance columns. Batipps *et al.* (1981) have compared the rates of local cerebral glucose utilization in albino and Norway brown rats during exposure to ambient light. The rates in the two strains were essentially the same throughout the brain except in the components of the primary visual system. The metabolic rates in the superior colliculus, lateral geniculate, and visual cortex of the albino rat were significantly lower than those in the pigmented rat. Miyaoka *et al.* (1979a) have studied the influence of the intensity of retinal stimulation with randomly spaced light flashes on the metabolic rates in the visual systems of the two strains. In dark-adapted animals there is relatively little difference between the two strains. With increasing intensity of light, the rates of glucose utilization first increase in the primary projection areas of the retina, e.g., superficial layer of the superior colliculus and lateral geniculate body, and the slopes of the increase are steeper in the albino rat (Fig. 9). At 7 lux, however, the metabolic rates peak in the albino rat and then decrease with increasing light intensity. In contrast, the metabolic rates in the pigmented rat rise until they reach a plateau at about 700 lux, approximately the ambient light intensity in the laboratory. At this level, the metabolic rates in the visual structures of the albino rat are considerably below those of the pigmented rat. These results are consistent with the greater intensity of light reaching

SUPERIOR COLLICULUS

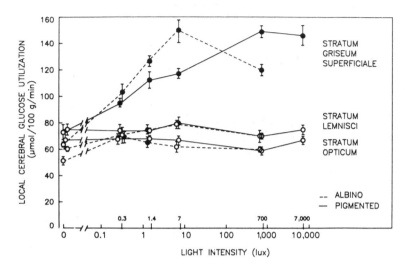

POSTEROLATERAL NUCLEUS OF THE THALAMUS

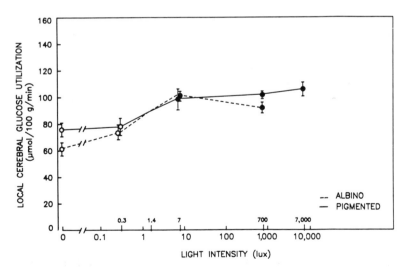

FIG. 9. Effects of intensity of retinal illumination with randomly spaced light flashes on local cerebral glucose utilization in components of the visual system of the albino and

LATERAL GENICULATE NUCLEUS

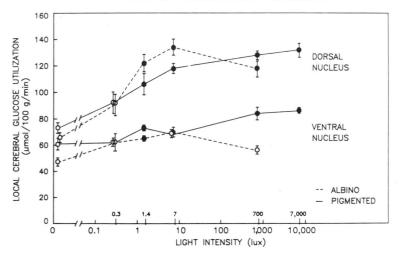

VISUAL CORTEX

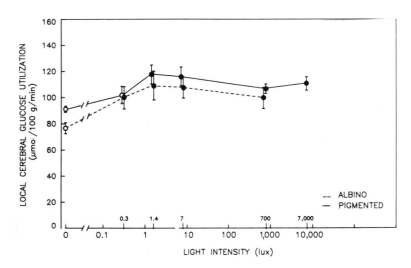

Norway brown rat. Note that the local glucose utilization is proportional to the logarithm of the intensity of illumination, at least at lower levels of intensity, in the primary projection areas of the retina. (From Miyaoka *et al.*, 1979a.)

the visual cells of the retina in the albino rats because of lack of pigment and the subsequent damage to the rods at higher light intensities. It is of considerable interest that the rates of glucose utilization in these visual structures obey the Weber–Fechner Law, i.e., the metabolic rate is directly proportional to the logarithm of the intensity of stimulation (Miyaoka *et al.*, 1979a). Inasmuch as this law was first developed from behavioral manifestations, these results imply that there is a quantitative relationship between behavioral and metabolic responses.

Although less extensive, there have also been applications of the method to other sensory systems. In studies of the olfactory system Sharp *et al.* (1975) have found that olfactory stimulation with specific odors activates glucose utilization in localized regions of the olfactory bulb. In addition to the experiments in the auditory system described above, there have been studies of tonotopic representation in the auditory system. Webster *et al.* (1978) have obtained clear evidence of selective regions of metabolic activation in the cochlear nucleus, superior olivary complex, nuclei of the lateral lemnisci, and the inferior colliculus in cats in response to different frequencies of auditory stimulation. Similar results have been obtained by Silverman *et al.* (1977) in the rat and guinea pig. Studies of the sensory cortex have demonstrated metabolic activation of the "whisker barrels" by stimulation of the vibrissae in the rat (Durham and Woolsey, 1977; Hand *et al.*, 1978). Each vibrissa is represented in a discrete region of the sensory cortex; their precise location and extent have been elegantly mapped by Hand *et al.* (1978) and Hand (1981) by means of the [^{14}C]deoxyglucose method.

Thus far, there has been relatively little application of the method to the physiology of motor functions. Kennedy *et al.* (1980) have studied monkeys that were conditioned to perform a task with one hand in response to visual cues; in the monkeys which were performing they observed metabolic activation throughout the appropriate areas of the motor as well as sensory systems from the cortex to the spinal cord.

An interesting physiological application of the [^{14}C]deoxyglucose method has been to the study of circadian rhythms in the central nervous system. Schwartz and his co-workers (1977, 1980) found that the suprachiasmatic nucleus in the rat exhibits circadian rhythmicity in metabolic activity, high during the day and low during the night (Fig. 10). None of the other structures in the brain that they examined showed rhythmic activity. The normally low activity present in the nucleus in the dark could be markedly increased by light, but darkness did not reduce the glucose utilization during the day. The rhythm is entrained to light; reversal of the light–dark cycle leads not only to reversal of the rhythm in running activity but also in the cycle of metabolic activity in the suprachiasmatic nucleus. These studies lend support to a role of the suprachiasmatic nucleus in the organization of circadian rhythms in the central nervous system.

Studies of circadian rhythms with the deoxyglucose method have been extended to natural sleep in monkeys. The results have demonstrated that during slow-wave, non-REM sleep, glucose utilization is diffusely depressed 25–30% throughout the central nervous system (Kennedy *et al.*, 1982). No structure in the brain showed an increased rate of glucose utilization, not even structures proposed as hypnogenic centers which allegedly are activated and depress functional activity in the other parts of the nervous system. The generalized uniformity of the metabolic depression suggests a chemical rather than a neurophysiological mechanism as the basis of slow-wave sleep. Studies in REM sleep have not yet been successfully carried out because of the short duration of REM episodes relative to the time resolution of the method.

Much of our knowledge of neurophysiology has been derived from studies of the electrical activity of the nervous system. Indeed, from the heavy emphasis that has been placed on electrophysiology one might gather that the brain is really an electric organ rather than a chemical one that functions mainly by the release of chemical transmitters at synapses. Nevertheless, electrical activity is unquestionably fundamental to the process of conduction, and it is appropriate to inquire how the local metabolic activities revealed by the [^{14}C]deoxyglucose method are related to the electrical activity of the nervous system. This question has been examined by Yarowsky and his co-workers (1983) in the superior cervical ganglion of the rat. The advantage of this structure is that its preganglionic input and postganglionic output can be isolated and electrically stimulated and/or monitored *in vivo*. The results thus far indicate a clear relationship between electrical input to the ganglion and its metabolic activity. Glucose utilization in the superior cervical ganglion is enhanced by electrical stimulation of the afferent nerves. The metabolic activation is frequency dependent in the range of 5 to 15 Hz,

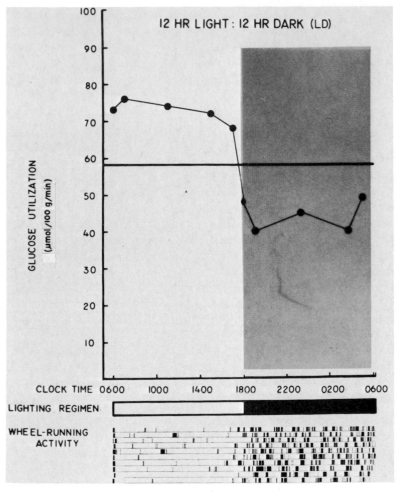

F<small>IG.</small> 10. Cicadian rhythm in glucose utilization in suprachiasmatic nucleus in the rat. *Left panel*, animals entrained to 12 hours of light during day and 12 hours of darkness during night. *Right panel*, animals entrained to opposite light–dark regimen. (From Schwartz *et al.*, 1980.)

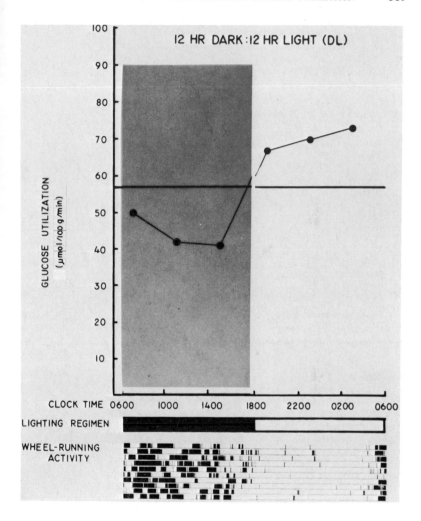

increasing in magnitude with increasing frequency of the stimulation (Fig. 11). Similar effects of electrical stimulation on the oxygen and glucose consumption of the excised ganglion studied *in vitro* have been observed (Larrabee, 1958; Horowicz and Larrabee, 1958; Friedli, 1978). Recent studies have also shown that antidromic stimulation of

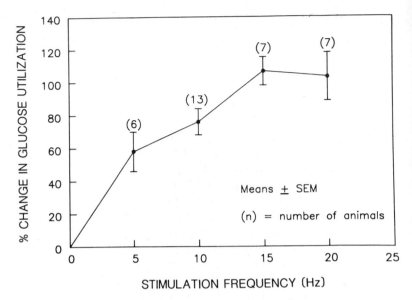

Fig. 11. Relationship between frequency of electrical stimulation of cervical sympathetic trunk and the percentage increase in the rate of glucose utilization in the superior cervical ganglion above that of the control ganglion on the other side. The values represent the means ± SEM of the individual percentage effects. (From Yarowsky *et al.*, 1983.)

the postganglionic efferent pathways from the ganglion has similar effects; stimulation of the external carotid nerve antidromically activates glucose utilization in the region of distribution of the cell bodies of this efferent pathway, indicating that not only the preganglionic axonal terminals are metabolically activated, but the postganglionic cell bodies as well (Yarowsky *et al.*, 1980). As already demonstrated in the neurohypophysis (Mata *et al.*, 1980), the effects of electrical stimulation on energy metabolism in the superior cervical ganglion are also probably due to the ionic currents associated with the spike activity and the consequent activation of the Na^+, K^+-ATPase activity to restore the ionic gradients. Electrical stimulation of the afferents to sympathetic ganglia have been shown to increase extracellular K^+ concentration (Friedli, 1978; Galvan *et al.*, 1979). Each spike is normally associated with a sharp transient rise in extracellular K^+ concentration which then rapidly falls and transiently undershoots before returning to the normal level (Galvan *et al.*, 1979); ouabain slows the decline in K^+ concentration after the spike and eliminates the undershoot. Continuous stimulation at a frequency of 6 Hz produces a sustained increase in cellular K^+ concentration (Galvan *et al.*, 1979). It is likely that the increased extracellular K^+ concentration and, almost certainly, increased intracellular Na^+ concentration activate the Na^+, K^+-ATPase, which in turn leads to the increased glucose utilization activation of the Na^+, K^+-ATPase activity to restore the ionic gradients. Electrical stimulation of the afferents to sympathetic ganglia have been shown to increase extracellular K^+ concentration (Friedli, 1978; Galvan *et al.*, 1979). Each spike is normally associated with a sharp transient rise in extracellular K^+ concentration which then rapidly falls and transiently undershoots before returning to the normal level (Galvan *et al.*, 1979); ouabain slows the decline in K^+ concentration after the spike and eliminates the undershoot. Continuous stimulation at a frequency of 6 Hz produces a sustained increase in cellular K^+ concentration (Galvan *et al.*, 1979). It is likely that the increased extracellular K^+ concentration and, almost certainly, increased intracellular Na^+ concentration activate the Na^+, K^+-ATPase, which in turn leads to the increased glucose utilization.

B. Neuroendocrinological Applications

The deoxyglucose method has thus far been applied only sparingly to neuroendocrinology. Several studies have, however, been carried out or are in progress.

1. Hypothalamoneurohypophyseal System

Physiological stimulation of the neurohypophyseal system by salt loading, which enhances vasopressin secretion, has been found to be associated with increased glucose utilization in the posterior pituitary (Fig. 12) (Schwartz *et al.*, 1979). Surprisingly, there were no detectable effects in the supraoptic and paraventricular nuclei, the loci of the cell bodies which project to the posterior pituitary. Obviously the entire

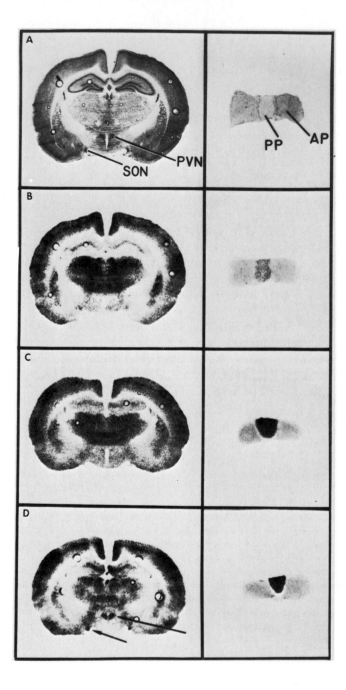

pathway had been activated by the osmotic stimulation. The posterior pituitary is composed (approximately 42%) of axonal terminals of the hypothalamohypophyseal tract (Nordmann, 1977), and the discrepancy between the effects on the cell bodies and in the regions of termination of their projections may reflect the greater sensitivity of axonal terminals and/or synaptic elements than that of perikarya to metabolic activation. That the supraoptic and paraventricular nuclei can be metabolically activated is evident from the effects of the α-adrenergic blocking agent, phenoxybenzamine (Fig. 12), or any other condition that produces hypotension (Savaki et al., 1982). In hypotension, however, these nuclei are activated by reflex activity, and it may well be that it is the afferent axonal terminals in these nuclei rather than the cell bodies that exhibit the increased utilization of glucose.

Kadekaro et al. (1983) have applied the deoxyglucose method to studies of the Brattleboro rat, a variant of the Long–Evans strain with a recessive genetic defect in vasopressin synthesis. This rat exhibits the characteristic signs of diabetes insipidus, an abnormally high water intake and a high output of hypo-osmolar urine. Despite the deficiency in vasopressin synthesis, glucose utilization was found to be markedly increased in the posterior pituitary and also in the subfornical organ, a structure that has been found to mediate drinking behavior in response to high plasma levels of angiotensin II, and angiotensin II is elevated in the Brattleboro rat. As in the normal rat stimulated by salt loading, the supraoptic and paraventricular nuclei were not metabolically more active in the Brattleboro rat. The reason for the high metabolic rate in the

---

FIG. 12. [¹⁴C]Deoxyglucose autoradiographs (B, C, D) and stained histological sections (A) of coronal brain sections (left) and pituitary sections (right). The photographs in (A) illustrate the positions of the supraoptic (SON) and paraventricular (PVN) nuclei in the brain section after cresyl violet (Nissl) staining. The positions of the posterior pituitary (PP) and anterior pituitary (AP) are illustrated on the right side in (A) after toluidine blue staining. The autoradiographs in (B) are characteristic of control rats, which were allowed to drink water freely. (C) Autoradiographs of brain and pituitary typical of dehydrated rats, which were given 2% NaCl to drink for 5 days. Note the intense labeling in the posterior pituitary, without comparable change in the SON or PVN. (D) Autoradiographs characteristic of normal rats given an intravenous injection of an α-adrenergic blocker, phenoxybenzamine (20 mg/kg), approximately 45 to 60 minutes before injection of [¹⁴C]deoxyglucose. Note the dramatic increase in labeling of the SON, PVN, and PP. (From Schwartz et al., 1979.)

posterior pituitary of the Brattleboro rat is still obscure, but it may be related to histological changes that also are present in the gland.

2. Altered Thyroid Function

Hyperthyroidism is known to have no effects on the average energy metabolism in the mature brain as a whole (Sokoloff *et al.*, 1953). Studies with the deoxyglucose method (D. Dow-Edwards and C. B. Smith, unpublished observations) reveal that in hyperthyroidism there are also no changes in glucose utilization in any anatomical components of the mature brain of the rat. The thyroid hormones are, however, fundamentally involved in the structural and functional maturation of the brain (Eayrs, 1961). Dow-Edwards *et al.* (1982) have applied the deoxyglucose method to rats radiothyroidectomized at birth but studied at approximately 5 months of age when the brain of normal rats has achieved maturity. Glucose utilization was significantly reduced in all regions of the brain examined. Most affected were the cerebral cortical regions and the sensory systems, particularly the auditory system. These metabolic changes are consistent with the histological pattern of impaired brain development in cretinism.

3. Sex Hormones and Sexual Behavior

The deoxyglucose method has been used to demonstrate selective metabolic activation of a number of structures in the female rat brain by vaginocervical stimulation that also elicited lordotic behavior (Allen *et al.*, 1981). The structures so activated were the medial preoptic nucleus, mesencephalic reticular formation, red nucleus of the stria terminalis, dorsal raphe nucleus, and the globus pallidus. Some but not all of these areas had been previously shown by electrical recording, lesioning, and stimulating techniques to participate in the behavioral and physiological responses to coitus. These results provide additional information about the concurrent processing of sensory stimulation in the brain and also indicate that the medial preoptic area is a receptive area for copulatory stimulation.

The female gonadal hormones, estrogen and progesterone, influence sexual behavior and have potent influences on the central nervous system, particularly the hypothalamus. Porrino *et al.* (1982) have used the deoxyglucose method in an attempt to identify regions of the brain affected by these hormones. In ovariectomized rats estradiol treatment stimulated glucose utilization in anterior, ventromedial, lateral, and posterior areas of the hypothalamus. Progesterone alone had very little effect in these areas. When progesterone was administered to animals which had been implanted previously with estradiol, glucose utilization was reduced in the lateral preoptic, medial preoptic area, and anterior hypothalamus below the levels of the ovariectomized controls. These data suggest an anatomical separation of the effects of gonadal steroids in the hypothalamus; estradiol may facilitate neural activity in the mid and posterior areas of the hypothalamus whereas estrogen in combination with progesterone suppresses activity in the anterior preoptic area. These two patterns in the anterior and posterior hypothalamus may reflect differential involvement in feminine sexual behavior.

C. Neuropharmacological Applications

The ability of the deoxyglucose method to map the entire brain for localized regions of altered functional activity on the basis of changes in energy metabolism offers a potent tool to identify the neural sites of action of agents with neuropharmacological and psychopharmacological actions. It does not, however, discriminate between the direct and indirect effects of the drug. An entire pathway may be activated even though the direct action of the drug may be exerted only at the origin of the pathway. This is of advantage for relating behavioral effects to central actions, but it is a disadvantage if the goal is to identify the primary site of action of the drug. To discriminate between direct and indirect actions of a drug the [^{14}C]deoxyglucose method must be combined with selectively placed lesions in the CNS that interrupt afferent pathways to the structure in question. If the metabolic effect of the drug then remains, then it is due to direct action; if lost, the effect is likely to be indirect and mediated via the interrupted pathway. Nevertheless, the method has proved to be useful in a number of pharmacological studies.

1. Effects of γ-Butyrolactone

γ-Hydroxybutyrate and γ-butyrolactone, which is hydrolyzed to γ-hydroxybutyrate in plasma, produce trance-like behavioral states associated with marked suppression of electroencephalographic activity

(Roth and Giarman, 1966). These effects are reversible, and these drugs have been used clinically as anesthetic adjuvants. There is evidence that these agents lower neuronal activity in the nigrostriatal pathway and may act by inhibition of dopaminergic synapses (Roth, 1976). Studies in rats with the [^{14}C]deoxyglucose technique have demonstrated that γ-butyrolactone produces profound dose-dependent reductions of glucose utilization throughout the brain (Wolfson *et al.*, 1977). At the highest doses studied, 600 mg/kg of body weight, glucose utilization was reduced by approximately 75% in gray matter and 33% in white matter, but there was no obvious further specificity with respect to the local cerebral structures affected. The reversibility of the effects and the magnitude and diffuseness of the depression of cerebral metabolic rate suggest that this drug might be considered as a chemical substitute for hypothermia in conditions in which profound reversible reduction of cerebral metabolism is desired.

2. Effects of D-Lysergic Acid Diethylamide

The effects of the potent psychotomimetic agent, D-lysergic acid diethylamide, have been examined in the rat (Shinohara *et al.*, 1976). In doses of 12.5 to 125 μg/kg, it caused dose-dependent reductions in glucose utilization in a number of cerebral structures. With increasing dosage more structures were affected and to a greater degree. There was no pattern in the distribution of the effects, at least none discernible at the present level of resolution, that might contribute to the understanding of the drug's psychotomimetic actions.

3. Effects of Morphine Addiction and Withdrawal

Acute morphine administration depresses glucose utilization in many areas of the brain, but the specific effects of morphine could not be distinguished from those of the hypercapnia produced by the associated respiratory depression (Sakurada *et al.*, 1976). In contrast, morphine addiction, produced within 24 hours by a single subcutaneous injection of 150 mg/kg of morphine base in an oil emulsion, reduces glucose utilization in a large number of gray structures in the absence of changes in arterial pCO_2. White matter appears to be unaffected. Naloxone (1 mg/kg subcutaneously) reduces glucose utilization in a number of structures when administered to normal rats, but when given to the morphine-addicted animals produces an acute withdrawal syndrome and reverses the reductions of glucose utilization in several structures, most strikingly in the habenula (Sakurada *et al.*, 1976).

4. Pharmacological Studies of Dopaminergic Systems

The most extensive applications of the deoxyglucose method to pharmacology have been in studies of dopaminergic systems. Ascending dopaminergic pathways appear to have a potent influence on glucose utilization in the forebrain of rats. Electrolytic lesions placed unilaterally in the lateral hypothalamus or pars compacta of the substantia nigra caused marked ipsilateral reductions of glucose metabolism in numerous forebrain structures rostral to the lesion, particularly the frontal cerebral cortex, caudate putamen, and parts of the thalamus (Schwartz *et al.*, 1976; Schwartz, 1978). Similar lesions in the locus coeruleus had no such effects.

The administration of the agonist of dopamine, apomorphine (Brown and Wolfson, 1978), or of amphetamine (Wechsler *et al.*, 1979), which stimulates release of dopamine at the synapse, produces marked increases in glucose consumption in some of the components of the extrapyramidal system known or suspected to contain dopamine-receptive cells. With both drugs, the greatest increases noted were in the zona reticulata of the substantia nigra and the subthalamic nucleus. Surprisingly, none of the components of the dopaminergic mesolimbic system appeared to be affected.

The studies with amphetamine (Wechsler *et al.*, 1979) were carried out with the fully quantitative [^{14}C]deoxyglucose method. The results in Table V illustrate the comprehensiveness with which this method surveys the entire brain for sites of altered activity due to actions of the drug. It also allows for quantitative comparison of the relative potencies of related drugs. For example, in Table V, the comparative effects of *d*-amphetamine and the less potent dopaminergic agent, *l*-amphetamine, are compared; the quantitative results clearly reveal that the effects of *l*-amphetamine on local cerebral glucose utilization are more limited in distribution and of lesser magnitude than those of *d*-amphetamine. Indeed, in similar quantitative studies with apomorphine, McCulloch *et al.* (1979, 1980a) have been able to generate complete dose–response curves for the effects of the drug on the rates of glucose utilization in various components of dopaminergic systems. They have also demon-

TABLE V

Effects of d-Amphetamine and l-Amphetamine on Local Cerebral Glucose Utilization in the Conscious Rat[a,b]

Structure	Control	d-Amphetamine	l-Amphetamine
Gray matter			
Visual cortex	102 ± 8	135 ± 11*	105 ± 8
Auditory cortex	160 ± 11	162 ± 6	141 ± 6
Parietal cortex	109 ± 9	125 ± 10	116 ± 4
Sensory–motor cortex	118 ± 8	139 ± 9	111 ± 4
Olfactory cortex	100 ± 6	93 ± 5	94 ± 3
Frontal cortex	109 ± 10	130 ± 8	105 ± 4
Prefrontal cortex	146 ± 10	166 ± 7	154 ± 4
Thalamus—lateral nucleus	97 ± 5	114 ± 8	117 ± 6
Ventral nucleus	85 ± 7	108 ± 6*	96 ± 4
Habenula	118 ± 10	71 ± 5**	82 ± 2**
Dorsomedial nucleus	92 ± 6	111 ± 8	106 ± 6
Medial geniculate	116 ± 5	119 ± 4	116 ± 4
Lateral geniculate	79 ± 5	88 ± 5	84 ± 4
Hypothalamus	54 ± 5	56 ± 3	52 ± 3
Suprachiasmatic nucleus	94 ± 4	75 ± 4**	67 ± 1**
Mamillary body	117 ± 8	134 ± 5	142 ± 5 *
Lateral olfactory nucleus[c]	92 ± 6	95 ± 5	99 ± 6
A_{13}	71 ± 4	91 ± 4**	81 ± 4
Hippocampus—Ammon's horn	79 ± 5	73 ± 2	81 ± 6
Dentate gyrus	60 ± 4	55 ± 3	67 ± 7
Amygdala	46 ± 3	46 ± 3	44 ± 2
Septal nucleus	56 ± 3	55 ± 2	54 ± 3
Caudate nucleus	109 ± 5	132 ± 8*	127 ± 3*
Nucleus accumbens	76 ± 5	80 ± 3	78 ± 3
Globus pallidus	53 ± 3	64 ± 2*	65 ± 3*
Subthalamic nucleus	89 ± 6	149 ± 10**	107 ± 2
Substantia nigra—zona reticulata	58 ± 2	105 ± 4	72 ± 4
Zona compacta	65 ± 4	88 ± 6**	72 ± 3
Red nucleus	76 ± 5	94 ± 5*	86 ± 2
Vestibular nucleus	121 ± 11	137 ± 5	130 ± 4
Cochlear nucleus	139 ± 6	126 ± 1	141 ± 5
Superior olivary nucleus	144 ± 4	143 ± 4	147 ± 6
Lateral lemniscus	107 ± 3	96 ± 5	98 ± 3
Inferior colliculus	193 ± 10	169 ± 5	150 ± 8**

(continued)

TABLE V (Continued)

Structure	Control	d-Amphetamine	l-Amphetamine
Gray matter			
Dorsal tegmental nucleus	109 ± 5	112 ± 7	122 ± 6
Superior colliculus	80 ± 5	89 ± 3	91 ± 3
Pontine gray	58 ± 4	65 ± 3	60 ± 1
Cerebellar flocculus	124 ± 10	146 ± 15	153 ± 10
Cerebellar hemispheres	55 ± 3	68 ± 6	64 ± 2
Cerebellar nuclei	102 ± 4	105 ± 8	110 ± 3
White matter			
Corpus callosum	23 ± 3	24 ± 2	23 ± 1
Genu of corpus callosum	29 ± 2	30 ± 2	26 ± 2
Internal capsule	21 ± 1	24 ± 2	19 ± 2
Cerebellar white	28 ± 1	31 ± 2	31 ± 2

[a] From Wechsler et al. (1979).

[b] All values are the means ± standard error of the mean for five animals.

[c] It was not possible to correlate precisely this area on autoradiographs with a specific structure in the rat brain. It is, however, most likely the lateral olfactory nucleus.

* Significant difference from the control at the $p < 0.05$ level.

** Significant difference from the control at the $p < 0.01$ level.

strated metabolically the development of supersensitivity to apomorphine in rats maintained chronically on the dopamine antagonist, haloperidol (J. McCulloch, H. E. Savaki, A. Pert, W. Bunney, and L. Sokoloff, unpublished observations). In the course of these studies with apomorphine, McCulloch et al. (1980b) obtained evidence of a retinal dopaminergic system that projects specifically to the superficial layer of the superior colliculus in the rat. Apomorphine administration activated metabolism in the superficial layer of the superior colliculus, as well as in other structures, but the effect in the superficial layer was prevented by prior enucleation (Fig. 13). Miyaoka (unpublished observations) subsequently observed that intraocular administration of minute amounts of apomorphine caused increased glucose utilization only in the superficial layer of the superior colliculus of the contralateral side.

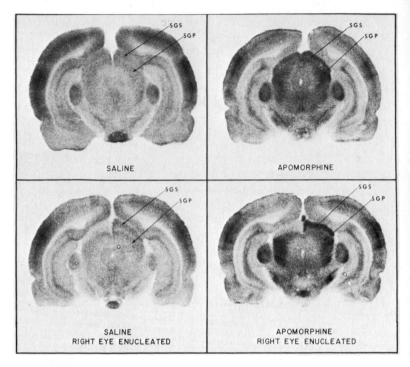

FIG. 13. Representative autoradiographs at the level of superior colliculus in dark-adapted rats studied in the dark. Abbreviations: SGS, stratum griseum superficiale; SGP, stratum griseum profundum. *Upper left:* saline, intact visual system. *Upper right:* apomorphine (1.5 mg/kg), intact visual system. Note bilaterally increased optical density (that is, elevated glucose utilization) in both superficial and deep laminae of the superior colliculus. *Lower left:* saline, right eye enucleated. Asymmetrical optical density with reduction on contralateral side is apparent within the superficial layer, whereas in the deeper layer optical density remains symmetrical. *Lower right:* apomorphine (1.5 mg/kg), right eye enucleated. Note increased optical density bilaterally in the deeper layer but only in the right or ipsilateral superficial layer of the superior colliculus. (From McCulloch *et al.*, 1980b.)

5. *Effects of α- and β-Adrenergic Blocking Agents*

Savaki *et al.* (1978) have studied the effects of the α-adrenergic blocking agent, phentolamine, and the β-adrenergic blocking agent, propranolol. Both drugs produced widespread dose-dependent depressions of glucose utilization throughout the brain, but exhibit particularly striking and opposite effects in the complete auditory pathway from the cochlear nucleus to the auditory cortex. Propranolol markedly depressed and phentolamine markedly enhanced glucose utilization in this pathway. The functional significance of these effects is unknown, but they seem to correlate with corresponding effects on the electrophysiological responsiveness of this sensory system. Propranolol depresses and phentolamine enhances the amplitude of all components of evoked auditory responses (T. Furlow and J. Hallenbeck, personal communication).

D. Neuropathophysiological Applications

The application of the deoxyglucose method to the study of pathological states has been limited because of uncertainties about the values for the lumped and rate constants to be used. There are, however, pathophysiological states in which there is no structural damage to the tissue and the standard values of the constants can be used. Several of these conditions have been and are continuing to be studied by the [^{14}C]deoxyglucose technique, both qualitatively and quantitatively.

1. Convulsive States

The local injection of penicillin into the motor cortex produces focal seizures manifested in specific regions of the body contralaterally. The [^{14}C]deoxyglucose method has been used to map the spread of seizure activity within the brain and to identify the structures with altered functional activity during the seizure. The partial results of one such experiment in the monkey are illustrated in Fig. 6. Discrete regions of markedly increased glucose utilization, sometimes as much as 200%, are observed ipsilaterally in the motor cortex, basal ganglia, particularly the globus pallidus, thalamic nuclei, and contralaterally in the cerebellar cortex (Kennedy et al., 1975). Kato et al. (1980), Caveness et al. (1980), Hosokawa et al. (1980), and Caveness (1980) have carried out the most extensive studies of the propagation of the seizure activity in newborn and pubescent monkeys. The results indicate that the brain of the newborn monkey exhibits similar increases of glucose utilization in specific structures, but the pattern of distribution of the effects is less well defined than in the pubescent monkeys. Collins et al. (1976) have carried out similar studies in the rat with similar results but also obtained evidence on the basis of a local stimulation of glucose utilization of a "mirror focus" in the motor cortex contralateral to the side with the penicillin-induced epileptogenic focus.

Engel *et al.* (1978) have used the [^{14}C]deoxyglucose method to study seizures kindled in rats by daily electroconvulsive shocks. After a period of such treatment, the animals exhibit spontaneous seizures. Their results show marked increases in the limbic system, particularly the amygdala. The daily administration of the local anesthetic, lidocaine, kindles similar seizures in rats; Post *et al.* (1979) have obtained similar results in such seizures with particularly pronounced increases in glucose utilization in the amygdala, hippocampus, and the enterorhinal cortex.

2. Spreading Cortical Depression

Shinohara *et al.* (1979) studied the effects of local applications of KCl on the dura overlying the parietal cortex of conscious rats or directly on the pial surface of the parietal cortex of anesthetized rats in order to determine if K^+ stimulates cerebral energy metabolism *in vivo* as it is well known to do *in vitro*. The results demonstrate a marked increase in cerebral cortical glucose utilization in response to the application of KCl; NaCl has no such effect (Fig. 14). Such application of KCl, however, also produces the phenomenon of spreading cortical depression. This condition is characterized by a spread of transient intense neuronal activity followed by membrane depolarization, electrical depression, and a negative shift in the cortical DC potential in all directions from the site of initiation at a rate of 2–5 mm/min. The depressed cortex also exhibits a number of chemical changes, including an increase in extracellular K^+, lost presumably from the cells. At the same time when the cortical glucose utilization is increased, most sub-

---

FIG. 14. Autoradiographs of sections of rat brains during spreading cortical depression and during recovery. The autoradiographs are pictorial representations of the relative rates of glucose utilization in various parts of the brain; the greater the density, the greater the rate of glucose utilization. The left sides of the brain are represented by the left hemispheres in the autoradiographs. In all the experiments illustrated, the control hemisphere was treated the same as the experimental side except that equivalent concentrations of NaCl rather than KCl were used. The NaCl did not lead to any detectable differences from

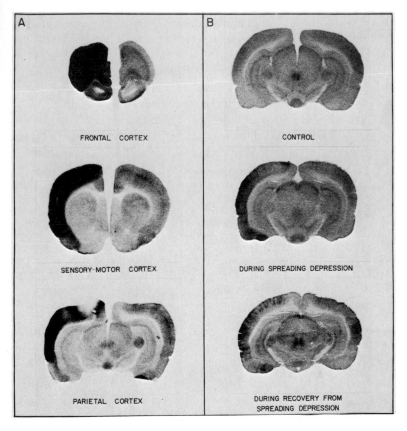

hemispheres over which the skull was left intact and no NaCl was applied. (A) Auto-radiographs of sections of brain at different levels of cerebral cortex from a conscious rat during spreading cortical depression induced on the left side by application of 5 M KCl to the intact dura overlying the left parietal cortex. The spreading depression was sustained by repeated applications of the KCl at 15- to 20-minute intervals throughout the experimental period. (B) Autoradiographs from sections of brain at the level of the parietal cortex from three animals under barbiturate anesthesia. The top section is from a normal anesthetized animal; the middle section is from an animal during unilateral spreading cortical depression induced and sustained by repeated applications of 80 mM KCl in artificial cerebrospinal fluid directly on the surface of the left parietooccipital cortex. At the bottom is a comparable section from an animal studied immediately after the return of cortical DC potential to normal after a single wave of spreading depression induced by a single application of 80 mM KCl to the parietooccipital cortex of the left side. (From Shinohara *et al.*, 1979.)

cortical structures that are functionally connected to the depressed cortex exhibit decreased rates of glucose utilization. During recovery from the spreading cortical depression, the glucose utilization in the cortex is still increased, but it is distributed in columns oriented perpendicularly through the cortex. This columnar arrangement may reflect the columnar functional and morphological arrangement of the cerebral cortex. It is likely that the increased glucose utilization in the cortex during spreading cortical depression is the consequence of the increased extracellular K^+ and activation of the Na^+, K^+-ATPase.

3. Opening of Blood–Brain Barrier

Unilateral opening of the blood–brain barrier in rats by unilateral carotid injection with a hyperosmotic mannitol solution leads to widely distributed discrete regions of intensely increased glucose utilization in the ipsilateral hemisphere (Pappius et al., 1979). These focal regions of hypermetabolism may reflect local regions of seizure activity. The prior administration of diazepam prevents in most cases the appearance of these areas of increased metabolism (Pappius et al., 1979), and electroencephalographic recordings under similar experimental conditions reveal evidence of seizure activity (Fieschi et al., 1980).

4. Hypoxemia

Pulsinelli and Duffy (1979) have studied the effects of controlled hypoxemia on local cerebral glucose utilization by means of the qualitative [^{14}C]deoxyglucose method. Hypoxemia was achieved by artificial ventilation of the animals with a mixture of N_2, N_2O, and O_2, adjusted to maintain the arterial pO_2 between 28 and 32 mm Hg. All the animals had had one common carotid artery ligated to limit the increase in cerebral blood flow and the amount of O_2 delivered to the brain. Their autoradiographs provide striking evidence of marked and disparate changes in glucose utilization in the various structural components of the brain. The hemisphere ipsilateral to the carotid ligation was not unexpectedly more severely affected. The most striking effects were markedly higher increases in glucose utilization in white matter than in gray matter, presumably due to the Pasteur effect, and the appearance of transverse cortical columns of high activity alternating with columns of low activity. By studies with black plastic microspheres, they were able to show that the cortical columns were anatomically related to penetrating cortical arteries with the columns of high metabolic activity lying between the arteries.

Miyaoka *et al.* (1979b) have also studied the effects of moderate hypoxemia in normal, spontaneously breathing conscious rats without carotid ligation. The hypoxemia was produced by lowering the O_2 in the inspired air to approximately 7%. Although this procedure reduced arterial pO_2 to approximately 30 mm Hg, the cerebral hypoxia was probably less than in the studies of Pulsinelli and Duffy (1979) because of the intact cerebral circulation. The animals remained fully conscious under these experimental conditions although they appeared subdued and less active. The quantitative [^{14}C]deoxyglucose method was employed, and rates of glucose utilization were determined. The results revealed many similarities to those of Pulsinelli and Duffy (1979). There was a complete redistribution of the local rates of glucose utilization from the normal pattern. Metabolism in white matter was markedly increased. Many areas showed decreased rates of metabolism. Columns were seen in the cerebral cortex, and the caudate nucleus exhibited a strange lace-like heterogeneity quite distinct from its normal homogeneity. Despite the widespread changes, however, overall average glucose utilization remained unchanged. These results are of relevance to the studies by Kety and Schmidt (1948b), who found in man that the breathing of 10% O_2 produced a wide variety of mental symptoms without altering the average O_2 consumption of the brain as a whole. The mental symptoms were probably the result of metabolic and functional changes in specific regions of the brain detectable only by methods like the deoxyglucose method that measure metabolic rate in the structural components of the brain.

5. Normal Aging

Although, strictly speaking, aging is not a pathophysiological condition, many of its behavioral consequences are directly attributable to decrements in functions of the central nervous system (Birren *et al.*, 1963). Normal human aging has been found to be associated with a decrease in average glucose utilization of the brain as a whole (Sokoloff, 1966). Smith *et al.* (1980) have employed the quantitative [^{14}C]deoxyglucose method to study normal aging in Sprague–Dawley rats between 5–6 and 36 months of age. Their results show widespread but not homogeneous reductions of local cerebral glucose utilization with age. The sensory systems, particularly auditory and visual, are particularly severely affected. Components of the extrapyramidal motor system are also metabolically depressed, and preliminary experiments indicate that they lose responsivity to dopamine agonists, such as apomorphine, with age (C. Smith and J. McCulloch, unpublished observations). This loss of response to a maximal dose of a dopamine agonist suggests loss of functional dopamine receptors. A striking effect was the loss of metabolically active neuropil in the cerebral cortex; layer IV is markedly decreased in metabolic activity and extent. Some of these changes may be related to specific functional disabilities that develop in old age.

VII. Microscopic Resolution

The resolution of the present [^{14}C]deoxyglucose method is at best approximately 100–200 μm (Smith, 1983). The use of [^{3}H]deoxyglucose does not greatly improve the resolution when the standard autoradiographic procedure is used. The limiting factor is the diffusion and migration of the water-soluble labeled compound in the tissue during the freezing of the brain and the cutting of the brain sections (Smith, 1983). Des Rosiers and Descarries (1978) attempted to extend the resolution of the method to the light and electron microscopic levels by the use of [^{3}H]deoxyglucose and dipping emulsion techniques applied to brain that was fixed, dehydrated, and embedded by perfusion *in situ*. They could localize grain counts over individual cells or portions of them, but loss of label and, therefore, also of quantitative reliability, undoubtedly occurred. An alternative promising approach to microscopic resolution is the use of freeze-substitution techniques (Ornberg *et al.*, 1979; Sejnowski *et al.*, 1980; Smith, 1983).

VIII. The [^{18}F]Fluorodeoxyglucose Technique

The deoxyglucose method was originally designed for use in animals with quantitative autoradiography and the radioactive isotopes most suitable for film autoradiography, ^{14}C or ^{3}H. Its basic physiological and biochemical principles apply, however, to man as well, and it is applicable to man provided the local tissue concentrations of isotope can be measured in the brain. Film autoradiography is a type of emission tomography that for obvious reasons cannot be used in man, but recent developments in computerized tomography have made it possible to determine local concentrations of γ-emitting isotopes in the cerebral tissues. The only possible γ-emitting isotopes that can be incorporated into 2-deoxyglucose are ^{11}C or ^{15}O, but the short half-lives of these isotopes present problems in the synthesis of the compounds. Alternatively, an analog of 2-deoxyglucose with another γ-emitting isotope but with similar biochemical properties could be used. It is a common experience that the substitution of the very small atom, F, in place of a hydrogen at a judicious site in the molecule often does not alter the basic biochemical behavior of metabolic substrates. 2-[^{18}F]Fluoro-2-deoxy-D-glucose has been synthesized, found to retain the biochemical properties of 2-deoxyglucose, and used to measure cerebral glucose utilization in man by means of single photon emission tomography (Reivich et al., 1979). ^{18}F is actually a positron emitter, and the absorption of positrons in the tissues gives rise to two coincident annihilation γ rays of equal energy traveling at almost 180° to each other. Positron emission tomography takes advantage of these coincident annihilation γ rays and, therefore, is inherently capable of better spatial resolution than single photon tomography. The [^{18}F]fluorodeoxyglucose method is, therefore, now generally used with positron emission tomography (Phelps et al., 1979). Positron emission tomography with [^{18}F]fluorodeoxyglucose is still relatively slow, and it may take up to 2 hours to obtain sufficient counts for accurate measurements of local ^{18}F concentrations in all parts of the brain. Although low in brain, glucose-6-phosphatase activity is not zero, and its effect becomes significant after the first 45 minutes after the pulse of tracer (Sokoloff, 1982). It has, therefore, been necessary to modify the model to include a rate constant for the hydrolysis of the phosphorylated product by glucose-6-phosphatase and to derive a new operational equation that takes this activity into account (Huang et al., 1980; Phelps et al., 1979; Sokoloff, 1982). The [^{18}F]fluorodeoxyglucose technique for the measurement of local cerebral glucose utilization in man is now operational and in use for studies of the human brain in health and disease in a number of laboratories. It has been used in studies of the visual and auditory systems (Phelps et al., 1981) and of clinical conditions, such as focal epilepsy (Kuhl et al., 1979, 1980), Huntington's disease (Kuhl et al., 1982b), aging (Kuhl et al., 1982a) and dementia (Kuhl et al., 1983; Foster et al., 1983), and cerebral gliomas (DiChiro *et al.,* 1983). MacGregor *et al.* (1981) and Reivich *et al.* (1982) have recently succeeded in synthesizing [^{11}C]deoxyglucose and applied it to the measurement of local cerebral glucose utilization in man with positron emission tomography. Because of the short half-life of ^{11}C this development should be very useful for sequential measurements in the same subject in a short time period.

IX. SUMMARY

The deoxyglucose method provides the means to determine quantitatively the rates of glucose utilization simultaneously in all structural and functional components of the central nervous system and to display them pictorially superimposed on the anatomical structures in which they occur. Because of the close relationship between local functional activity and energy metabolism, the method makes it possible to identify all structures with increased or decreased functional activity in various physiological, pharmacological, and pathophysiological states. The images provided by the method do resemble histological sections of nervous tissue, and the method is, therefore, sometimes misconstrued to be a neuroanatomical method and contrasted with physiological methods, such as electrophysiological recording. This classification obscures the most significant and unique feature of the method. The images are not of structure but of a dynamic biochemical process, glucose utilization, which is as physiological as electrical activity. In most situations changes in functional activity result in changes in energy metabolism, and the images can be used to visualize and identify the sites of altered activity. The images are, therefore, analogous to infrared maps; they record quantitatively the rates of a kinetic process and display them pictorially exactly where they exist. The fact that they depict the anatomical structures is fortuitous; it indicates that the rates of glucose utilization are distributed according to structure, and specific functions in the nervous system are associated with specific anatomical structures. The deoxyglucose method represents, therefore, in a real sense, a new type of encephalography, metabolic encephalography. At the very least, it should serve as a valuable supplement to more conventional types, such as electroencephalography. Because, however, it provides a new means to examine another aspect of function simultaneously in all parts of the brain, it is hoped that it and its derivative, the

[^{18}F]fluorodeoxyglucose technique, will open new roads to the understanding of how the brain works in health and disease.

ACKNOWLEDGMENTS

The author wishes to express his appreciation to Mrs. Brenda Sandler for her excellent editorial and bibliographic assistance and to Mr. J. D. Brown for his skilled photographic reproductions.

REFERENCES

Abrams, R., Ito, M., Frisinger, J. E., Patlak, C. S., Pettigrew, K. D., and Kennedy, C. (1984). *Am. J. Physiol.*, **246**, R608.

Allen, T. O., Adler, N. T., Greenberg, J. H., and Reivich, M. (1981). *Science* **211**, 1070.

Bachelard, H. S. (1971). *J. Neurochem.* **18**, 213.

Batipps, M., Miyaoka, M., Shinohara, M., Sokoloff, L., and Kennedy, C. (1981). *Neurology* **31**, 58.

Bidder, T. G. (1968). *J. Neurochem.* **15**, 867.

Birren, J. E., Butler, R. N., Greenhouse, S. W., Sokoloff, L., and Yarrow, M. R., eds. (1963). "Human Aging: A Biological and Behavioral Study." Public Health Service Publ. No. 986. U.S. Govt. Printing Office, Washington, D.C.

Brown, L., and Wolfson, L. (1978). *Brain Res.* **148**, 188.

Caveness, W. F. (1969). *In* "Basic Mechanisms of the Epilepsies" (H. H. Jasper, A. A. Ward, and A. Pope, eds.), pp. 517–534. Little, Brown, Boston.

Caveness, W. F. (1980). *Ann. Neurol.* **7**, 230.

Caveness, W. F., Kato, M., Malamut, B. I.., Hosokawa, S., Wakisaka, S., and O'Neill, R. R. (1980). *Ann. Neurol.* **7**, 213.

Collins, R. C., Kennedy, C., Sokoloff, L., and Plum, F. (1976). *Arch. Neurol.* **33**, 536.

Des Rosiers, M. H., and Descarries, L. (1978). *C.R. Acad. Sci. Paris, Ser. D* **287**, 153.

Des Rosiers, M. H., Sakurada, O., Jehle, J., Shinohara, M., Kennedy, C., and Sokoloff, L. (1978). *Science* **200**, 447.

DiChiro, G., Brooks, R. A., Sokoloff, L., Patronas, N. J., DeLaPaz, R. L., Smith, B. H., and Kornblith, P. L. (1983). *In* "Positron Emission Tomography of the Brain" (E.-D. Heiss and M. E. Phelps, eds.), pp. 181–191. Springer-Verlag, Berlin and New York.

Dow-Edwards, D. L., Crane, A., Kennedy, C., and Sokoloff, L. (1982). *Soc. Neurosci. Abstr.* **8**, 82.

Duffy, T. E., Cavazutti, M., Cruz, N. F., and Sokoloff, L. (1982). *Ann. Neurol.* **11**, 233.

Durham, D., and Woolsey, T. A. (1977). *Brain Res.* **137**, 169.

Eayrs, J. (1961). *J. Endocrinol.* **22**, 409.

Eklöf, B., Lassen, N. A., Nilsson, L., Norberg, K., and Siesjö, B. K. (1973). *Acta Physiol. Scand.* **88**, 587.

Engel, J., Jr., Wolfson, L., and Brown, L. (1978). *Ann. Neurol.* **3**, 538.

Fieschi, C., Lenzi, G. L., Zanette, E., Orzi, F., and Passero, S. (1980). *Life Sci.* **27**, 239.

Foster, N. L., Chase, T. N., Fedio, P., Patronas, N. J., Brooks, R. A., and DiChiro, G. (1983). *Neurology* **33**, 961.

Freygang, W. H., Jr., and Sokoloff, L. (1958). *Adv. Biol. Med. Phys.* **6**, 263.

Friedli, C. (1978). *Adv. Exp. Med. Biol.* **94**, 747–754.

Galvan, M., Ten Bruggencate, G., and Senekowitsch, R. (1979). *Brain Res.* **160**, 544.

Gjedde, A. and Diemer, N. H. (1983). *J. Cerebral Blood Flow Metab.* **3**, 303.

Gjedde, A., Caronna, J. J., Hindfelt, B., and Plum, F. (1975). *Am. J. Physiol.* **229**, 113.

Goochee, C., Rasband, W., and Sokoloff, L. (1980). *Ann. Neurol.* **7**, 359.

Hand, P. J. (1981). *In* "Neuroanatomical Tract Tracing Methods" (L. Heimer and M. J. Robards, eds.), pp. 511–538. Plenum, New York.

Hand, P. J., Greenberg, J. H., Miselis, R. R., Weller, W. L., and Reivich, M. (1978). *Soc. Neurosci. Abstr.* **4**, 553.

Hawkins, R., Phelps, M., Huang, S. C., and Kuhl, D. (1981). *J. Cerebral Blood Flow Metab.* **1** (Suppl. 1), S9.

Hers, H. G. (1957). "Le Métabolisme du Fructose," p. 102. Ed. Arscia, Brussels.

Horowicz, P., and Larrabee, M. G. (1958). *J. Neurochem.* **2**, 102.

Hosokawa, S., Iguchi, T., Caveness, W. F., Kato, M., O'Neill, R. R., Wakisaka, S., and Malamut, B. L. (1980). *Ann. Neurol.* **7**, 222.

Huang, S. C., Phelps, M. E., Hoffman, E. J., Sideris, K., Selin, C. J., and Kuhl, D. E. (1980). *Am. J. Physiol.* **238**, E69.

Hubel, D. H., and Wiesel, T. N. (1968). *J. Physiol. (London)* **195**, 215.

Hubel, D. H., and Wiesel, T. N. (1972). *J. Comp. Neurol.* **146**, 421.

Hubel, D. H., Wiesel, T. N., and Stryker, M. P. (1978). *J. Comp. Neurol.* **177**, 361.

Kadekaro, M., Gross, P. M., Holcomb, H. H., Sokoloff, L., and Saavedra, J. M. (1983). *Brain Res.* **275**, 189.

Kato, M., Malamut, B. L., Caveness, W. F., Hosokawa, S., Wakisaka, S., and O'Neill, R. R. (1980). *Ann. Neurol.* **7**, 204.

Kennedy, C., Des Rosiers, M., Jehle, J. W., Reivich, M., Sharp, F., and Sokoloff, L. (1975). *Science* **187**, 850.

Kennedy, C., Des Rosiers, M. H., Sakurada, O., Shinohara, M., Reivich, M., Jehle, J. W., and Sokoloff, L. (1976). *Proc. Natl. Acad. Sci. U.S.A.* **73**, 4230.

Kennedy, C., Sakurada, O., Shinohara, M., Jehle, J., and Sokoloff, L. (1978). *Ann. Neurol.* **4**, 293.

Kennedy, C., Miyaoka, M., Suda, S., Macko, K., Jarvis, C., Mishkin, M., and Sokoloff, L. (1980). *Trans. Am. Neurol. Assoc.* **105**, 13.

Kennedy, C., Gillin, J. C., Mendelson, W., Suda, S., Miyaoka, M., Ito, M., Nakamura, R. K., Storch, F. I, Pettigrew, K., Mishkin, M., and Sokoloff, L. (1982). *Nature* **297**, 325.

Kety, S. S. (1950). *Am. J. Med.* **8**, 205.

Kety, S. S. (1957). *In* "Metabolism of the Nervous System" (D. Richter, ed.), pp. 221–237. Pergamon, Oxford.

Kety, S. S. (1960). *Methods Med. Res.* **8**, 228.

Kety, S. S., and Schmidt, C. F. (1948a). *J. Clin. Invest.* **27**, 476.

Kety, S. S., and Schmidt, C. F. (1948b). *J. Clin. Invest.* **27**, 484.

Kuhl, D., Engel, J., Phelps, M., and Selin, C. (1979). *Acta Neurol. Scand. Suppl.* **60**, 538.

Kuhl, D. E., Engel, J., Jr., Phelps, M. E., and Selin, C. (1980). *Ann. Neurol.* **8**, 348.

Kuhl, D. E., Metter, E. J., Riege, W. H., and Phelps, M. E. (1982a). *J. Cerebral Blood Flow Metab.* **2**, 163.

Kuhl, D. E., Phelps, M. E., Markham, C. H., Meter, E. J., Riege, W. H., and Winter, J. (1982b). *Ann. Neurol.* **12,** 425.

Kuhl, D. E., Metter, E. J., Riege, W. H., Hawkins, R. A., Mazziotta, J. C., Phelps, M. E., and Kling, A. S. (1983). *J. Cerebral Blood Flow Metab.* **3,** S494.

Landau, W. M., Freygang, W. H., Jr., Rowland, L. P., Sokoloff, L., and Kety, S. S. (1955). *Trans. Am. Neurol. Assoc.* **80,** 125.

Larrabee, M. G. (1958). *J. Neurochem.* **2,** 81.

Lashley, K. S. (1934). *J. Comp. Neurol.* **59,** 341.

Lassen, N. A. (1959). *Physiol. Rev.* **39,** 183.

Lassen, N. A., and Munck, O. (1955). *Acta Physiol. Scand.* **33,** 30.

McCulloch, J., Savaki, H. E., McCulloch, M. C., and Sokoloff, L. (1979). *Nature (London)* **282,** 303.

McCulloch, J., Savaki, H. E., and Sokoloff, L. (1980a). *Brain Res.* **194,** 117.

McCulloch, J., Savaki, H. E., McCulloch, M. C., and Sokoloff, L. (1980b). *Science* **207,** 313.

MacGregor, R., Fowler, J. S., Wolfe, A. P., Shive, C., Lade, R. E., and Wan, C. (1981). *J. Nucl. Med.* **22,** 800.

Macko, K. A., Jarvis, C. D., Kennedy, C., Miyaoka, M., Shinohara, M., Sokoloff, L., and Mishkin, M. (1982). *Science* **218,** 394.

Mata, M., Fink, D. J., Gainer, H., Smith, C. B., Davidsen, L., Savaki, H., Schwartz, W. J., and Sokoloff, L. (1980). *J. Neurochem.* **34,** 213.

Miyaoka, M., Shinohara, M., Batipps, M., Pettigrew, K. D., Kennedy, C., and Sokoloff, L. (1979a). *Acta Neurol. Scand. Suppl.* **60,** 16.

Miyaoka, M., Shinohara, M., Kennedy, C., and Sokoloff, L. (1979b). *Trans. Am. Neurol. Assoc.* **104,** 151.

Montero, V. M., and Guillery, R. W. (1968). *J. Comp. Neurol.* **134,** 211.

Nelson, T., Kaufman, E., and Sokoloff, L. (1984). *J. Neurochem.* **43,** 949.

Nordmann, J. J. (1977). *J. Anat.* **123,** 213.

Oldendorf, W. H. (1971). *Am. J. Physiol.* **221,** 1629.

Ornberg, R. L., Neale, E. A., Smith, C. B., Yarowsky, P., and Bowers, L. M. (1979). *J. Cell Biol. Abstr.* **83,** CN142A.

Pappius, H. M., Savaki, H. E., Fieschi, C., Rapoport, S. I., and Sokoloff, L. (1979). *Ann. Neurol.* **5,** 211.

Phelps, M. E., Huang, S. C., Hoffman, E. J., Selin, C., Sokoloff, L., and Kuhl, D. E. (1979). *Ann. Neurol.* **6,** 371.

Phelps, M. E., Kuhl, D. E., and Mazziotta, J. C. (1981). *Science* **211,** 1445.

Plum, F., Gjedde, A., and Samson, F. E. (1976). *Neurosci. Res. Program Bull.* **14,** 457.

Porrino, L., Namba, H., Crane, A., Jehle, J., and Sokoloff, L. (1982). *Soc. Neurosci. Abstr.* **8,** 69.

Post, R. M., Kennedy, C., Shinohara, M., Squillace, K., Miyaoka, M., Suda, S., Ingvar, D. H., and Sokoloff, L. (1979). *Soc. Neurosci. Abstr.* **5,** 196.

Pulsinelli, W. A., and Duffy, T. E. (1979). *Science* **204,** 626.

Rakic, P. (1976). *Nature (London)* **261,** 467.

Reivich, M., Jehle, J., Sokoloff, L., and Kety, S. S. (1969). *J. Appl. Physiol.* **27,** 296.

Reivich, M., Kuhl, D., Wolf, A., Greenberg, J., Phelps, M., Ido, T., Cassella, V., Fowler, J., Hoffman, E., Alavi, A., Som, P., and Sokoloff, L. (1979). *Circ. Res.* **44,** 127.

Reivich, M., Alavi, A., Wolf, A., Greenberg, J. H., Fowler, J., Christman, D., Mac-Gregor, R., Jones, S. C., London, J., Shine, C., and Yonekura, Y. (1982). *J. Cerebral Blood Flow Metab.* **2,** 307.

Roth, R. H. (1976). *Pharmacol. Ther.* **2,** 71.

Roth, R. H., and Giarman, N. J. (1966). *Biochem. Pharmacol.* **15,** 1333.

Sacks, W. (1957). *J. Appl. Physiol.* **10,** 37.

Sakurada, O., Shinohara, M., Klee, W. A., Kennedy, C., and Sokoloff, L. (1976). *Soc. Neurosci. Abstr.* **2,** 613.

Savaki, H. E., Kadekaro, M., Jehle, J., and Sokoloff, L. (1978). *Nature (London)* **276,** 521.

Savaki, H. E., McCulloch, J., Kadekaro, M., and Sokoloff, L. (1982). *Brain Res.* **233,** 347.

Scheinberg, P., and Stead, E. A., Jr. (1949). *J. Clin. Invest.* **28,** 1163.

Schoppmann, A., and Stryker, M. P. (1981). *Nature (London)* **293,** 574.

Schuier, F., Orzi, F., Suda, S., Kennedy, C., and Sokoloff, L. (1981). *J. Cerebral Blood Flow Metab.* **1,** S63.

Schwartz, W. J. (1978). *Brain Res.* **158,** 129.

Schwartz, W. J., and Gainer, H. (1977). *Science* **197,** 1089.

Schwartz, W. J., Sharp, F. R., Gunn, R. H., and Evarts, E. V. (1976). *Nature (London)* **261,** 155.

Schwartz, W. J., Smith, C. B., Davidsen, L., Savaki, H., Sokoloff, L., Meta, M., Fink, D. J., and Gainer, H. (1979). *Science* **205,** 723.

Schwartz, W. J., Davidsen, L. C., and Smith, C. B. (1980). *J. Comp. Neurol.* **189,** 157.

Sejnowski, T. J., Reingold, S. C., Kelley, D. B., and Gelperin, A. (1980). *Nature (London)* **287,** 449.

Sharp, F. R., Kauer, J. S., and Shepherd, G. M. (1975). *Brain Res.* **98,** 596.

Shinohara, M., Sakurada, O., Jehle, J., and Sokoloff, L. (1976). *Soc. Neurosci. Abstr.* **2,** 615.

Shinohara, M., Dollinger, B., Brown, G., Rapoport, S., and Sokoloff, L. (1979). *Science* **203,** 188.

Silverman, M. S., Hendrickson, A. E., and Clopton, B. M. (1977). *Soc. Neurosci. Abstr.* **3,** 11.

Smith, C. B. (1983). *In* "Current Methods in Cellular Neurobiology" (J. L. Barker and J. F. McKelvy, eds.), pp. 269–317. Wiley, New York.

Smith, C. B., Goochee, C., Rapoport, S. I., and Sokoloff, L. (1980). *Brain* **103,** 351.

Sokoloff, L. (1960). *Handb. Physiol. Neurophysiol.* **III,** 1843–1864.

Sokoloff, L. (1966). *Res. Publ. Assoc. Nerv. Ment. Dis.* **41,** 237.

Sokoloff, L. (1969). *In* "Psychochemical Research in Man" (A. J. Mandell and M. P. Mandell, eds.), pp. 237–252. Academic Press, New York.

Sokoloff, L. (1976). *In* "Basic Neurochemistry" (G. J. Siegel, R. W. Albers, R. Katzman, and B. W. Agranoff, eds.), 2nd ed., pp. 388–413. Little, Brown, Boston.

Sokoloff, L. (1977). *J. Neurochem.* **29,** 13.

Sokoloff, L. (1978a). *Trends Neurosci.* **1,** 75.

Sokoloff, L. (1978b). *Ciba Found. Symp.* **56,** 171–197.

Sokoloff, L. (1979). *Acta Neurol. Scand. Suppl.* **60,** 640.

Sokoloff, L. (1982). *In* "Advances in Neurochemistry," Vol. 4 (B. W. Agranoff and M. H. Aprison, eds.), pp. 1–82. Plenum, New York.

Sokoloff, L., Wechsler, R. L., Mangold, R., Balls, K., and Kety, S. S. (1953). *J. CLin. Invest.* **32,** 202.

Sokoloff, L., Reivich, M., Kennedy, C., Des Rosiers, M. H., Patlak, C. S., Pettigrew, K. D., Sakurada, O., and Shinohara, M. (1977). *J. Neurochem.* **28,** 897.

Sols, A., and Crane, R. K. (1954). *J. Biol. Chem.* **210,** 581.

Suda, S., Shinohara, M., Miyaoka, M., Kennedy, C., and Sokoloff, L. (1981). *J. Cerebral Blood Flow Metab.* **1,** S62.

Tootell, R. B. H., Silverman, M. S., Switkes, E., and De Valois, R. L. (1982). *Science* **218,** 902.

Webster, W. R., Serviere, J., Batini, C., and LaPlante, S. (1978). *Neurosci. Lett.* **10,** 43.

THE ENDOCRINE CONTROL OF SEXUAL DIFFERENTIATION*

JEAN D. WILSON

Department of Internal Medicine
The University of Texas Health Science Center at Dallas
Southwestern Medical School
Dallas, Texas

I. INTRODUCTION

E MBRYOS of both sexes develop in an identical fashion for the first portion of gestation, and thereafter anatomical and physiological development diverge to result in the formation of the male and female phenotypes. The fundamental mechanism of sexual differentiation was elucidated by Alfred Jost and was the subject of a previous Harvey Lecture (Jost, 1959). According to his formulation—now the central dogma of sexual development—this process is sequential, ordered, and straightforward. Chromosomal sex, established at the time of conception, directs the development of either ovaries or testes. If testes develop, their hormonal secretions induce development of the male secondary sex characteristics, collectively known as the male phenotype. If an ovary develops or if no gonad is present, anatomical development is female in character. Thus, whatever the mechanisms by which chromosomal or genetic sex is translated into gonadal sex, the gonads act as endocrine organs to promote the sexual phenotypes.

Stimulated by this powerful paradigm, subsequent investigators have sought to identify the specific hormones that are secreted by the fetal testis, to elucidate the control mechanisms that regulate the secretion of these hormones at the critical time in embryonic development, and to characterize—at the molecular and genetic level—the mechanisms by which the testicular hormones induce the conversion of the sexually indifferent embryo into the male phenotype. As a consequence, the

---

*Lecture delivered February 16, 1984.

145

original formulation of Jost has been refined and expanded, and insight has been obtained into the pathogenesis of many derangements of sexual development.

II. FORMATION OF THE SEXUAL PHENOTYPES

The first phase of sexual differentiation involves the establishment of chromosomal sex at the time of fertilization, the heterogametic complement (XY) being male and the homogametic state (XX) female (Jost, 1959). The second involves the development of gonadal sex. The germ cells originate in the yolk sac and migrate to their ultimate destination in the genital ridges of the embryo (Peters, 1970). After the migration, the gonads in male and female embryos appear identical and consist of three components—the primordial germ cells, the connective tissue of the genital ridge, and a covering layer of epithelium. The specific determinants by which the Y chromosome directs testicular development are the subject of intense scrutiny (Ohno, 1978; Wachtel, 1980; Silvers *et al.*, 1982). Histological differentiation of the gonads begins when the germ cells in the testis line up to form the spermatogenic cords. Shortly thereafter, Leydig (interstitial) cells appear in the connective tissue of the testis; these cells synthesize testosterone. In contrast to the early, rapid development of the testes, fetal overies show little histological development until the second third of gestation when ovarian follicles appear.

The anatomical events in the development of the male and female urogenital tracts are diagrammed schematically in Figs. 1 and 2 (Wilson, 1978). In brief, the primordial genital tract of both sexes consists of three components: (1) the gonads, (2) two genital duct systems (wolffian and mullerian), and (3) a common opening for the genital ducts and the urinary tract to the outside through the genital folds on the abdominal wall.

The internal genital tracts in the two sexes develop from the wolffian and mullerian ducts. Male urogenital tract development (termed virilization) begins shortly after the formation of the spermatogenic cords of the testis. The initial event is regression of the mullerian ducts followed by virilization of the wolffian ducts. The upper portion of the wolffian duct forms the epididymis, the central portion develops a thick muscular coat to become the vas deferens, and the terminal portion

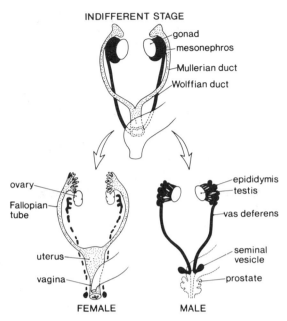

INDIFFERENT STAGE

gonad
mesonephros
Mullerian duct
Wolffian duct

ovary
Fallopian tube
uterus
vagina
FEMALE

epididymis
testis
vas deferens
seminal vesicle
prostate
MALE

Fig. 1. Formation of the internal genital tracts in male and female embryos. [Reprinted with permission from Wilson (1979).]

gives rise to the ejaculatory duct and seminal vesicle (Fig. 1). Simultaneously, the prostate gland develops from endodermal buds that appear in the lining of the primitive urethra. In the female embryo the wolffian ducts regress, and the mullerian ducts develop into the fallopian tubes and uterus and contribute to development of the vagina (Fig. 1).

The external genitalia in the two sexes develop from common anlage, which consist of the urethral fold and groove, which serves as the opening for the urogenital sinus, a genital swelling on each side of the urethral fold, and the genital tubercle (Fig. 2). The external genitalia of the female enlarge but otherwise undergo little change from the indifferent stage. The genital tubercle becomes the clitoris, the genital swellings give rise to the labia majora, and the genital folds become the labia minora. Development of the male external genitalia begins shortly after the onset of virilization of the wolffian ducts. The genital folds elongate

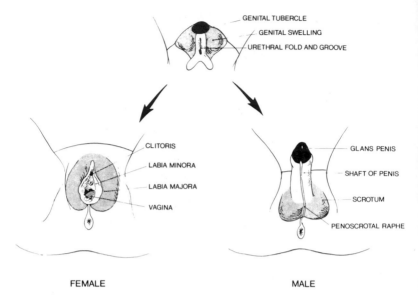

FIG. 2. Formation of the external genitalia in male and female embryos. [Reprinted with permission from Wilson and Griffin (1983).]

and fuse to form the shaft of the penis and bring the male urethra to the end of the genital tubercle (glans penis). The fusion converts the urogenital swellings into a bilobed scrotum that serves as the receptable for descent of the testes.

Anatomical development of the internal and external genitalia is accomplished largely by the end of the first trimester of gestation. During this time the testes remain in the abdominal cavity, and no differential growth of the external genitalia takes place so that there is no difference in the size of the phallus in male and female embryos when formation of the male urethra is complete. In the latter two-thirds of gestation descent of the testes and differential growth of the male genitalia occur. Descent of the testes in man takes place over a 7-month period, beginning about the sixth week of gestation and finishing in some instances after birth. Growth commences in the external genitalia, the prostate, and the structures derived from the wolffian duct during the second trimester of male development and continues throughout gestation.

III. Control of Phenotypic Development

A. *Role of Testicular Secretions*

The role of testicular secretions in the transformation of the indifferent urogenital tract and external genitalia into the male phenotype was established by studies of the effects of castration in the rabbit embryo (Jost, 1959). Removal of the gonads from embryos of either sex prior to the onset of phenotypic differentiation results in the development of a female phenotype. Thus, the male phenotype is induced by testicular secretions whereas female differentiation is not dependent on the presence of an ovary and therefore does not require secretions from the embryonic gonad. Two hormones of the fetal testis are involved in male development—mullerian-inhibiting substance and androgen.

1. *Mullerian-Inhibiting Substance*

Mullerian-inhibiting substance is an incompletely characterized peptide hormone that acts in the male to cause regression of the mullerian ducts. Its formation commences shortly after the onset of testicular differentiation and constitutes the initial endocrine function of the embryonic testis. The inhibiting substance is a glycoprotein of about M_r 70,000 and is formed by the spermatogenic tubules (Blanchard and Josso, 1974; Donahoe *et al.*, 1977; Picard *et al.*, 1978). The mechanism by which it acts to suppress mullerian duct development is uncertain. The essential nature of its action, i.e., proof that mullerian duct regression is an active process and not just a failure of the ducts to grow, is supported by the existence of a single gene defect (the persistent mullerian duct syndrome) in which genetic and phenotypic men have fallopian tubes and uteri together with male wolffian duct structures (Sloan and Walsh, 1976). This disorder is inherited as a recessive trait, either autosomal or X linked, and is believed to be due either to a failure to produce the mullerian-inhibiting substance or to an inability of the tissue to respond to the hormone.

2. *Androgen*

Jost deduced that the second developmental hormone of the fetal testis is an androgenic steroid. The principal steroid hormone formed by

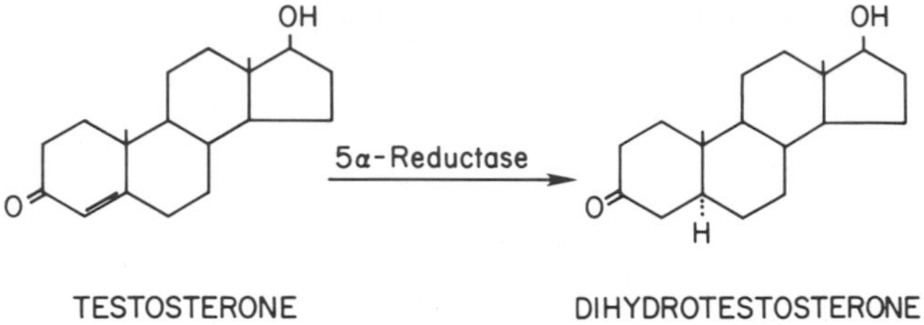

TESTOSTERONE   DIHYDROTESTOSTERONE

Fig. 3. Conversion of testosterone to dihydrotestosterone.

the testis in postnatal life is testosterone (Fig. 3). Testosterone is also the androgen formed by the testes of rabbit and human embryos at the time of male phenotypic development (Lipsett and Tullner, 1965; Wilson and Siiteri, 1973; Siiteri and Wilson, 1974). More importantly, the fetal testis forms no other major steroids at this critical time (Wilson and Siiteri, 1973; Siiteri and Wilson, 1974). Thus, testosterone is the principal fetal androgen as well as the postnatal androgen in the male. The onset of testosterone formation by the testes commences shortly after the onset of differentiation of the spermatogenic tubules and concomitant with the histological differentiation of the Leydig cells of the testis (Wilson and Siiteri, 1973; Siiteri and Wilson, 1974; George et al., 1978a).

Testosterone performs two functions in male development. First, it acts locally within the testis to promote maturation of the spermatogonia. Second, it is secreted into the fetal circulation where it induces development of the male phenotype and is probably responsible as well for programming of those systems in the central nervous system that regulate testicular function and certain male behavior patterns.

The critical role of testosterone in development of the male urogenital tract was established on four types of evidence: First, the fact that the onset of testosterone synthesis immediately precedes the initiation of virilization in a variety of species suggested a cause and effect relation between the two events (Lipsett and Tullner, 1965; Attal, 1969; Wilson and Siiteri, 1973; Siiteri and Wilson, 1974; Rigaudiere, 1979). Second, the administration of testosterone analogs induces male development of the internal and external genitalia in female embryos (Schultz and Wilson, 1974). Third, administration at the appropriate time in embryonic development of pharmacologic agents that inhibit the synthesis or action of androgens prevents male development (Goldman, 1971; Neumann *et al.*, 1970). Fourth, five separate genetic defects in the human are known to cause inadequate testosterone synthesis and incomplete virilization of the male embryo during embryogenesis (New *et al.*, 1983; Griffin and Wilson, 1980; Wilson, 1978). Each defect involves a discrete enzyme (or enzyme complex) required for the synthesis of testosterone, and each causes incomplete virilization of the male urogenital tract. The fact that the fallopian tubes and uterus are not present in such patients indicates that regression of the mullerian ducts takes place normally during embryogenesis and that mullerian regression is independent of testosterone biosynthesis.

B. *Regulation of Testosterone Synthesis in the Fetal Testis*

In the human embryo onset of testosterone synthesis occurs abruptly between the sixth and eighth weeks of development (Siiteri and Wilson, 1973). In the male rabbit embryo synthesis commences reproducibly during a 12-hour period between days 17 and 17.5 of gestation (Catt *et al.*, 1975). The sexual fate of the individual—both anatomical and behavioral—is determined by whether this increase in testosterone production occurs at the appropriate time and in sufficient magnitude. Understanding the factors that regulate testosterone biosynthesis at this time is central to understanding sexual differentiation. Perhaps the most important question about this system is whether testosterone synthesis at its onset—as is true for later stages of embryogenesis and for postnatal life—is under control of the pituitary, i.e., is the central nervous system involved in the programming of sexual differentiation? A definitive answer to this question is not available.

Prior to the onset of steroid hormone synthesis the primordial rabbit ovary and testis contain all but two enzymes (or enzyme complexes) in the testosterone synthetic pathway—the cholesterol side-chain cleavage enzyme and 3β-hydroxysteroid dehydrogenase. Enzymes required for the remaining three reactions in the conversion of cholesterol to testosterone are present in excess in both types of gonads. On approximately day 17.5 there is a rapid increase in cholesterol side-chain cleavage activity in ovaries and testis and a simultaneous increase in 3β-hydroxysteroid dehydrogenase activity only in the testes so that by day 18 the activity of the latter enzyme is at least 50 times as great in testes as in ovaries. The appearance of this latter enzyme in the testis corresponds exactly with the onset of testosterone formation and with the transformation in the undifferentiated interstitial cells of the testis into mature Leydig cells with abundant smooth endoplasmic reticulum (George *et al.*, 1978a).

The rabbit ovary begins to form potent estrogens at the same time as the onset of testosterone synthesis in the testes (Milewich *et al.*, 1977; George *et al.*, 1978b), indeed before histological differentiation of the ovary has been recognized. Similarly, the onset of endocrine function of human fetal testes and ovaries occurs simultaneously (Siiteri and Wilson, 1974; George and Wilson, 1978). Estrogen synthesis occurs because the fetal ovary has the capacity to convert the small amount of testosterone synthesized in the tissue into estradiol whereas the testis lacks this capacity. Differences in the enzymatic profiles of the gonads exist among species, but in all cases examined to date the embryonic synthesis of testosterone and estrogen appears to be activated simultaneously (Milewich *et al.*, 1977; Mauleon *et al.*, 1977; George and Wilson, 1978; George *et al.*, 1978b; Sholl and Goy, 1978). Thus, differences in the rates of a small number of enzymatic reactions in the gonads at a critical time in development have profound consequences for the further life of the individual.

The question as to whether the rates of formation of the gonadal steroids are themselves regulated at the onset by other hormones has been harder to evaluate. Late in embryogenesis, as in the postnatal state, gonadotropins from the pituitary and/or placenta regulate the rates of estradiol and testosterone formation in the ovary and testis, primarily by controlling the rate of cholesterol side-chain cleavage, thereby regulating the availability of substrate for androgen formation. In the rabbit, furthermore, differentiation of the anterior pituitary occurs at about the same time as the onset of testosterone synthesis in the fetal testis, suggesting the possibility that hormones from the pituitary may control testosterone synthesis at the time of its initiation (Schechter, 1970). A receptor for luteinizing hormone is present in rabbit testis at the time of the onset of testosterone synthesis, and from its first appearance in the Leydig cell this receptor is functionally coupled to the side-chain cleavage process by which cholesterol is converted to pregnenolone (Catt *et al.*, 1975; George *et al.*, 1979).

Other evidence suggests the alternative possibility, namely that the onset of testosterone synthesis is independent of control by the pituitary or other hormones. First, the endocrine differentiation of the gonads occurs in organ culture (Picon, 1967; George *et al.*, 1978a; George and Wilson, 1980). That is, day 16 rabbit embryo testes and ovaries undergo their characteristic enzymatic differentiation at the appropriate time when cultured for 2 to 4 days in synthetic media devoid of hormones. Second, gonadotropin is not required for testosterone formation in the fetal rabbit testis until late in embryogenesis when cholesterol side-chain cleavage (and the availability of substrate) becomes rate limiting in the enzymatic sequence of testosterone biosynthesis (George *et al.*, 1979). Thus, the differentiation of the gonads as endocrine organs may be controlled by factors intrinsic to the gonads themselves, and the embryonic ovary and testis may function initially as independent or autonomous endocrine organs. If this interpretation is correct, differentiation of the sexual phenotypes takes place independently of the pituitary. Since testosterone production late in embryogenesis is gonadotropin dependent, the late testosterone-mediated events in male development such as growth of the male genitalia are modulated indirectly by the pituitary and/or placenta. Indeed, infants with congenital gonadotropin deficiency often have microphallus and cryptorchidism despite otherwise normal male anatomy (Walsh *et al.*, 1978).

C. *Mechanism of Androgen Action in the Embryo*

The current concepts of androgen action in postnatal life are summarized schematically in Fig. 4. Testosterone (T), the androgen secreted by the testis and the major androgen in plasma, enters target tissues by a passive diffusion process. Inside the cell testosterone can be converted to dihydrotestosterone (D) by the 5α-reductase enzyme (Fig. 3). Testosterone or dihydrotestosterone is then bound to the same high-affinity androgen receptor protein (R). The hormone–receptor complexes (TR and DR) either form in the nucleus or move from cytosol to the nucleus, where they interact with acceptor sites on the chromosomes. The nature of the acceptor sites within the nucleus (i.e., whether protein or DNA) and the number of the acceptor sites have not been defined, but the overall result of the interaction of the hormone–receptor complexes with chromatin is to increase transcription of specific structural genes

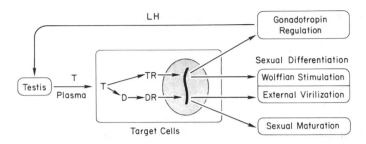

FIG. 4. Current concepts of the mechanism of action of testosterone. T, testosterone; D, dihydrotestosterone; R, androgen receptor protein; LH, luteinizing hormone. [Reprinted with permission from Wilson *et al.* (1979).]

with the subsequent appearance of new messenger RNAs and new proteins in the cytoplasm of the cell.

As the result of studies in normal embryos it is know that androgens act in the embryo by the same mechanisms as in the postnatal state (Fig. 4) (Griffin and Wilson, 1980). The testosterone–receptor complex is responsible for regulation of gonadotropin secretion by the hypothalamic–pituitary system and for virilization of the wolffian duct during embryogenesis, whereas the dihydrotestosterone–receptor complex induces virilization of the urogenital sinus and external genitalia during embryogenesis and is responsible in large part for the maturational events at male puberty.

Perhaps the most puzzling aspect of this model is how two hormones can bind to the same receptor protein but nevertheless have different effects (Wilbert *et al.*, 1983). Indeed, the question of why dihydrotestosterone formation is important in androgen action has been a central preoccupation in androgen physiology for more than a decade, an issue that has become resolved only as a result of study of mutations that impair this pathway.

Three types of single gene mutations have been informative in proving that this scheme applies to events in the embryo. Each mutation affects one of the three major processes in the pathway of normal androgen action, namely, the 5α-reductase enzyme, the androgen receptor, or the subsequent phases of hormone action, and each results in hereditary resistance to androgen action and incomplete virilization during embryogenesis (and in subsequent life) despite the fact that testosterone formation and regression of the mullerian duct are normal.

1. Role of Testosterone and Dihydrotestosterone

Separate roles for testosterone in mediating virilization of the wolffian ducts and for dihydrotestosterone in causing development of the external genitalia of the male were established in studies of androgen metabolism in normal embryos (Wilson and Lasnitzki, 1971; Wilson, 1971; Siiteri and Wilson, 1974). Namely, in the embryos of the rat, rabbit, guinea pig, and human, 5α-reductase activity is maximal in the anlage of the prostate and external genitalia prior to virilization, whereas the enzyme is virtually undetectable in the wolffian duct derivatives until after virilization of the tissues is advanced. This deduction received genetic substantiation from studies of patients with a rare form of abnormal sexual development originally termed pseudovaginal perineoscrotal hypospadias by Nowakowski and Lenz (1961). Affected persons are 46,XY males who have an autosomal recessive disorder characterized by an external female phenotype, bilateral testes, and normally virilized wolffian structures (epididymis, vas deferens, seminal vesicle, and ejaculatory duct) that terminate in a vagina (Fig. 5). At the time of expected puberty the external genitalia virilize to a variable

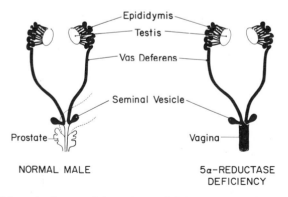

NORMAL MALE   5α-REDUCTASE DEFICIENCY

FIG. 5. Schematic diagram of the anatomy of the internal reproductive tract in 5α-reductase deficiency. [Reprinted with permission from Wilson *et al.* (1979).]

extent, axillary and pubic hair develop normally, and testosterone production increases to the male range. Gynecomastia does not develop. This is the phenotype that would be predicted if dihydrotestosterone-mediated events in male phenotypic development were deficient but the testosterone-mediated phases were normal (Fig. 4). Direct evidence for a defect in 5α-reductase activity in this disorder was reported in 1974 in two families—one in the Dominican Republic (Imperato-McGinley *et al.*, 1974; Peterson *et al.*, 1977) and one from Dallas (Walsh *et al.*, 1974). Additional patients were described subsequently (Cantu *et al.*, 1976, 1980; Saenger *et al.*, 1978; Hodgins *et al.*, 1977; Jaffiol *et al.*, 1978; Fisher *et al.*, 1978; Pinsky *et al.*, 1978; Greene *et al.*, 1978; Imperato-McGinley *et al.*, 1980; Savage *et al.*, 1980; Kuttenn *et al.*, 1979; Mauvais-Jarvis *et al.*, 1981; Okon *et al.*, 1980). The disorder is now termed 5α-reductase deficiency.

In affected persons elevated ratios of plasma testosterone to dihydrotestosterone following administration of human chorionic gonadotropin can be demonstrated prior to puberty, and normal to elevated plasma testosterone levels and low plasma dihydrotestosterone levels are present in adults. Elevated ratios of urinary 5β-reduced to 5α-reduced steroids, decreased *in vivo* conversion of testosterone to dihydrotestosterone, diminished 5α-reductase activity in tissue biopsy specimens, and deficient or abnormal 5α-reductase activity in fibroblasts cultured from genital skin are consistent features.

Affected men have less facial and body hair and less temporal hairline recession than unaffected men from the same families. Acne does not occur. No prostatic tissue is palpable, and no prostatic utricle can be visualized on cystoscopy. Thus, temporal hairline regression, growth of facial and body hair, and appearance of acne in the male at puberty, as well as development of the external genitalia and prostate during embryogenesis, appear to be mediated by dihydrotestosterone.

Although plasma luteinizing hormone (LH) is elevated, it is lower than in castrated men or in subjects with disorders of the androgen receptor (Wilson *et al.*, 1983). In some untreated patients virilization at the time of expected puberty appears to be accompanied by a change in gender role from female to male (Imperato-McGinley *et al.*, 1979, 1980). Other subjects who have been raised as females, castrated, and given subsequent estrogen replacement therapy have made successful adjustments as women. The frequency and cause of the apparent reversal in gender role have not been established.

The deficiency in 5α-reductase is believed to be due to the homozygous state of an autosomal recessive gene that is manifest clinically only in males. Homozygous 46,XX persons have normal fertility, and heterozygous 46,XY persons are clinically normal (Peterson *et al.*, 1977). The mutation has been described in individuals from a variety of ethnic backgrounds. Consanguinity has been documented in approximately a third of reported cases, and another third occur in communities with known high coefficients of inbreeding.

The molecular features of the mutation have been studied in cells cultured from 21 subjects from 16 pedigrees (Fig. 6). The enzyme in normal genital skin fibroblasts has a pH optimum of 5.5; measurement of this activity has proved to be the most sensitive means to detect the

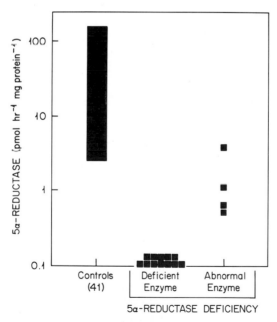

Fig. 6. 5α-reductase activity at pH 5.5 in sonicates of genital skin fibroblasts cultured from individuals from 16 families with 5α-reductase deficiency.

enzyme (Wilson, 1975; Moore *et al.*, 1975; Moore and Wilson, 1976; Leshin *et al.*, 1978; Imperato-McGinley *et al.*, 1980). In the initial families studied 5α-reductase activity was markedly deficient and has been similarly defective in fibroblasts from members of 10 additional families studied to date. However, in cells cultured from patients from one family (Fisher *et al.*, 1978), the activity of the enzyme is in the low normal range in cultured skin fibroblasts despite the demonstration of a severe deficiency of the enzyme in fresh tissues from the same patients (Leshin *et al.*, 1978). In contrast to the enzyme in cells from the families with enzyme deficiency the enzyme from this family has a normal pH optimum and a normal K_m for testosterone. However, affinity for reduced nicotinamide adenine dinucleotide phosphate (NADPH), the cofactor for the reaction, is decreased, and the enzyme is unstable and has a rapid turnover (Leshin *et al.*, 1978). Fibroblasts from patients from three other families have intermediate levels of 5α-reductase and altered affinities for both testosterone and NADPH (Imperato-McGinley *et al.*, 1980) (Fig. 6). Our interpretation of these results is that different structural mutations of the 5α-reductase enzyme can give rise to the disorder. The common mutations affect the binding of the steroid substrate to the enzyme (Dallas and the Dominican Republic); others affect primarily the binding of NADPH. Still other mutations affect both functions. This genetic heterogeneity among families with similar clinical manifestations is similar to that noted for other inherited enzyme deficiencies, such as glucose-6-phosphate dehydrogenase deficiency (Beutler and Yoshida, 1973).

A major unresolved issue is why the external genitalia of patients with 5α-reductase deficiency virilize more at puberty than during embryogenesis. In collaboration with Besser and his colleagues we have recently studied four patients with 5α-reductase deficiency who underwent change of gender role from female to male at the time of expected puberty. All were underandrogenized, and all had normal levels of testosterone and low but measurable levels of dihydrotestosterone in plasma. When these men were treated with supraphysiological levels of testosterone (which raised plasma testosterone more than three fold above the normal range) each man underwent a profound virilization, and in each the plasma dihydrotestosterone rose into the normal range (Price *et al.*, 1984). Thus, the partial pubertal virilization in this disorder may be due to the accumulation of a small amount of dihydrotestosterone in plasma as a result of the action of the residual 5α-reductase present in all patients.

2. Role of the Androgen Receptor

Several disorders of the androgen receptor cause abnormal sexual development in man and animals.

a. The Tfm Mouse. The first disorder of androgen resistance to be characterized in molecular terms was the testicular feminization (*Tfm*) mutation in the mouse, an X-linked disorder in which affected males have testes and normal testosterone production but differentiate as phenotypic females (Lyon and Hawkes, 1970). No mullerian duct derivatives can be identified, indicating that the mullerian regression function of the testis is intact, but there is a total failure of androgen-mediated aspects of male development in the wolffian duct, urogenital sinus, and external genitalia. A blind-ending vagina is usually present. Such animals are resistant to the action of their own androgens and to exogenous testosterone and dihydrotestosterone during embryogenesis as well as in postnatal life (Goldstein and Wilson, 1972). Dihydrotestosterone formation is normal, but the androgen receptor protein of the cell cytosol is undetectable; consequently, the hormone cannot reach the nucleus of the cell and interact with the chromosomes (Gehring *et al.*, 1971; Bullock *et al.*, 1971; Goldstein and Wilson, 1972; Verhoeven and Wilson, 1976). Elucidation of the pathophysiology of this mutation documented the critical role of the androgen receptor in the normal embryonic action of androgen and established that a single receptor protein serves as the mediator of the actions of both testosterone and dihydrotestosterone.

b. Disorders of the Human Androgen Receptor: Clinical Features. Disorders of the androgen receptor result in several distinct phenotypes (Wilson *et al.*, 1983). Despite differences in clinical presentation and molecular pathology these disorders are similar in regard to endocrinology and basic pathophysiology, and all are inherited as apparent X-linked defects. Women with *testicular feminization* are usually ascertained because of primary amenorrhea (postpubertally) or the presence of an inguinal hernia (prepubertally) (Morris, 1953). Facial and scalp hair and breast development are those of a normal woman, and the general habitus and distribution of body fat are female in character.

Axillary, pubic hair, and vulvar hair are absent or scanty. The external genitalia are unambiguously female, and the vagina is blind-ending and may be absent or shallow. The internal genital tract is absent except for testes with absence of spermatogenesis but normal or increased Leydig cells. Occasionally, remnants of mullerian or wolffian origin can be identified in the paratesticular fascia or in fibrous bands extending from the testes. The testes may be located in the abdomen, along the course of the inguinal canal, or in the labia majora. The fact that the chromosomal complement is 46,XY and that the chromosomes are of normal structure documented that the affected individuals are genetic males.

Subjects with *incomplete testicular feminization* resemble women with the complete disorder but have some ambiguity of the external genitalia and experience partial virilization as well as feminization at puberty (Morris and Mahesh, 1963; Madden *et al.*, 1975). Affected individuals have the habitus and general appearance of women and like women with the complete form of disorder most commonly present because of primary amenorrhea. The karyotype is 46,XY; the testes are in the abdomen or in the inguinal canals and are indistinguishable from those in complete testicular feminization. Partial fusion of the labioscrotal folds and a variable degree of clitoromegaly are distinctive features. The vagina is short and ends blindly. Mullerian duct derivatives are absent, and wolffian duct structures are present although underdeveloped in comparison with those of a normal man. This latter feature, together with the partial virilization of the external genitalia, separates the phenotype from that of testicular feminization.

Some families with X-linked hereditary male pseudohermaphroditism exhibit less complete failure of virilization than in incomplete testicular feminization. The common phenotype is male, but the spectrum of phenotypes within a given family may range from almost complete failure of virilization to nearly complete masculinization. The first family with this disorder was described by Sir Charles Ford (1941) and subsequently by Walker *et al.* (1970). The disorder has been reported under a variety of eponymic terms including the Reifenstein syndrome (Reifenstein, 1947), the Lubs syndrome (Lubs *et al.*, 1959), the Gilbert-Dreyfus syndrome (Gilbert-Dreyfus *et al.*, 1957), the Rosewater syndrome (Rosewater *et al.*, 1965), and familial incomplete male pseudohermaphroditism, type 1 (Wilson *et al.*, 1974); common appelation is the *Reifenstein syndrome*. Evidence that these disorders are in fact variable manifestations of a similar mutation was derived from pedigree analyses.

The usual presentation is a 46,XY male with perineoscrotal hypospadias, azoospermia and infertility, incomplete virilization, and gynecomastia that develops at the expected time of puberty. Axillary and pubic hair are normal, but chest and facial hair tend to be feminine in character. Temporal recession of the hairline is minimal, and the voice tends to be somewhat high pitched. Less severely affected members may exhibit only a bifid scrotum, infertility, and incomplete virilization at puberty. More severely affected individuals can have almost complete male psudohermaphroditism, including incomplete wolffian duct derivatives and formation of a vagina. Incomplete virilization of the urogenital sinus results in a prostatic utricle but no true prostate. The lower ejaculatory duct system has not been studied in detail. Cryptorchidism is common, and the testes are small. The testes contain normal Leydig cells and spermatogenic tubules with Sertoli cells and germinal epithelium but no maturation of the germ cells beyond the primary spermatocyte stage.

Most are raised as men. Gender identity in subjects raised as men appears to be unambiguously male in character, and some have had successful marriages. Infertility is the most consistent feature of the syndrome and appears to result both from defective spermatogenesis and from the anatomic abnormalities of the ejaculatory system.

In a family study of the Reifenstein syndrome, it was recognized that minimally affected men had the same apparent degree of androgen resistance as assessed by endocrinological criteria and the same abnormality of the androgen receptor in cultured skin fibroblasts as did the more severely affected individuals (Wilson *et al.*, 1974; Griffin *et al.*, 1976). Subsequently, it was found that some *infertile men with azoospermia* or severe oligospermia but no family history of the Reifenstein syndrome have endocrine evidence of androgen resistance and clear-cut abnormality of the androgen receptor (Aiman *et al.*, 1979). The frequency of this form of androgen resistance as a cause of male infertility is not established, but in one survey it accounted for as much as a fifth to a third of infertility associated with idiopathic azoospermia or severe oligospermia (Aiman and Griffin, 1982). Thus, the infertile male syndrome may be the most common abnormality of the androgen receptor and the most common form of primary resistance to the action of any hormone.

Endocrinology. The endocrine pathology is similar in all forms of androgen receptor disorders but has been best characterized in complete testicular feminization. Resistance to the feedback regulation of LH production by circulating androgen results in elevated plasma LH levels, and this in turn results in the enhanced secretion by the testes of both testosterone and estradiol. The fact that gonadotropin levels rise even higher (and that symptoms of menopausal flushing develop) when the testes are removed indicates that gonadotropin secretion is under some type of regulatory control; presumably, in the steady state and in the absence of an effect of androgen, estrogen alone regulates LH secretion in subjects with testicular feminization. This feedback control is purchased at the expense of a higher plasma estrogen level than in normal men (MacDonald *et al.*, 1980).

Pathogenesis. Androgen resistance in testicular feminization is due to abnormalities of the androgen receptor. Keenan and co-workers documented that a specific dihydrotestosterone receptor protein is present in fibroblasts cultured from the skin of normal subjects (1974, 1975). The receptor level is greater in fibroblasts cultured from genital skin sites (foreskin, scrotum, labia majora) than from nongenital sites. The receptor has a dissociation constant of approximately 1 nM and is believed to be the same intracellular receptor protein as in androgen target tissues. Furthermore, skin fibroblasts from some women with complete testicular feminization showed no detectable dihydrotestosterone binding (Keenan *et al.*, 1974, 1975), a finding that has been confirmed (Griffin *et al.*, 1976; Kaufman *et al.*, 1976). The lack of androgen binding in fibroblasts from some patients with testicular feminization provides an explanation for the profound resistance to all androgen actions in this disorder. Whether absent binding of dihydrotestosterone in such cases is due to absence of the androgen receptor protein or the presence of a mutant protein that cannot bind the ligand is now known.

Other subjects with complete testicular feminization have qualitative abnormalities of the receptor protein. The initial evidence for a qualitative abnormality of the receptor was found in fibroblasts from two sisters with complete testicular feminization who had about half-normal levels of binding under the usual assay conditions at 37°C and normal binding at 26°C. When the assay was performed at an elevated temperature (42°C) dihydrotestosterone binding decreased to less than a fifth that seen at 37°C. The binding was rapidly restored on lowering the assay temperature to 37°C, suggesting that the alteration of the structure at elevated temperatures is reversible (Griffin, 1979). Similar receptor thermolability has been observed by Pinsky *et al.* (1981). Additional qualitative abnormalities of the receptor were identified by examining the ultracentrifugation characteristics of the cytosol receptor in the presence of molybdate, which stabilizes the normal 8 S androgen receptor but not the receptor from many subjects with androgen resistance (Griffin and Durrant, 1982).

The characteristics of the androgen receptor in fibroblasts grown from biopsies of individuals from 35 families that fulfill the phenotypic and endocrine requirements to be designated androgen resistance, including 15 families with complete testicular feminization, are summarized in Fig. 7. In nine of the families binding was virtually undetectable in fibroblast monolayers at any temperature and was designated as absent; these families are representative of the receptor-negative catego-

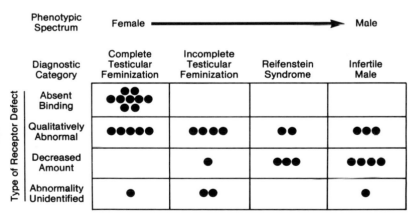

FIG. 7. Androgen receptor assays in subjects from 35 families with androgen resistance and putative defects in the androgen receptor. The 35 families include 31 families with established defects of the androgen receptor and 4 with no abnormality identified (receptor-positive resistance). Absent binding is associated with the phenotype of complete testicular feminization, but the qualitative and quantitative defects in the receptor can be associated with a spectrum of phenotypes from complete testicular feminization to infertile men. [Reprinted with permission from Griffin *et al.* (1982).]

ry of testicular feminization identified in the early studies of the problem. The pathogenesis of androgen resistance in these families is similar to that in the mouse with testicular feminization (Bullock *et al.*, 1971; Gehring *et al.*, 1971; Goldstein and Wilson, 1972). However, such a defect could not be the explanation for the androgen resistance in the remaining families with complete testicular feminization. In five families with complete testicular feminization the receptor was measurable but was qualitatively abnormal, and in one family the receptor was normal in amount and without a detectable qualitative abnormality. Likewise, when binding was compared in fibroblasts from affected individuals from seven families with incomplete testicular feminization, a qualitative abnormality was demonstrated in four, a diminished amount of binding was present in one family, and no defect could be identified in the other two families. Similarly, in our initial studies of the Reifenstein syndrome and the infertile male syndrome the only defect identified was a diminished amount of binding. However, when additional patients were studied, the androgen receptor was found to be qualitatively abnormal in two Reifenstein families and three infertile men and was diminished in amount in three Reifenstein families [including fibroblasts from a member of the original Ford pedigree reported by Thies *et al.* (1979) and in four unrelated infertile men]. In affected subjects of three families (two with the phenotype of incomplete testicular feminization and one infertile male) no abnormality of the androgen receptor was demonstrable, despite endocrine evidence of profound androgen resistance (see Receptor Positive Resistance, below).

To summarize, absent binding appears to be associated with the syndrome of complete testicular feminization. Qualitatively abnormal receptors and decreased amount of receptors are associated with a spectrum of phenotypes from female to male; we assume but cannot yet prove that there is some correlation between the phenotype that results and the severity of impairment of receptor function. The mutations that give rise to qualitatively abnormal receptors, like the genes for normal and absent receptors, are X linked, and it is likely that the various mutations that influence the androgen receptor are allelic (Elawady *et al.*, 1983). What is needed is better means of assessing structure–function relationships. Further study of the qualitatively abnormal androgen receptors from one family has been particularly informative.

Before the androgen–receptor complex can bind to anionically charged substances such as DNA it must undergo a heat-dependent transformation process (Kovacs *et al.*, 1983). (Whether this is a dissociation of a protein aggregate into subunits or enzymatic processing is not clear.) The dihydrotestosterone–receptor complex normally transforms to the DNA-binding state much more effectively than does the testosterone–receptor complex, and we believe that this is the reason that dihydrotestosterone formation is important in androgen action (Kovacs *et al.*, 1984). Two first cousins with the phenotype of incomplete testicular feminization were ascertained by Dr. David Weaver and his colleagues at the University of Indiana; the girls have 46,XY karyotypes, normal epididymis and ejaculatory ducts, normal 5α-reductase enzyme, and normal amounts of androgen receptor. Their phenotypes suggested that the mutation impairs the action of dihydrotestosterone more completely than that of testosterone, and, indeed, the transformation of the dihydrotestosterone–receptor complexes from these girls to the DNA-binding state is defective (Kovacs *et al.*, 1984). These findings suggest that dihydrotestosterone amplifies the androgen signal in target tissues because of its more efficient conversion to the DNA-binding state and that such amplification is less critical in target tissues in which testosterone suffices for androgenic effects. Other types of mutant androgen receptors have been described in the recent past (Eil, 1983; Gyorky *et al.*, 1983; Kaufman *et al.*, 1982).

3. Receptor-Positive Resistance

A category of androgen resistance that does not appear to involve either the 5α-reductase or the androgen receptor was identified by Amrhein *et al.* (1976) in three affected members of one family with the phenotype of testicular feminization and who have normal 5α-reductase, normal amounts of androgen receptor, and normal nuclear localization of dihydrotestosterone. Subsequent subjects have been described with a variety of phenotypes ranging from incomplete testicular feminization to the Reifenstein syndrome (Amrhein *et al.*, 1977; Keenan *et al.*, 1977; Collier *et al.*, 1978). The site of the molecular abnormality in these patients is unclear. A qualitative abnormality of the receptor that is too subtle to be detected by current methods may be responsible. Indeed the original family identified with receptor-positive resistance has subsequently been shown to have a qualitatively abnormal receptor (Brown *et al.*, 1982). Alternatively, the defect may reside at some step in androgen action distal to the receptor, such as the site of generation of specific messenger RNA. In the subjects we have assessed—labeled "abnormality unidentified" in Fig. 7—all parameters of receptor function studied to date are normal including affinity of binding, turnover rate, nuclear localization of the hormone–receptor complex, and stability of binding both to elevated temperature and to ultracentrifugation. The disorder may constitute a heterogeneous group of molecular abnormalities.

IV. Conclusion

The validity of the Jost formulation for sexual development is now amply documented. Genetic sex determines gonadal sex, and the gonads in turn determine the development of the sexual phenotypes through their function as endocrine organs. A striking feature of this model is its overall simplicity. As the result of a difference in the activity of one or a few enzymes in the gonads at a critical time in development, testosterone synthesis is activated in the fetal testis. This hormone in turn causes profound developmental effects in the male that account in large part for the differences between men and women.

In at least two regards the Jost model must now be amplified. First, sex is so complex that it cannot be explained solely by chromosomal sex. In the human at least one X-linked gene is essential for testicular development, and autosomal genes necessary for differentiation of the ovaries and testes have been identified in several species (reviewed by Wilson, 1978). Some of these genes influence migration of the primordial germ cells, others probably regulate the processing or function of the Y chromosome-linked determinants that appear to be involved in testicular development, some code for the enzymes required for steroid hormone synthesis, and the function of the remainder is unknown. The important point is that gonadal development is determined by genes located on the autosomes as well as on the X and Y chromosomes. Second, the process by which male phenotypic sex develops depends on the expression of several gene products necessary for androgen action so that sexual development can actually be characterized as a series of sequential interactions between the genetic machinery and regulatory factors.

We now have considerable insight into the nature of the various genes involved in this process. This fortunate circumstance is the result of the fact that aberrations at any stage of sexual development, whether due to environmental causes, chromosomal abnormalities, or single gene mutations, have profound consequences, each of which is expressed as a characteristic defect in sexual development. Investigation of the pathogenesis of such defects in man and animals has provided insight into many of the endocrine, molecular, and genetic determinants that regulate the normal process.

The analysis of the single gene mutations that produce abnormal sexual development in man and animals has been particularly informative in this regard. A minimum of 19 genes have been implicated in sexual differentiation in man (Wilson and Goldstein, 1975). The involvement of such a large number of genes does not imply a greater complexity for sexual differentiation than for other developmental processes but rather reflects the comparative ease with which mutant genes affecting the normal process of sexual development can be ascertained. Normal sexual development is essential for reproduction and hence for the survival of species but not for the life of individuals. In contrast, developmental defects in organ systems essential to life usually cause abnormalities that result in abortion or early death. Therefore, individuals with even the most profound abnormalities of sexual development survive, usually come to the attention of physicians, and have been subjected to detailed pathophysiological studies.

Some fundamental issues in the embryonic development of the genital tract are still poorly understood. One relates to the mechanism by which specific tissues develop the capacity early in embryogenesis that allows them to respond to a hormonal stimulus later in development. As the result of careful studies in the embryo, Cunha and his colleagues have established that the capacity to respond to androgens is acquired by tissues of the embryonic urogenital tract early in development; the mesenchyme of the embryonic urogenital tract contains the receptor mechanism that regulates the epithelial response to androgen, namely the development and proliferation of the prostatic buds (Cunha *et al.*, 1980). It is not known how mesenchymal tissue of the urogenital tract acquires this differentiative capacity, and the mechanism by which the appropriate signal is transferred from mesenchyme to epithelium is unclear. Another problem relates to the precise mechanisms by which the same hormonal signal is translated into different physiological effects in different tissues. For example, the diverse effects of androgen during embryogenesis include regression of the mammary duct (in the rodent at least), budding and proliferation in the urogenital sinus and wolffian duct, fusion of cells in the urethral fold, and differential growth of the entire male genital tract late in embryogenesis. At present we have no insight into the mechanisms by which these apparently different functions are accomplished. Ultimately, these fundamental issues of embryogenesis will have to be clarified before it will be possible to understand the entire program by which the myriad of genetic determinants and hormones interact to cause sexual differentiation.

ACKNOWLEDGMENTS

These studies have been performed in collaboration with several valued colleagues. Fredrick W. George and Pentti K. Siiteri were involved in the studies on the regulation of androgen formation in the fetus, and the work on the molecular defects in androgen action has been directed by James E. Griffin, Mark Leshin, and William J. Kovacs. Paul C. MacDonald has characterized the endocrine features of these various mutations. The work has been supported by Grant AMO3892 from the National Institutes of Health.

REFERENCES

Aiman, J., and Griffin, J. E. (1982). *J. Clin. Endocrinol. Metab.* **54,** 725–732.

Aiman, J., Griffin, J. E., Gazak, J. M., Wilson, J. D., and MacDonald, P. C. (1979). *N. Engl. J. Med.* **300,** 223–227.

Amrhein, J. A., Meyer, W. J., III, Jones, H. W., Jr., and Migeon, C. J. (1976). *Proc. Natl. Acad. Sci. U.S.A.* **73,** 891–894.

Amrhein, J. A., Klingensmith, G. J., Walsh, P. C., McKusick, V. A., and Migeon, C. J. (1977). *N. Engl. J. Med.* **297,** 350–356.

Attal, J. (1969). *Endocrinology* **85,** 280–289.

Beutler, E., and Yoshida, A. (1973). *Ann. Hum. Genet.* **37,** 151–155.

Blanchard, M. G., and Josso, N. (1974). *Pediatr. Res.* **8,** 968–971.

Brown, T. R., Maes, M., Rothwell, S. W., and Migeon, C. J. (1982). *J. Clin. Endocrinol. Metab.* **55,** 61–69.

Bullock, L. P., Bardin, C. W., and Ohno, S. (1971). *Biochem. Biophys. Res. Commun.* **44,** 1537–1543.

Cantu, J. M., Hernandez–Montes, H., Del Castillo, V., Cortes-Gallegos, V., Sandoval, R., Armendares, S., and Parra, A. (1976). *Rev. Invest. Clin. (Mex.)* **28,** 177–182.

Cantu, J. M., Corona-Rivera, E., Diaz, M., Medina, C., Esquinca, E., Cortes-Gallegos, V., Vaca, G., and Hernandez, A. (1980). *Acta Endocrinol.* **94,** 273–279.

Catt, K. J., Dufau, M. L., Neaves, W. B., Walsh, P. C., and Wilson, J. D. (1975). *Endocrinology* **97,** 1157–1165.

Collier, M. E., Griffin, J. E., and Wilson, J. D. (1978). *Endocrinology* **103,** 1499–1505.

Cunha, G. R., Chung, L. W. K., Shannon, J. M., and Reese, B. A. (1980). *Biol. Reprod.* **22**, 19–42.

Donahoe, P. K., Ito, Y., Price, J. M., and Herndon, W. H., III. (1977). *Biol. Reprod.* **16**, 238–243.

Eil, C. (1983). *J. Clin. Invest.* **71**, 850–858.

Elawady, M. K., Allman, D. R., Griffin, J. E., and Wilson, J. D. (1983). *Am. J. Hum. Genet.* **35**, 376–384.

Fisher, L. K., Kogut, M. D., Moore, R. J., Goebelsmann, U., Weitzman, J. J., Issacs, H., Jr., Griffin, J. E., and Wilson, J. D. (1978). *J. Clin. Endocrinol. Metab.* **47**, 653–664.

Ford, E. (1941). *Med. J. Aust.* **1**, 450–451.

Gehring, U., Tomkins, G. M., and Ohno, S. (1971). *Nature (London) New Biol.* **232**, 106–107.

George, F. W., and Wilson, J. D. (1978). *J. Clin. Endocrinol. Metab.* **47**, 550–555.

George, F. W., and Wilson, J. D. (1980). *Nature (London)* **283**, 861–863.

George, F. W., Catt, K. J., Neaves, W. B., and Wilson, J. D. (1978a). *Endocrinology* **102**, 665–673.

George, F. W., Milewich, L., and Wilson, J. D. (1978b). *Nature (London)* **274**, 172–173.

George, F. W., Simpson, E. R., Milewich, L., and Wilson, J. D. (1979). *Endocrinology* **105**, 1100–1106.

Gilbert-Dreyfus, S., Sebaoun, C. A., Belaisch, J. (1957). *Ann. Endocrinol.* **18**, 93–101.

Goldman, A. S. (1971). *Endocrinology* **88**, 527–531.

Goldstein, J. L., and Wilson, J. D. (1972). *J. Clin. Invest.* **51**, 1647–1658.

Greene, S. A., Symes, E., and Brook, C. G. D. (1978). *Arch. Dis. Child.* **53**, 751–753.

Griffin, J. E. (1979). *J. Clin. Invest.* **64**, 1624–1631.

Griffin, J. E., and Durrant, J. L. (1982). *J. Clin. Endocrinol. Metab.* **55**, 455–474.

Griffin, J. E., and Wilson, J. D. (1980). *N. Engl. J. Med.* **302**, 198–209.

Griffin, J. E., Punyashthiti, K., and Wilson, J. D. (1976). *J. Clin. Invest.* **57**, 1342–1351.

Griffin, J. E., Leshiu, M., and Wilson, J. D. (1982). *Am. J. Physiol.* **243**, E-81-E-87.

Gyorki, S., Warne, G. L., Khalid, B. A. K., and Funder, J. W. (1983). *J. Clin. Invest.* **72**, 819–825.

Hodgins, M. B., Clayton, R. N., and London, D. R. (1977). *J. Endocrinol.* **75**, 24P.

Imperato-McGinley, J., Guerrero, L., Gautier, T., and Peterson, R. E. (1974). *Science* **186**, 1213–1215.

Imperato-McGinley, J., Peterson, R. E., Gautier, T., and Sturla, E. (1979). *N. Engl. J. Med.* **300**, 1233–1237.

Imperato-McGinley, J., Peterson, R. E., Leshin, M., Griffin, J. E., Cooper, G., Draghi, S., Berenyi, M., and Wilson, J. D. (1980). *J. Clin. Endocrinol. Metab.* **50**, 15–22.

Jaffiol, C., Robin, M., Corratge, P., and Mirouze, J. (1978). *Ann. Endocrinol. (Paris)* **39**, 47–48.

Jost, A. (1959–1960). *Harvey Lect. Ser.* **55**, 201–227.

Kaufman, M., Straisfeld, C., and Pinsky, L. (1976). *J. Clin. Invest.* **58**, 345–350.

Kaufman, M., Pinsky, L., Simard, L., and Wong, S. C. (1982). *Mol. Cell. Endocrinol.* **25**, 151–162.

Keenan, B. S., Meyer, W. J., III, Hadjian, A. J., Jones, H. W., and Migeon, C. J. (1974). *J. Clin. Endocrinol. Metab.* **38**, 1143–1146.

Keenan, B. S., Meyer, W. J., III, Hadjian, A. J., and Migeon, C. J. (1975). *Steroids* **25**, 535–552.

Keenan, B. S., Kirkland, J. L., Kirkland, R. T., and Clayton, G. W. (1977). *Pediatrics* **59**, 224–231.

Kovacs, W. J., Griffin, J. E., and Wilson, J. D. (1983). *Endocrinology* **113**, 1574–1581.

Kovacs, W. J., Griffin, J. E., Weaver, D. D., Carlson, B. R., and Wilson, J. D. (1984). *J. Clin. Invest.,* **73**, 1095–1104.

Kuttenn, F., Mowszowicz, I., Wright, F., Baudot, N., Jaffiol, C., Robin, M., and Mauvais-Jarvis, P. (1979). *J. Clin. Endocrinol. Metab.* **49**, 861–865.

Leshin, M., Griffin, J. E., and Wilson, J. D. (1978). *J. Clin. Invest.* **62**, 685–691.

Lipsett, M. B., and Tullner, W. W. (1965). *Endocrinology* **77**, 273–277.

Lubs, H. A., Jr., Vilar, O., and Bergenstal, D. M. (1959). *J. Clin. Endocrinol. Metab.* **19**, 1110–1120.

Lyon, M. F., and Hawkes, S. G. (1970). *Nature (London)* **227**, 1217–1219.

MacDonald, P. C., Madden, J. D., Brenner, P. F., Wilson, J. D., and Siiteri, P. K. (1980). *J. Clin. Endocrinol. Metab.* **49**, 905–916.

Madden, J. D., Walsh, P. C., MacDonald, P. C., and Wilson, J. D. (1975). *J. Clin. Endocrinol. Metab.* **41**, 751–760.

Mauleon, P., Bezard, J., and Terqui, M. (1977). *Ann. Biol. Anim. Biochim. Biophys.* **17**, 399–401.

Mauvais-Jarvis, P., Kuttenn, F., Mowszowicz, I., and Wright, F. (1981). *Clin. Endocrinol.* **14**, 459–469.

Milewich, L., George, F. W., and Wilson, J. D. (1977). *Endocrinology* **100**, 187–196.

Moore, R. J., and Wilson, J. D. (1976). *J. Biol. Chem.* **251**, 5895–5900.

Moore, R. J., Griffin, J. E., and Wilson, J. D. (1975). *J. Biol. Chem.* **250**, 7168–7172.

Morris, J. M. (1953). *Am. J. Obstet. Gynecol.* **65**, 1192–1211.

Morris, J. M., and Mahesh, V. B. (1963). *Am. J. Obstet. Gynecol.* **87**, 731–748.

Neumann, F., von, Berswordt-Wallrabe, R., Elger, W., Steinbeck, H., Hahn, J. D., and Kramer, M. (1970). *Recent Prog. Horm. Res.* **26**, 337–410.

New, M. I., Dupont, B., Grumbach, K., and Levine, L. S. (1983). *In* "The Metabolic Basis of Inherited Disease" (J. B. Stanbury, J. B. Wyngaarden, D. S. Fredrickson, J. L. Goldstein, and M. S. Brown eds.), 5th Ed., pp. 973–1000. McGraw-Hill, New York.

Nowakowski, H., and Lenz, W. (1961). *Recent Prog. Horm. Res.* **17**, 53–95.

Ohno, S. (1978). *J. Am. Med. Assoc.* **239**, 217–220.

Okon, E., Livni, N., Rosler, A., Yorkoni, S., Segal, S., Kohn, G., and Schenker, J. G. (1980). *Arch. Pathol. Lab. Med.* **104**, 363–367.

Peters, H. (1970). *Philos. Trans. R. Soc. London Ser. B* **259**, 91–101.

Peterson, R. E., Imperato-McGinley, J., Gautier, T., and Sturla, E. (1977). *Am. J. Med.* **62**, 170–191.

Picard, J. -Y., Tran, D., and Josso, N. (1978). *Mol. Cell. Endocrinol.* **12**, 17–30.

Picon, R. (1967). *Arch. Anat. Microsc. Morphol. Exp.* **56**, 281–290.

Pinsky, L., Kaufman, M., Straisfeld, C., Zilahi, B., and Hall, C. St.-G. (1978). *Am. J. Med. Genet.* **1**, 407–416.

Pinsky, L., Kaufman, M., and Summit, R. L. (1981). *Am. J. Med. Genet.* **10**, 91–99.

Price, P., Wass, J. A. H., Griffin, J. E., Leshin, M., Wilson, J. D., Savage, M. O., Lange, D. M., Anderson, D. C., and Besser, G. M. (1984). *J. Clin. Invest.*, **74**, 1496–1508.

Reifenstein, E. C., Jr. (1947). *Proc. Am. Fed. Clin. Res.* **3**, 86.

Rigaudiere, N. (1979). *Acta Endocrinol.* **92**, 174–186.

Rosewater, S., Gwinup, G., and Hamwi, G. J. (1965). *Ann. Intern. Med.* **63**, 377–385.

Saenger, P., Goldman, A. S., Levine, L. S., Korth-Schutz, S., Muecke, E. C., Katsumata, M., Doberne, Y., and New, M. I. (1978). *J. Clin. Endocrinol. Metab.* **46**, 627–634.

Savage, M. O., Preece, M. A., Jeffcoate, S. L., Ransley, P. G., Rumsby, G., Mansfield, M. D., and Williams, D. I. (1980). *Clin. Endocrinol.* **12**, 397–406.

Schechter, J. (1970). *Gen. Comp. Endocrinol.* **14**, 53–67.

Schultz, F. M., and Wilson, J. D. (1974). *Endocrinology* **94**, 979–986.

Sholl, S. A., and Goy, R. W. (1978). *Biol. Reprod.* **18**, 160–169.

Siiteri, P. K., and Wilson, J. D. (1974). *J. Clin. Endocrinol. Metab.* **38**, 113–125.

Silvers, W. K., Gasser, D. L., and Eicher, E. M. (1982). *Cell* **28**, 439–440.

Sloan, W. R., and Walsh, P. C. (1976). *J. Urol.* **115**, 459–461.

Thies, N., Warne, G., Connelly, J. F., Montalto, J., Funder, J., Walker, A. C., and Wettenhall, H. N. B. (1979). *Aust. Paediatr. J.* **15**, 209.

Verhoeven, G., and Wilson, J. D. (1976). *Endocrinology* **99**, 79–92.

Wachtel, S. S. (1980). *Biol. Reprod.* **22**, 1–8.

Walker, A. C., Stack, E. M., and Horsfall, W. A. (1970). *Med. J. Aust.* **1**, 156–160.

Walsh, P. C., Madden, J. D., Harrod, M. J., Goldstein, J. L., MacDonald, P. C., and Wilson, J. D. (1974). *N. Engl. J. Med.* **291**, 944–949.

Walsh, P. C., Wilson, J. D., Allen, T. D., Madden, J. D., Porter, J. C., Neaves, W. B., Griffin, J. E., and Goodwin, W. E. (1978). *J. Urol.* **120**, 90–95.

Wilbert, D. M., Griffin, J. E., and Wilson, J. D. (1983). *J. Clin. Endocrinol. Metab.* **56**, 113–120.

Wilson, J. D. (1971). *Symp. Dtsch. Ges. Endokrinol.* **17**, 11–18.

Wilson, J. D. (1975). *J. Biol. Chem.* **250**, 3498–3504.

Wilson, J. D. (1978). *Annu. Rev. Physiol.* **40**, 279–306.

Wilson, J. D. (1979). *In* "Campbell's Textbook of Urology" (J. H. Harrison, R. F. Gittes, A. D. Perlmutter, T. A. Stamey, and P. C. Walsh, eds.), pp. 1469–1483. Saunders, Philadelphia.

Wilson, J. D., and Griffin, J. E. (1983). *In* "Harrison's Principles of Internal Medicine" (R. G. Petersdorf, R. D. Adams, E. Braunwald, K. S. Isselbacher, J. B. Martin, and J. D. Wilson, eds.), pp. 724–739. McGraw-Hill, New York.

Wilson, J. D., and Goldstein, J. L. (1975). *Birth Defects Orig. Artic. Ser.* **11**, 1–16.

Wilson, J. D., and Lasnitski, I. (1971). *Endocrinology* **89**, 659–668.

Wilson, J. D., and Siiteri, P. K. (1973). *Endocrinology* **92**, 1182–1191.

Wilson, J. D., Harrod, M. J., Goldstein, J. L., Hemsell, D. L., and MacDonald, P. C. (1974). *N. Engl. J. Med.* **290,** 1097–1103.

Wilson, J. D., Griffin, J. E., and George, F. W. (1979). *Arthritis Rheum.* **22,** 1275–1283.

Wilson, J. D., Griffin, J. E., Leshin, M., and MacDonald, P. C. (1983). *In* "The Metabolic Basis of Inherited Disease" (J. B. Stanbury, J. B. Wyngaarden, D. S. Fredricksen, J. E. Goldstein, and M. S. Brown, eds.), 5th Ed., pp. 1001–1026. McGraw-Hill, New York.

BIOLOGICAL FUNCTIONS OF CALMODULIN*

WAI YIU CHEUNG

Departments of Biochemistry
St. Jude Children's Research Hospital, and
The University of Tennessee Center for the Health Sciences
Memphis, Tennessee

I. Introduction

MAMMALS are composed of billions of different cells that share information with one another by means of cellular contact or by chemical or electrical signals. Cellular organelles and compartments also communicate with each other, usually with the help of chemical signals such as cyclic AMP (cAMP) or calcium ions (Ca^{2+}). Our interest is in how these signals regulate various cellular activities. Cellular regulation has been a topic of interest for a long time, but only within the last three decades has information become available at the molecular level. level. It was a landmark in the history of endocrinology when cAMP was discovered in the late 1950s by Earl Sutherland and his co-workers as an agent that mediates the glycogenolytic action of glucagon in the liver (1).

The importance of Ca^{2+} as a cellular regulator was appreciated long before the discovery of cAMP. In 1883, Ringer reported that Ca^{2+} was required in the bathing medium to maintain the contraction of an isolated frog heart (2); some 70 years later, Heilbrunn demonstrated the contractile effect of Ca^{2+} when it was injected into a muscle fiber (3). The effect of calcium ions is not restricted to muscular function; they play a role in such diverse processes as endocytosis, exocytosis, cell motility, energy metabolism, synthesis and release of neurotransmitters, chromosome movement, and cell division. Indeed, the effects of Ca^{2+} touch nearly all aspects of cellular physiology.

Despite the prominent role of Ca^{2+} in cell function, its mechanism of action remained largely unexplored until recently. The first suggestion

*Lecture delivered April 19, 1984.

of how Ca^{2+} functions at the molecular level came from work demonstrating that troponin C binds Ca^{2+} and mediates the contraction of skeletal and cardiac muscle (4). The action of Ca^{2+} in the contraction of smooth muscle, and its numerous effects within other tissues, were still unknown.

As happens so often in the progress of science, serendipity intervened. I shall trace the discovery of calmodulin drawing primarily from our own experiments and discuss its paramount role in cellular regulation.

II. Discovery of Calmodulin

In 1964, I joined Dr. Britton Chance of the Johnson Research Foundation, University of Pennsylvania, as a postdoctoral fellow. I was working on the regulatory properties of a bovine brain phosphodiesterase, an enzyme that degrades cAMP to adenosine-5'-monophosphate and terminates its action.

I was initially interested in this enzyme only for determining the purity of a commercial sample of cAMP which affected NADH oscillation in a yeast extract (5). Later my interest in phosphodiesterase was aroused by some of its biological properties. Brain cortex is rich in phosphodiesterase and adenylate cyclase, which catalyzes the synthesis of cAMP. The activity of phosphodiesterase is some 100 times higher than adenylase cyclase (6,7), yet, cAMP increased markedly in brain cortex shortly after decapitation and in brain slices incubated in the presence of neurohormones (8,9). Adenylate cyclase is associated with the cell membrane (7), whereas phosphodiesterase is found in particulate and cytosolic fractions (6). Cyclic AMP formed under these conditions may not be freely accessible to phosphodiesterase, allowing the nucleotide to accumulate transiently. Another possibility is that phosphodiesterase is subject to some control mechanisms not yet elucidated.

Adenylate cyclase was being actively studied by Sutherland's group; I decided to examine phosphodiesterase, a task that required purification of the enzyme. During such an attempt, I passed an enzyme preparation through an ion-exchange chromatography column (10), and to my surprise, the activity of the enzyme decreased dramatically. Systematic analysis disclosed that the enzyme lost activity because an activator protein, now called calmodulin, had been removed (11).

Two observations were instrumental in demonstrating the presence of calmodulin: the loss of phosphodiesterase activity as the enzyme was purified, and the stimulation of the purified (but not crude) enzyme by snake venom, which was used as a source of 5′-nucleotidase required for the assay of phosphodiesterase. Table I shows a typical pattern of the specific activity of bovine brain phosphodiesterase at the different stages of purification. The specific activity was increased from 54 in the homogenate to 340 in an eluate from a calcium phosphate gel. Further purification on a DEAE–cellulose column resulted in a precipitous loss of activity.

A common way to monitor the activity of phosphodiesterase in the 1960s entailed use of an auxiliary enzyme, 5′-nucleotidase, which is abundant in snake venom (6). The assay could be completed in one stage by including 5′-nucleotidase in the reaction mixture, or in two stages by stopping the reaction at the level of adenosine-5′-monophosphate and then adding snake venom to convert it to adncosine and inorganic phosphate, which were determined chemically. It was common experience that the two procedures gave comparable enzyme ac-

TABLE I

PARTIAL LOSS OF PHOSPHODIESTERASE ACTIVITY DURING
PROCESS OF PURIFICATION[a]

Fraction (tubes a through e)	Phosphodiesterase activity (nmol/mg protein/min)
a. Homogenate	54.1
b. pH 5.9 supernatant fluid	91.3
c. 30–50% $(NH_4)_2SO_4$	181.5
d. Calcium phosphate gel eluate	342.0
e. DEAE–cellulose eluate	45.2

[a] Phosphodiesterase was purified by extracting bovine brain cerebra with water, followed by pH fractionation, differential centrifugation, $(NH_4)_2SO_4$ fractionation, calcium phosphate gel adsorption, and DEAE–cellulose chromatography. An aliquot of each of the fractions obtained at the different stages of the purification procedure was assayed for enzymatic activity according to a two-stage procedure (from 11).

tivities. Both phosphodiesterase and 5'-nucleotidase required divalent cations for activity. In studies of the metal requirements of phosphodiesterase (12), I had to use the two-stage assay to ascertain that the addition or omission of a particular divalent cation to the reaction system did not affect the activity of 5'-nucleotidase. Unexpectedly, I found that the assay procedure markedly affected the activity of partially purified (but not crude) phosphodiesterase and that snake venom, itself inactive toward cAMP, greatly stimulated only the purified enzyme (Table II) (13). The stimulation of snake venom was traced to its endogenous proteolytic activity (10). The finding that crude phosphodiesterase is fully active whereas the purified enzyme depends on venom for maximum activity could be explained in several ways. One was that an activator originally present with phosphodiesterase was removed during the course of purification and that snake venom somehow mimicked the effect of the activator. This hunch proved to be correct.

Table III compares the activity of a crude and a purified phosphodiesterase assayed individually with a mixture of these two enzymes assayed together. The activity of the mixture was nearly twice the summed activities of the individual preparations (14). This experiment demonstrated the synergistic effect of the mixture but did not reveal which component was the activating agent. The stimulation of only the purified phosphodiesterase by snake venom is illuminating in this respect. The activity of the mixture was comparable to the summed activities of the crude and the purified enzyme subsequent to its activation by the venom. Since only the purified enzyme was stimulated by the

TABLE II

Effect of Snake Venom on the Activity of Purified
Phosphodiesterase[a]

| | Activity (OD/sample) | |
Enzyme	With venom	without venom
Crude phosphodiesterase	0.625	0.621
Purified phosphodiesterase	0.476	0.061

[a] The two-stage procedure was used for the assay (from 13).

TABLE III

EFFECT OF SNAKE VENOM ON THE ACTIVITY OF CRUDE AND
PURIFIED PHOSPHODIESTERASE[a]

	Fractions	Activity (nanomoles)
a.	Crude phosphodiesterase	262
b.	Crude phosphodiesterase + venom	279
c.	Purified phosphodiesterase	80
d.	Purified phosphodiesterase + venom	454
e.	Crude + purified phosphodiesterase	658

[a] Phosphodiesterase was assayed using a two-stage procedure. When indicated, venom was added in the first stage of incubation (from 14).

venom, the activator was probably associated with the crude enzyme. Moreover, this activating agent was as effective as the venom in stimulating the purified enzyme.

Phosphodiesterase was a stable enzyme, and other experiments showed that stimulation of the purified enzyme by the venom was not due to protection of some unstable phosphodiesterase activity afforded by proteins in the venom (10). Thus, the increased activity of the purified enzyme in the presence of the homogenate was due to stimulation of the enzyme. From such considerations, I concluded that the relative inactivity of the purified enzyme was caused by removal of an activator during the course of enzyme purification.

Figure 1 depicts the elution pattern of the enzyme from a DEAE–cellulose column and shows phosphodiesterase activity in its stimulated and nonstimulated state. The activity in the peak tubes depended upon venom but that in the tubes trailing the peak did not. In fact, the activity of tubes 69–73 was essentially the same whether or not venom was present during the incubation before the assay. This suggested that the enzyme in these tubes retained sufficient activator which was eluted after the enzyme. Tubes were pooled into two groups (Fig. 1) to test this possibility. Fraction I was mostly inactive, and fraction II exhibited no phosphodiesterase activity (Table IV). However, fraction II augmented the activity of fraction I some sixfold. The experiment confirmed that an

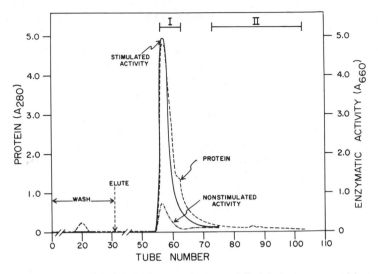

FIG. 1. Resolution of phosphodiesterase into a partially inactive enzyme and its activator on a DEAE–cellulose column. Phosphodiesterase was assayed by a two-stage
procedure, once with snake venom in the first stage of incubation to stimulate activity,
and again without venom. Tubes were pooled as follows: fraction I, tubes 56 to 63;
fraction II, tubes 70 to 100 (from 11).

TABLE IV

EFFECT OF ACTIVATOR ON ACTIVITY OF PURIFIED
PHOSPHODIESTERASE[a]

Fraction (tubes a through c)	Activity (nmol cAMP/tube/10 min)
a. Fraction I	48
b. Fraction II	0
c. Fraction I + fraction II	290

[a] Fraction I (purified phosphodiesterase) and fraction II (the activator) were assayed for phosphodiesterase activity individually
and together in a mixture according to a two-stage procedure (from
11).

activator was removed from phosphodiesterase during the course of enzyme purification.

To examine the distribution of the activator in the fractions representing different stages of purification, I studied the effect of these fractions on the activity of the purified phosphodiesterase (DEAE–cellulose eluate). Table V shows the activities of the individual as well as the combined fractions. The first column shows the activities of the individual fractions, the second column those of a mixture of the DEAE–cellulose eluate and one of the other fractions, and the third column the algebraic sums of the activities of the corresponding individual assays. The difference between the observed activity and the calculated activity for any fraction is due to the stimulating effect of that fraction. The difference was most definite in the fractions obtained during the early stages of purification, i.e., the homogenate and the pH 5.9 supernatant fluid. This suggested that the initial fractions contained abundant quantities of the activator. The 30 to 50% $(NH_4)_2SO_4$ fraction and the calcium phosphate gel eluate produced no significant difference, suggesting that the amount of the activator in these fractions was no longer in excess. This is supported by the observation that whereas most of the phosphodiestease activity was sedimented with the 30 to 50% $(NH_4)_2SO_4$ fraction, a large amount of the activator remained in the 50% supernatant fluid and was discarded, indicating that as purification proceeded, more activator was removed from the enzyme. The reverse experiment, showing the effect of the activator on phosphodiesterase activity in the different fractions, is presented in the last column. No significant effect was seen on the enzymatic activity of the homogenate and the pH 5.9 supernatant. This was consistent with the notion that these fractions already contained abundant activator. The stimulation of the activity of the $(NH_4)_2SO_4$ and calcium phosphate gel fractions was small, indicating that further purification caused a slight deficiency in the activator. The effect of the activator on the DEAE–cellulose eluate was pronounced, the stimulation being severalfold.

These results revealed that removal of the activator from the enzyme took place mainly at two stages. The first stage coincided with the $(NH_4)_2SO_4$ fractionation. Whereas most of the enzyme was precipitated with the 30 to 50% fraction, a large amount of the activator remained in the 50% supernatant fluid and was discarded. The second stage occurred on a DEAE–cellulose column, whereby more activator was re-

TABLE V

DISTRIBUTION OF ACTIVATOR AND ITS EFFECT ON DIFFERENT FRACTIONS
OBTAINED DURING PURIFICATION OF PHOSPHODIESTERASE[a]

| | | Activity (nmol/tube/10 min) | | |
| | | Individual fraction and DEAE–cellulose eluate | | |
Fraction	Individual fraction	Experimental	Theoretical	Individual fraction and activator
a. Homogenate	66	260	106	62
b. pH 5.9 supernatant	48	261	88	48
c. 30–50% $(NH_4)_2SO_4$	87	119	127	115
d. Calcium phosphate gel eluate	142	188	182	161
e. DEAE–cellulose eluate	40	—	—	304
f. Activator	0	—	—	—

[a] All fractions were dialyzed against Tris–chloride. The homogenate and the pH 5.9 supernatant fluid were centrifuged at 40,000 g for 20 minutes and an appropriate aliquot of the supernatant fluid was used. Each fraction was assayed individually, in the presence of a purified phosphodiesterase (DEAE–cellulose eluate), and again in the presence of the activator. The first column shows the activity of the individual fractions; the second column shows the observed activity of the combined assays; the third column shows the algebraic sum of the activities of the individual assays; and the last column shows the activities of the individual fractions in the presence of the activator (from 11).

moved from the enzyme. The further removal of the activator from the enzyme at this stage rendered the enzyme dependent on an exogenous activator for optimal activity.

Collectively, these data clearly indicated that the decreased phosphodiesterase activity was due to dissociation of an activator from the enzyme during the course of purification. The crude enzyme was fully active because the activator was present in excess; the purified enzyme was partially active because little of the activator remained; and fractions that contained excess activator were not affected by an endogenous activator but were capable of augmenting the activity of the purified enzyme.

Calmodulin was born.

III. Biological and Biochemical Properties of Calmodulin

Calmodulin has been found in all eukaryotes from amoeba and fungi to plants and animals. In some tissues, such as testis, brain (15), and the electroplax of *Electrophorus electricus* (16), the concentrations of calmodulin are particularly high. Calmodulin molecules from different phylogenetic sources show very similar, in some cases identical, biological and biochemical features. The amino acid sequence appears to have been highly conserved, an attribute not unexpected of a fundamental regulatory protein. Thus, calmodulin lacks both tissue and species specificity (17,18).

Calmodulin from bovine brain consists of 148 amino acids. A third of the residues are glutamate and aspartate, which furnish carboxylic groups to chelate Ca^{2+}. Figure 2 shows the amino acid sequence of calmodulin. The protein contains four homologous domains, each harboring a Ca^{2+}-binding site. The dissociation constant of these sites for Ca^{2+} is about 10^{-6} M, within the physiological range of the cation. This property allows calmodulin to sense the cellular flux of Ca^{2+}, an essential property for its being a Ca^{2+} receptor.

Most proteins are generally delicate; harsh treatments or extreme conditions invariably inactivate them. Calmodulin stands out as a stark contrast; it withstands exposure to acidic pH, boiling water (11), and 8 M urea (22), conditions that invariably disable other proteins. The remarkable stability of calmodulin greatly facilitated its isolation in the

182   WAI YIU CHEUNG

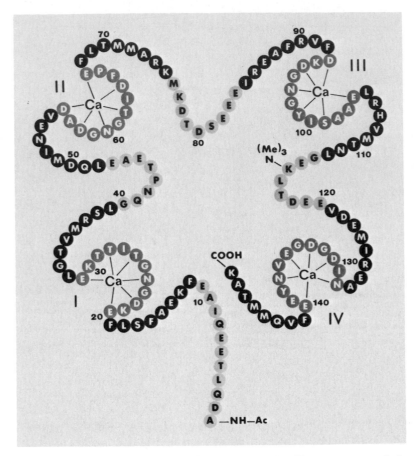

Fig. 2. Amino acid sequence of bovine brain calmodulin. The sequence was elucidated by Watterson *et al.* (19). The scheme depicts the four putative Ca²⁺-binding domains, each consisting of a 12-residue loop (gray circles) flanked on each side by an 8-residue helix (dark circles) as proposed by Kretsinger (20). The predicted Ca²⁺-binding residues are indicated by the solid lines in each loop. The amino acids are abbreviated: A, alanine; D, aspartic acid; E, glutamic acid; F, phenylalanine; G, glycine; H, histidine; I, isoleucine; K, lysine; L, leucine; M, methionine; N, asparagine; P, proline; Q, glutamine; R, arginine; S, serine; T, threonine; V, valine; Y, tyrosine (from 21).

TABLE VI

PHYSIOCHEMICAL PROPERTIES OF BOVINE BRAIN CALMODULIN

Determination	Value
M_r (molecular weight)	16,700
$f_i : f_o$ (frictional ratio)	1.20
pI (isoelectric point)	4.30
K_d (Ca_2^+ binding)	$3.5 \times 10^{-6} - 1.8 \times 10^{-5}\ M$
$s_{20,w}$ (sedimentation coefficient)	1.85 S
v (partial specific value)	0.72 cm^3/g
D (diffusion coefficient)	$1.09 \times 10^{-6}\ cm^2/S$
Stokes radius	20.9 Å
$E_{276}^{1\%}$	1.8
Amino acid	148

bulk quantities needed for physicochemical characterization (Table VI) during the early years of calmodulin research.

Calmodulin is found in the cytoplasm and in association with membranes and organelles (23–25), and its intracellular distribution varies with cell type. Even though its concentration within the cell can change during the cell cycle (26), the concentration usually is not rate limiting for the various enzyme systems (see Table VII).

Why is calmodulin such a hardy protein, and what makes it so versatile in cellular regulation? The amino acid composition of calmodulin is unique: it does not include easily oxidizable residues such as tryptophan and cysteine (without cysteine, there is no formation of disulfide bridges), nor does it include proline, which usually appears at turns of a polypeptide. Without such intrinsic restrictions, calmodulin is highly flexible, capable of assuming its native conformation even after it has been distorted by otherwise incapacitating conditions. This inherent flexibility allows calmodulin to transmit the Ca^{2+} signal to elicit first a conformational change in calmodulin, and then in the receptors of calmodulin (17). Its structural versatility thus offers calmodulin a unique attribute as a principal intracellular receptor or partner of Ca^{2+}.

Calcium, alone among divalent cations, serves as a key messenger. First, Ca^{2+} is ubiquitous and abundant in all biological systems, although its steady state concentration in the cytoplasm is $10^{-7}\ M$ or lower, some 1,000 to 10,000 times lower than that in the fluid outside the cell. In fact, the cell does not tolerate a high intracellular level of calcium ions; they form insoluble salts with organic phosphates such as adenosine triphosphate, a universal energy currency for the cell. The steep concentration differential between extracellular and intracellular space is maintained because the cell membrane is normally highly impermeable to Ca^{2+}. When the cell is stimulated, the cell membrane becomes momentarily permeable and allows an influx of Ca^{2+}, which is detected as an informational signal. The increased calcium level within the cell is short lived. The cation is either actively extruded by the Ca^{2+} pump situated in the cell membrane or sequestered in the mitochondria or endoplasmic reticulum.

Secondly, Ca^{2+} has physicochemical properties unique among divalent cations in the living cell. It has the appropriate dimension to fit snugly into the Ca^{2+}-binding domain of proteins. Magnesium (Mg^{2+}), which is also widely found in biological systems, has a smaller ionic radius and is more rigid in its requirements for proper coordination with proteins (27). Other divalent cations, such as Cd^{2+}, Hg^{2+}, and Pb^{2+} that have comparable ionic radii, may substitute for Ca^{2+} to activate calmodulin (28), but they are not normally present in significant quantities in the living system. When they do accumulate under certain pathological conditions, they are highly toxic, as will be discussed in a later section.

IV. MECHANISM OF CALMODULIN ACTION

Kakiuchi *et al.* (29) observed that the calmodulin-dependent phosphodiesterase required both Ca^{2+} and Mg^{2+} for maximum activity, and that calmodulin rendered the enzyme more sensitive to the activation by Ca^{2+}. This finding directly links Ca^{2+} to the metabolism of cAMP. By 1970, some of the basic properties of calmodulin were known: its heat stability, its lack of any intrinsic enzymatic activity, and its activation of phosphodiesterase through a stoichiometric process. Figure 3A reproduces a titrimetric trace showing the stoichiometric effect of calmodulin on the rate of hydrolysis of cAMP. As cAMP was hydrolyzed, an equivalent amount of H^{3+} was released, which was measured by the consumption of NaOH. No detectable lag was observed after the addition of the calmodulin. The rate was linear and was maintained until another addition of calmodulin was made, whereby a new rate was established and maintained thereafter; the increase was constant after each addition of calmodulin. As a comparison, a trace showing the catalytic activation of phosphodiesterase by trypsin is reproduced in Fig. 3B. The rate of hydrolysis increases with time after the addition of trypsin.

Although the process of activation by the two agents appears to be different mechanistically, the final effects are comparable. Either calmodulin or trypsin was capable of causing maximal stimulation, after which no further effect was observed by the addition of the other agent. Chymotrypsin, pronase, and snake venom stimulated the purified enzyme in a manner similar to trypsin (30).

Teo and Wang (31) and Lin and Liu in our laboratory (32) showed that calmodulin is a Ca^{2+}-binding protein. Under our experimental conditions, calmodulin displayed two classes of binding sites, three sites with a K_d of $3.5 \times 10^{-6} M$ and one site with a K_d of $1.8 \times 10^{-5} M$ (Fig. 4). The mechanism of calmodulin activation was soon elucidated in several laboratories (31–34). Calmodulin itself is not active, nor is Ca^{2+}. Upon binding Ca^{2+}, calmodulin assumes a more helical structure (35), as monitored by optical rotary dispersion, a sensitive probe to follow conformational change in proteins. A protein with a more helical structure exhibits a larger rotatory power. Figure 5 depicts a typical optical rotatory dispersion spectrum of calmodulin in the near ultraviolet region, and shows a trough at 231 nm in the presence or absence of Ca^{2+}. In the absence of Ca^{2+}, the reduced mean residue rotation, $[m']_{231}$, was -5700, and in the presence of 100 μM Ca^{2+}, it increased to -7500, corresponding to 39 and 57% of α-helical content, respectively. This experiment shows that Ca^{2+} increases the helical content of calmodulin, a finding subsequently confirmed by others using various other physical measurements.

The change of conformation in calmodulin results in expression of a hydrophobic region (36,37) believed to interact with the inactive apoenzyme to form the active holoenzyme, which assumes a new conformation. Exposure of a hydrophobic domain affords calmodulin a recognition site in a generally aqueous environment of the cell to interact with its receptor enzymes. Figure 6 depicts a gel filtration experiment that shows the formation of an active complex of calmodulin·phosphodiesterase. A mixture of phosphodiesterase and calmodulin

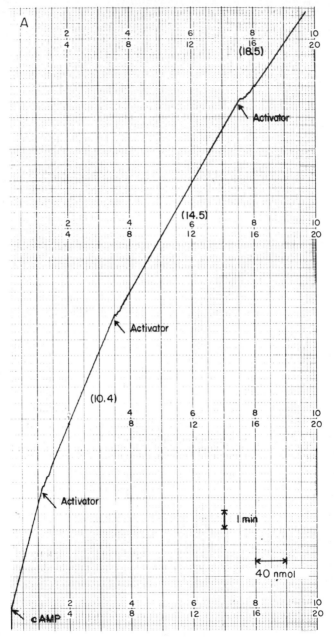

Fig. 3. Comparison between activation of phosphodiesterase by calmodulin and by trypsin. (A) In a titrimetric trace showing the effect of calmodulin on the activity of

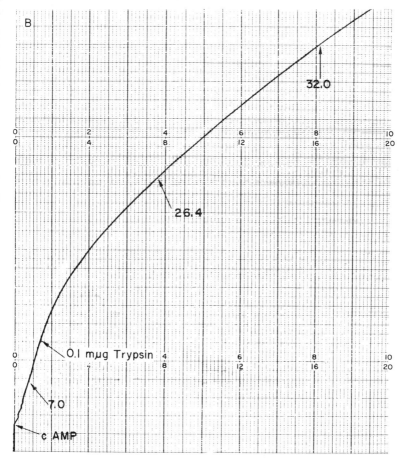

phosphodiesterase, a microversion of the Metrohm Combi-Titrator 3D equipped with a 0.2-ml syringe was used. Assay was carried out at 30°C in a final volume of 1.5 ml containing 40 mM NaCl, 0.1 mM MnCl$_2$, 240 μg of purified phosphodiesterase, and 1 mM cAMP. The substrate (15 μl of 0.1 M cAMP, pH 8.0) was added to initiate the reaction, and the rate of cAMP hydrolysis was followed by the generation of H$^+$, which was measured by the consumption of the titrant (2 mM NaOH). The reaction mixture was maintained at pH 8.0. The scales of the trace are as shown. Where indicated, 3.8 μg of activator was added. The figures in parentheses indicate the rate of cAMP hydrolysis expressed in nanomoles per minute. Before addition of calmodulin, the rate of hydrolysis was 6.2 nmol/min. Note the constant increase of the rate of hydrolysis after each addition of calmodulin. (B) Reproduction of a titrimetric trace showing the effect of trypsin on the activity of a purified phosphodiesterase. Assay was carried out as in (A), except that the purified enzyme was 95 μg. At the point indicated, 0.1 μg of trypsin was added. The rate of hydrolysis was 7 nmol/min before the addition of trypsin. The rate 13 minutes after the addition increased to 32 nmol/min (from 11).

188   WAI YIU CHEUNG

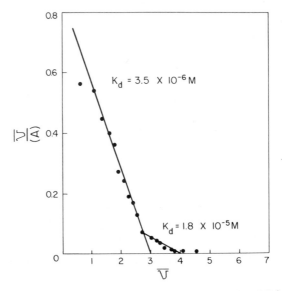

FIG. 4. Scatchard plot of Ca^{2+} binding by calmodulin. The moles of Ca^{2+} bound per mole of calmodulin, v, was calculated from the difference in radioactivity in the protein solution inside a dialysis tube and that in the buffer outside the tubing after equilibrium had been reached. (A) is the concentration of Ca^{2+} in the dialyzing buffer outside the dialysis tubing (from 32).

lin was passed through a Sephadex G-200 column equilibrated with EGTA. The phosphodiesterase was resolved into two active fractions (panel A). The first peak coincided with the exclusion volume, and the second corresponded to a molecular weight of 170,000. Phosphodiesterase activity in both fractions was low, but increased substantially when calmodulin was added to the assay solution. With filtration chromatography, known to give an abnormally high molecular weight for calmodulin, elution of calmodulin occurred at a position corresponding to a molecular weight of 33,000.

In a separate experiment (panel B), the enzyme mixture was passed through the same column that had been equilibrated with Ca^{2+} instead of EGTA. In contrast to the results shown in panel A, calmodulin was eluted with phosphodiesterase and the enzyme activity was found to be virtually the same with or without exogenous calmodulin. The second

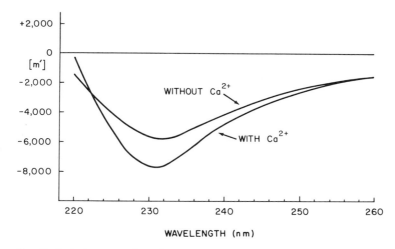

FIG. 5. Optical rotatory dispersion spectra of calmodulin. The concentration of calmodulin was 50 μg/ml and that of Ca^{2+} was 100 μM (from 34).

activity peak shifted to a position corresponding to a molecular weight of 230,000, suggesting that this form of the enzyme retained 2 mol of calmodulin. Recent experiments with homogeneous phosphodiesterase from bovine heart (39) and brain (40) showed that the enzyme exists as a dimer (M_r 120,000) and that each monomer binds one calmodulin.

In a controlled experiment (panel C), the enzyme and calmodulin were passed separately through the column equilibrated with Ca^{2+}. Both the enzyme and calmodulin were eluted at positions identical to those in panel A, thus demonstrating that Ca^{2+} did not affect the behavior of either protein during gel filtration. These experiments suggest that the enzyme and calmodulin form a complex in the presence of Ca^{2+}, but remain dissociated when Ca^{2+} is absent.

Although the experiments (Fig. 6) demonstrated the Ca^{2+}-dependent formation of the enzyme·calmodulin complex, they did not indicate the rate of formation or dissociation of the complex. Since the enzyme·calmodulin complex is the active species, the rate of increased phosphodiesterase activity by addition of Ca^{2+} would be a measure of the rate of complex formation. Similarly, the rate of decrease of enzyme activity by addition of EGTA would be a measure of the rate of complex

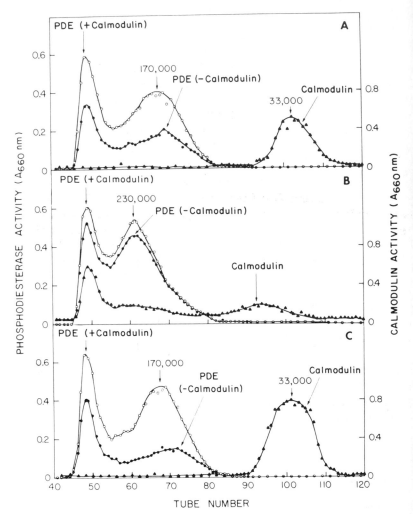

Fig. 6. Ca^{2+}-dependent association of phosphodiesterase and calmodulin in a Sephadex G-200 column (95 × 2.5 cm). (A) The column was equilibrated with a buffer containing 20 mM Tris–HCl (pH 8.0), 100 mM NaCl, 0.1 mM dithiothreitol, and 0.1 mM EGTA (buffer A) at 0°C. Thirteen milligrams of a calmodulin-deficient phosphodiesterase and 8 μg of calmodulin in 2.5 ml of a buffer containing 40 mM Tris–HCl (pH 8.0), 0.1 mM dithiothreitol, and 0.1 mM EGTA were incubated for 15 minutes at 30°C and then applied to the column. Both phosphodiesterase and calmodulin were prepared from bovine brain. The volume was eluted with buffer A; fractions of 3.5 ml were collected at a

dissociation. These rates were determined in an experiment using a detergent-solubilized adenylate cyclase of rat brain (Fig. 7). The initial portion of the curve represents the basal adenylate cyclase activity which rapidly changed upon the addition of Ca^{2+}. After Ca^{2+} was added to the reaction mixture, the rate of cAMP formation increased immediately. The enzyme activity remained elevated until the addition of EGTA, which reduced the activity to its prestimulated level (41). This experiment demonstrated that both the formation and dissociation of the enzyme·calmodulin complex were rapid and readily reversible.

Collectively, these experiments showed that Ca^{2+} changes first the conformation of calmodulin and then that of the receptor enzyme, resulting in an increase of enzyme activity, as outlined below.

$$Ca^{2+}_n + (CaM)_{inactive} \rightleftharpoons (Ca^{2+}_n \cdot CaM^*)_{active}$$
$$Ca^{2+}_n CaM^* + (E)_{inactive} \rightleftharpoons (Ca^{2+}_n \cdot CaM^* \cdot E^*)_{active}$$

The asterisk indicates a new conformation and n the number of bound Ca^{2+} ions. Kinetic analysis indicates that calmodulin assumes its active conformation with three to four bound Ca^{2+} (42,43).

Viewed another way, an increase of Ca^{2+} elicits a change in calmodulin conformation, which serves as a signal that is transmitted to the enzyme to change its activity. These reactions are freely reversible, and the direction of the reactions is determined by the intracellular level of Ca^{2+} which increases from a steady state level of approximately 10^{-7} M to 10^{-6} M when a cell is stimulated. The increased level of Ca^{2+} initiates a chain of reactions, first the activation of calmodulin and then that of its receptor protein. The excess Ca^{2+} is rapidly taken up by

---

flow rate of 24 ml/hr. Aliquots were assayed separately for calmodulin and for phosphodiesterase in the presence or absence of an exogenous calmodulin by a two-stage procedure. (B) The column was equilibrated with a buffer containing 20 mM Tris–HCl (pH 8.0), 100 mM NaCl, 0.1 mM dithiothreitol, and 0.1 mM $CaCl_2$ (buffer B). Thirteen milligrams of a calmodulin-deficient phosphodiesterase and 8 μg of calmodulin in 2.5 ml of a buffer containing 40 mM Tris–HCl (pH 8.0), 0.1 mM dithiothreitol, and 0.1 mM $CaCl_2$ were incubated for 15 minutes at 30°C and then loaded on the column. The column was eluted with buffer B. Fractions were collected and assayed as in (A). (C) Conditions were the same as those in (B) except that phosphodiesterase and calmodulin were applied to the column separately. The column was calibrated with known protein markers (from 38).

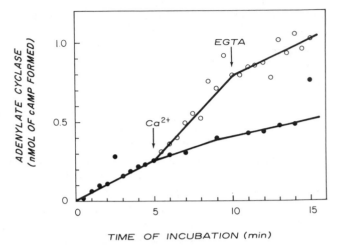

FIG. 7. Effect of Ca^{2+} or EGTA on the rate of cAMP synthesis catalyzed by rat brain adenylate cyclase solubilized by Lubrol-PX. A reaction mixture of 5 ml contained 40 mM Tris–HCl (pH 7.5), 40 mM caffeine, 10 mM NaF, 5 mM MgSO$_4$, 0.1 mM EGTA, 4 mM cAMP, 1 mM [^{3}H]ATP, 4 mM phosphoenolpyruvate, 40 μg/ml of pyruvate kinase, and 4.1 mg Lubrol-PX-solubilized rat brain adenylate cyclase, which was added last to initiate the reaction. At appropriate times, 0.1-ml aliquots were withdrawn from the reaction system and were transferred to small tubes containing 50 μl of 1 N HCl. At 5 minutes 1 ml of the reaction mixture was removed and transferred to another tube, which served as a control, and then Ca^{2+} was added to a final concentration of 0.1 mM. At 10 mM, EGTA was added to a final concentration of 0.1 mM. The [^{3}H]cAMP formed was determined (from 41).

mitochondria or endoplasmic reticulum, or extruded by the Ca^{2+} pump associated with the cell membrane. Lowering the concentration of Ca^{2+} to its steady state level dissociates the calmodulin·receptor complex and terminates the Ca^{2+} signal. Thus, the cellular level of Ca^{2+}, rather than that of calmodulin, is the pacesetter of many cellular processes. However, the level of calmodulin can be the limiting factor under certain conditions [see for example (26)].

Since calmodulin has four Ca^{2+}-binding sites, the question arises whether these sites are filled randomly or sequentially. Tb^{3+} is often used as a probe to study the interaction of Ca^{2+} with its receptor proteins, primarily because of its fluorescence characteristics. Of the four Ca^{2+}-binding sites, two (domains III and IV) contain one tyrosine apiece. When Tb^{3+} is bound to these domains, the potential exists for the transfer of fluorescence resonance energy from tyrosine to Tb^{3+}. An analysis of the fluorescence characteristics of resonance energy transfer would reveal the sequence of occupancy of these sites by Tb^{3+}. Figure 8 shows a schematic diagram of the differential excitation of Tb^{3+} bound to calmodulin by two wavelengths, "direct" excitation at 222 nm, and "indirect" excitation at 280 nm. "Direct" excitation utilizes a wavelength of 222 to excite Tb^{3+} (Fig. 8A). Tyrosine has an absorption peak at 222 nm. At this wavelength, the Tb^{3+} in domains III and IV are excited by direct absorption as well as by energy transfer from tyrosine. Thus, direct excitation actually involves direct perturbation of all four Tb^{3+} ions (Fig. 8A) and indirect perturbation of the two Tb^{3+} ions bound to domains III and IV through energy transfer from tyrosine. However, the latter does not contribute significantly to the Tb^{3+} fluorescence monitored at 545 nm (44) and is omitted in the figure for the sake of simplicity. "Indirect excitation" utilizes a wavelength of 280 nm to excite tyrosine, with a resultant energy transfer to Tb^{3+} (Fig. 8B). Tb^{3+} is not significantly excited at 280 nm. By exciting a solution of calmodulin in the presence of Tb^{3+} at 280 nm and monitoring the fluorescence at 545 nm, one can determine the selective binding of Tb^{3+} to the domain containing a tyrosine molecule.

Figure 9 shows the increase of fluorescence monitored at 545 nm as a function of the number of Tb^{3+} bound to bovine brain calmodulin using direct (222 nm) and indirect (280 nm) excitation. The titration curve with direct excitation increased linearly up to 4 mol of Tb^{3+}/mol of calmodulin before the onset of a plateau, in agreement with the expected maximum of four binding sites. The titration curve obtained with indirect excitation is sigmoidal and also reached a maximum at a ratio of 4 mol of Tb^{3+}/mol of calmodulin. When the tangents from the linear portions of this titration curve were constructed, they intercepted at the ratio of 1 and 3 mol of Tb^{3+}/mol of calmodulin. These findings suggest that resonance energy transfer takes place when calmodulin binds the second and third molecule of Tb^{3+}, but not the first or fourth. In other words, the first Ca^{2+} binding site filled was either domain I or II (neither of which contains tyrosine), and the next two sites filled were

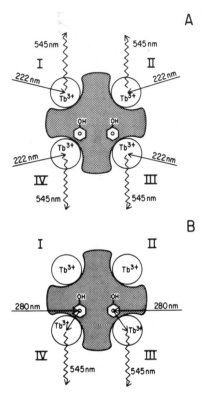

FIG. 8. A simplified scheme showing "direct" and "indirect" excitation of calmodu-
lin-bound Tb^{3+}. "Indirect excitation" utilizes a wavelength of 280 nm to excite tyrosine
with resultant energy transfer to Tb^{3+} (B). "Direct excitation" utilizes a wavelength of
222 nm to excite Tb^{3+} (A). Tyrosine has an absorption peak at 222 nm. At this wavelength, the Tb^{3+} in domains III and IV are excited by direct absorption as well as by
energy transfer from tyrosine. Thus, direct excitation actually comprises two components:
direct perturbation of all four Tb^{3+} (as shown in Panel A) and indirect perturbation of the
two Tb^{3+} bound to domains III and IV through energy transfer from tyrosine. The latter
apparently does not contribute significantly to the Tb^{3+} fluorescence monitored at 545
nm and is omitted in the figure for the sake of simplicity (from 44).

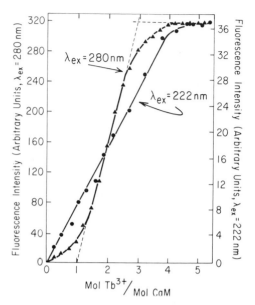

FIG. 9. Titration of bovine brain calmodulin with Tb^{3+} as monitored by fluorescence. Emission wavelength 545 nm, excitation wavelength 222 nm (●) or 280 nm (▲). The curves have been corrected for Tb^{3+} fluorescence in the absence of calmodulin. What is plotted in the figure is the difference in fluorescence with and without calmodulin for each concentration of Tb^{3+}. Concentration of calmodulin, 10 μM (from 44).

domains III and IV. These data, however, did not indicate whether these two sites were filled randomly or sequentially. The last domain filled was either II or I, depending on which had not been filled initially.

The experiments using fluorescence resonance energy transfer indicate that the binding of Tb^{3+} by calmodulin is sequential. Separate experiments indicate that Tb^{3+} competes with Ca^{2+} for the same binding sites. The dissociation constant of calmodulin for Ca^{2+} is approximately 1 μM whereas that for Tb^{3+} is estimated to be 20 nM. Although Tb^{3+} substitutes for Ca^{2+} in calmodulin in all aspects examined, the affinity of calmodulin for Tb^{3+} is significantly higher than that for Ca^{2+}; it is not certain whether Tb^{3+} and Ca^{2+} interact with calmodulin in the same manner.

The effect of calmodulin on the kinetic constants of adenylate cyclase was analyzed by means of the Lineweaver–Burke plot. Figure 10 shows

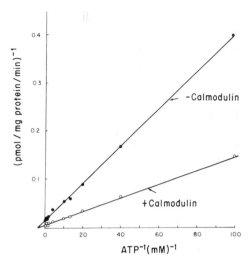

Fig. 10. Double reciprocal plot of adenylate cyclase in the presence or absence of calmodulin. The enzyme was a particulate fraction prepared from rat brain and was depleted of endogenous calmodulin by washing with a buffer containing 1 M NaCl and 2 mM EGTA. To remove the NaCl and EGTA, the fraction was washed with 20 mM Tris–HCl (pH 7.5) containing 3 mM DTT. The reaction mixture contained 20 μM Ca^{2+} or 60 μM EGTA in the presence or absence of an exogenous calmodulin (from 45).

that calmodulin increased the V_{max} but caused little or no change to the K_m (45). Thus, the primary effect of calmodulin is to increase the enzyme velocity rather than its substrate affinity. Similar observations have been made in our laboratory with phosphodiesterase (46), Ca^{2+}-ATPase (47), and protein phosphatase (48).

V. Biological Functions

Although phosphodiesterase is found in many tissues, levels of calmodulin in the same tissues do not correspond to the distribution of the enzyme. In certain cells and tissues, such as erythrocytes and testis, phosphodiesterase was undetected or hardly responsive to calmodulin, but calmodulin was present in high concentrations (15). The obvious question was whether or not calmodulin had other, still unidentified, functions. Brain adenylate cyclase, an enzyme that catalyzes the synthesis of cAMP, also required Ca^{2+} in addition to Mg^{2+} for maximum activity (49). Noting the similarity in the Ca^{2+} requirement between adenylate cyclase and phosphodiesterse, first Brostrom *et al.* (50) and then our group showed that calmodulin also stimulated the synthetic enzyme (51).

Calmodulin's regulation of adenylate cyclase supported the notion that it has other functions. Even in the brain, however, the concentration of calmodulin is still in molar excess of that required by adenylate cyclase and phosphodiesterase. As subsequent studies in many laboratories have shown, calmodulin regulates numerous other enzyme systems and appears to serve as a major intracellular receptor of Ca^{2+}.

The activation of both adenylate cyclase and phosphodiesterase by calmodulin may not occur simultaneously; concurrent activation would be wasteful. Adenylate cyclase is associated with the cell membrane, whereas the Ca^{2+}-dependent phosphodiesterase is localized within the cytoplasm. Stimulation of the cell may lead to an influx of calcium ions. As Ca^{2+} passes through the plasma membrane, it activates the synthetic enzyme; with subsequent diffusion into the cytoplasm, Ca^{2+} activates the hydrolytic enzyme. The sequential activation of adenyate cyclase and phosphodiesterase could result in a transient increase of cellular AMP that is commonly observed during stimulation of various tissues (Fig. 11). Piascik *et al.* (53) showed that the sensitivities of the two enzymes to Ca^{2+} differ. During the initial phase of Ca^{2+} influx, low levels of Ca^{2+} activate adenylate cyclase. As Ca^{2+} continues to increase, it then inhibits adenylate cyclase while it activates phosphodiesterase, thus returning intracellular cAMP to its steady state level.

Bond and Clough (54) demonstrated that the hemolysate of human erythrocytes contained a stimulatory factor for a Ca^{2+}-ATPase, the Ca^{2+} pump associated with the cell membrane. Gopinath and Vincenzi (55) and Jarret and Penniston (56) later identified the activator as calmodulin. Thus, calmodulin is not only a Ca^{2+}-modulated protein, but also a modulator of intracellular levels of Ca^{2+}, as the names implies (57). In regulating the Ca^{2+} pump, calmodulin provides the cell with a means of extruding cytosolic Ca^{2+} after it has increased, an ingenious self-compensatory device.

Much of our understanding of how calcium ions trigger muscle contraction is derived from studies on skeletal muscle. A nerve impulse

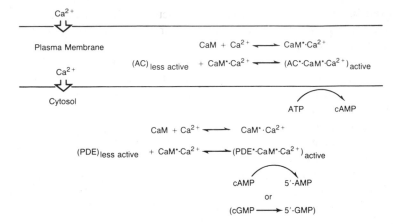

Fig. 11. Speculative scheme for the sequential activation of brain adenylate cyclase and phosphodiesterase by a cellular flux of Ca^{2+}. CaM, calmodulin; AC, adenylate cyclase; PDE, phosphodiesterase; the asterisk (*) indicates an active conformation (from 52).

arriving at the myofibril causes the release of Ca^{2+} from the sarcoplasmic reticulum. This Ca^{2+} binds to and alters the shape of troponin C, which pushes away tropomyosin to allow the interaction between actin and myosin. This reaction initiates the hydrolysis of ATP that furnishes the energy for muscle contraction. Although contraction of smooth muscle and nonmuscle cells is also controlled by Ca^{2+}, the effect is not mediated through the troponin C–tropomyosin system found in the striated muscle, but rather through a myosin light chain kinase, an enzyme that depends on calmodulin for activity (58). This enzyme catalyzes the phosphorylation of the regulatory light chain of myosin, and allows the interaction between actin and myosin and then the activation of the myosin ATPase to generate the energy needed for muscle contraction. Thus, in cardiac and skeletal muscle, Ca^{2+} acts through troponin C, whereas in nonmuscle and smooth muscle cells, Ca^{2+} acts through calmodulin.

Muscle contraction is metabolically coordinated with glycogen breakdown. Glycogen is a polymer of glucose, a readily mobilized source of stored energy that is used for the metabolic requirements of a tissue. The presence of glycogen greatly increases the amount of energy available between meals and during muscular activity. Although relative glycogen levels are higher in the liver, the amount of glycogen is larger in skeletal muscle because of its greater mass. Our knowledge of the pathway of glycogen metabolism owes much to the pioneering studies of Carl and Gerty Cori, and later to those of Edwin Krebs and Edmond Fischer. Glycogen degradation and synthesis are controlled by the enzymes phosphorylase and glycogen synthetase, respectively. Phosphorylation of phosphorylase by phosphorylase kinase converts it from the inactive b form to the active a form (59). Phosphorylase kinase consists of a tetramer, α, β, γ, and δ, with a quaternary structure of $(\alpha,\beta,\gamma,\delta)_4$, the δ subunit being calmodulin, the Ca^{2+} receptor of the kinase, whose activity is controlled by Ca^{2+} (61). When muscle is stimulated, the Ca^{2+} released from the sarcoplasmic reticulum triggers muscle contraction; at the same time, it stimulates glycogenolysis to generate the ATP needed for the contractile process.

The activity of glycogen synthetase is regulated by phosphorylation, which converts the active synthetase to an inactive form (59). Phosphorylation of glycogen synthetase is catalyzed by glycogen synthetase kinase, another calmodulin-dependent enzyme (61). Although the activities of both phosphorylase and glycogen synthetase are controlled by phosphorylation, the end results are opposite; phosphorylation augments the activity of the degradative enzyme while it decreases that of the synthetic enzyme. As Ca^{2+} is released from the sarcoplasmic reticulum in response to stimuli, calmodulin stimulates phosphorylase kinase while inhibiting glycogen synthetase. This results in the degradation of glycogen and the simultaneous suppression of its synthesis, an excellent example of coordinated metabolic control.

Many regulatory agents affect the phosphorylation of specific proteins, which are then able to control cellular functions. Indeed, phosphorylation of specific proteins may be a final pathway for some of the actions of a diverse spectrum of stimuli (62).

The three protein kinases involved in glycogen metabolism and smooth muscle contraction may be only some of the calmodulin-regulated kinases. Growing evidence indicates that there is a calmodulin-dependent kinase distinct from these three enzymes. Schulman and Greengard (63) and subsequent other investigators (64) have detected such an enzyme in many mammalian tissues that catalyzes the phosphorylation of numerous endogenous proteins. Burke and DeLorenzo

(65) found a calmodulin-dependent kinase in synaptosomes prepared from presynaptic terminals that catalyzes the phosphorylation of tubulin, resulting in a marked change in its physicochemical properties and in temperature-dependent formation of nonrandom, insoluble "filamentous-like" structures unlike microtubules. They believe that these microfilaments may interact with the presynaptic membrane to facilitate the release of norepinephrine, an important neurotransmitter (66). When released in the sympathetic nervous system, epinephrine heightens arousal and respiration and triggers rapid energy mobilization for the "fight or flight" response. In the brain, the neurons that release norepinephrine may be closely linked to alertness and concentration, as well as emotionality.

Calmodulin may do more than release neurotransmitters. Norepinephrine and other catecholamines such as dopamine and adrenalin are synthesized from a common precursor, tyrosine, through a multistep enzymatic reaction, the initial one being catalyzed by tyrosine 3-monooxygenase. Yamauchi and Fujisawa (67) showed that the activity of this enzyme depends on phosphorylation that is catalyzed by a calmodulin-dependent protein kinase. Moreover, tryptophan 5-monooxygenase, which catalyzes the formation of the neurotransmitter serotonin, is also controlled by a calmodulin-dependent phosphorylation process (68). Collectively, these findings suggest that the synthesis and the release of certain neurotransmitters is governed by a calmodulin-dependent protein kinase.

The pentose phosphate pathway occupies an important role in carbohydrate metabolism. Not only does it furnish intermediates for the synthesis of amino acids and nucleic acids, it also generates the reduced form of nicotinamide-adenine dinucleotide phosphate (NADPH) from NADP. These cofactors are needed for the biosynthesis of many cellular constituents such as steroids, dioxyribonucleotides, and fatty acids. NADP can be synthesized from NAD by a NAD kinase, a calmodulin-dependent enzyme (69). The ratio of NAD to NADP is important in determining certain cellular metabolic directions. Moreover, these cofactors are critical in cellular activities during early embryonic development. The involvement of Ca^{2+} in the fertilization of the egg by the sperm has been known for some time. A current view of egg activation after fertilization is that the increase in Ca^{2+} shortly after sperm–egg fusion is coupled to a transient calmodulin-mediated activation of NAD kinase (70). The increased formation of NADP presumably contributes to the many synthetic cellular processes underlying the early proliferative phase of embryonic development.

In protozoa, calmodulin activates a guanylate cyclase (71), an enzyme that catalyzes the synthesis of cGMP, believed to be another messenger but whose biological function(s) is still poorly understood. Calmodulin usually lacks tissue and species specificity, but the protozoan enzyme appears to be activated only by its own calmodulin (72). Mammalian guanylate cyclase also requires Ca^{2+} for maximum activity. Whether the effect of Ca^{2+} on the mammalian enzyme is mediated through calmodulin is unknown.

Calmodulin may be involved in Ca^{2+} effects not represented by the enzymes described above. One approach is to determine the component's subcellular localization by immunochemistry. Calmodulin is associated with the mitotic spindle of certain cultured cells, indicating a possible role of calmodulin in chromosomal movement during cell division (73). Further, calmodulin could regulate *in vitro* the assembly and disassembly of microtubules (74,75) believed to be important in many functions, including chromosome movement during cell division. In collaboration with John Wood, my group determined that calmodulin is localized at the postsynaptic densities and at microtubules associated with postsynaptic dendrites, indicating that calmodulin may have some postsynaptic function (24). Working with Alton Steiner and his colleagues, we found that calmodulin is associated with the nuclei of cells from adrenal cortex, and that the amount in the adrenal cells varied as a function of hormonal activity, indicating a possible role in nuclear function (23).

Mammalian brain and other tissues contain numerous calmodulin-binding proteins whose functions have not been determined. One of these, recently identified as a protein phosphatase, contains two subunits. Subunit A, M_r 60,000, harbors the catalytic site and interacts with calmodulin (76), and subunit B, M_r 16,500, binds four Ca^{2+} ions (77). Subunit B has many properties comparable to calmodulin, including 35% of sequence homology (78). The phosphatase is particularly rich in the basal ganglia of mouse brain (79) and is colocalized with calmodulin, primarily at the postsynaptic densities and the microtubules associated with the postsynaptic dendrites (24). Ontogeny studies show that the enzyme level markedly increases with synaptogenesis (80), indicating again that the enzyme has some role in synaptic function. Table VII lists the 10 enzymes for which there is solid evidence that their activities are regulated by calmodulin. The identification of these enzymes as calmodulin dependent is summarized chronologically in Table VIII.

The importance of calmodulin in cell function is unlikely to be limited to the processes described. Tissue extracts contain many calmodulin-binding proteins whose identities are not known and which may prove to be additional calmodulin-dependent enzymes. In addition, many of the Ca^{2+} effects do not appear to be mediated through calmodulin. It is important to identify which cellular functions are calmodulin regulated, and which are not. As more is known about calmodulin and

TABLE VII

CALMODULIN-DEPENDENT ENZYMES

	Enzyme	Molecular weight or subunit structure[a]		Reference
1.	Adenylate cyclase	176,000–200,000	(bovine brain)	81
2.	Guanylate cyclase	—	(tetrahymena)	72
3.	Ca^{2+}-dependent phosphodiesterase	59,000	(bovine heart)	39
4.	Ca^{2+}-ATPase	135,000–150,000	(human erythrocyte)	82
5.	NAD kinase	—	(plant)	83
6.	Phosphorylase kinase	1,300,000 $(\alpha\beta\gamma\delta)_4$ α—143,000 β—129,000 γ—51,000 δ—17,000	(rabbit skeletal muscle)	84
7.	Glycogen synthetase kinase	300,000	(rat liver)	85
8.	Myosin light chain kinase	124,000	(turkey gizzard)	58
9.	Calmodulin-dependent protein kinase	600,000 $(\alpha_9\beta_3)$ α—50,000 β—60,000	(rat brain)	64
10.	Calmodulin-dependent protein phosphatase	80,000 (A·B) A—60,000 B—19,500	(bovine brain)	76

[a] The molecular weights for tetrahymena guanylate cyclase and plant NAD kinase are not known.

TABLE VIII

CHRONOLOGICAL DEVELOPMENT OF CALMODULIN RESEARCH[a]

Findings	Investigators and references
1. Protein activator of phosphodiesterase is discovered	Cheung, 1967 (13), 1969 (10), 1970 (14)
2. The protein activates $Ca^{2+}-Mg^{2+}$-dependent phosphodiesterase	Kakiuchi et al., 1970 (29)
3. The activator's mechanism of action is elucidated	Teo and Wang, 1973 (31); Lin et al., 1974 (32); Teshima and Kakiuchi, 1974 (33); Brostrom and Wolff, 1974 (34)
4. The protein activates adenylate cyclase	Brostrom et al., 1975 (50); Cheung et al., 1975 (51)
5. Trifluoperazine inactivates the protein	Levin and Weiss 1976 (86)
6. The protein activates Ca^{2+}-ATPase	Gopinath and Vincenzi, 1977 (55); Jarrett and Penniston, 1977 (56)
7. The protein is the δ subunit of phosphorylase kinase	Cohen et al., 1978 (60)
8. The protein activates myosin light chain kinase	Dabrowska et al., 1978 (87); Yagi et al., 1978 (88)
9. The protein activates NAD kinase	Anderson and Cormier, 1978 (69)
10. Calmodulin is given as a proper name	Cheung et al., 1978 (57)
11. Calmodulin activates Ca^{2+}-dependent protein kinase	Schulman and Greengard, 1978 (63)
12. Calmodulin activates guanylate cyclase	Nagao et al., 1979 (71)
13. Amino acid sequence of calmodulin is elucidated	Watterson et al., 1980 (19)
14. Calmodulin activates glycogen synthase kinase	Payne and Soderling, 1980 (61)
15. Calmodulin activates protein phosphatase	Stewart et al., 1982 (89); Yang et al., 1982 (90)

[a] The above list is not meant to be exhaustive. The selections represent what appear to me to be highlights in the development of calmodulin research through 1982. The emphasis is on calmodulin-dependent enzymes; many other important findings have therefore been excluded from the table. The figure in parentheses is the reference number.

other Ca^{2+} receptors, a much better understanding of the role of calcium ions in cell biology will begin to emerge.

VI. Criteria for Calmodulin-Regulated Reactions

Levin and Weiss (86) reported that trifluoperazine, an antipsychotic agent, inhibited the activity of calmodulin. The drug presumably binds to the Ca^{2+}-exposed hydrophobic region and blocks its interaction with the various calmodulin receptors (17). Although this action is unrelated to its clinical activity, the drug aided immensely in the identification of some of the biological functions of calmodulin. Moreover, it spurred new interest in the mechanism of calmodulin action and in the design and identification of drugs that affect Ca^{2+} metabolism and action (91).

Although calmodulin has been implicated in many cellular reactions, not all of them have satisfied the criteria proposed for calmodulin-modulated reactions (17).

First, the experimental system should contain sufficient calmodulin. This condition is invariably met because all eukaryotic cells contain calmodulin, and some have exceedingly high levels.

Second, the depletion of endogenous calmodulin should alter the reaction rate, and reconstitution with an exogenous calmodulin should restore the activity to the original level. This is easily achieved with a purified enzyme, but is difficult with an *in vivo* system under physiological settings.

Third, the sequestration of Ca^{2+} with a chelator such as EGTA [ethylene glycol bis(β-aminoethyl ether)N,N,N',N'-tetraacetic acid], should reduce the calmodulin-supported activity to the basal level. This condition is generally satisfied in an *in vitro* system; an *in vivo* system is more complex, especially because Ca^{2+} affects so many processes that it is difficult to distinguish a direct from an indirect effect.

Fourth, the inactivation of calmodulin by antagonists should reduce the calmodulin-dependent activity to the basal level. A commonly used antagonist is trifluoperazine. Calmodulin binds avidly to this compound in the presence of Ca^{2+} and becomes biologically inactive. Since this drug, and others like it, has hydrophobic characteristics, it is necessary to ascertain that the action results from inactivation of calmodulin and not from a general hydrophobic effect. A case in point is the use of napthalenesulfonamide, W-12, and its chloro derivative W-13. With a chlorine substituent, W-13 should be considerably more hydrophobic than W-12, and thus a more potent antagonist of calmodulin (92). Unfortunately, W-12 has been frequently used as a control for W-13, on the assumption that the two compounds have nearly comparable hydrophobicity. Indeed, Asano and Hidaka (92) recently reported that W-13 is several times more hydrophobic than W-12. Sellinger-Barnette and Weiss (93) and Malencik and Anderson (94) have described a series of peptides that bind to calmodulin with high affinity. Of particular interest are the mastoparans, a closely related group of cytoactive tetradecapeptides. They bind to calmodulin with an affinity of 10^{-9} M in the presence of Ca^{2+}. These short peptides may prove to be effective and perhaps more specific antagonists for calmodulin.

Fifth, anticalmodulin should reverse the calmodulin-induced effect, provided that calmodulin in the experimental system is accessible to the antibody. The dissociation of an antibody from its antigen, however, is usually in the range of 10^{-6} M to 10^{-7} M, whereas that of calmodulin from its receptor protein is 10^{-9} M. In view of the disparate affinities of the antigen·antibody complex and the calmodulin·receptor complex, it may be necessary to use an excessively large amount of antibody to counteract the calmodulin effect, an undertaking not necessarily feasible with *in vivo* systems. In this respect, the mastoparans may be more effective because of their higher affinities for calmodulin. The question remains whether these peptides are specific for calmodulin.

VII. The Interlocking Regulatory Pathways of Ca^{2+} and cAMP

The interlocking metabolism and functions of Ca^{2+} and of cAMP have long been appreciated by many investigators (95,96). In the brain, and perhaps in other tissues, both the synthesis and degradation of cAMP is regulated by Ca^{2+}. The cytosolic level of Ca^{2+} is partially regulated by its uptake into the sarcoplasmic reticulum, a process enhanced by cAMP. In its various functions, calmodulin may act independently of, in conjunction with, or in opposition to cAMP-mediated reactions. For example, in the smooth muscle that lines the body's arteries, intestines, and respiratory tract, calmodulin and cAMP exert opposing effects on myosin light chain kinase. Calmodulin stimulates myosin light chain kinase to initiate contraction, but cAMP causes the enzyme to be refractory to calmodulin activation (97). Thus, in the presence of cAMP, calmodulin is less effective in initiating muscle contraction.

To understand the salient features of the two regulators, it is useful to compare their attributes. With Ca^{2+} as a messenger, there is no need for the synthesis of the signal. The cation is plentiful in the extracellular fluid and is present in many cellular components, and the signal is generated by a transient increase in response to stimuli. The Ca^{2+} system possesses more receptors than the cAMP system, as evidenced by the numerous calcium-binding proteins and receptors for calmodulin alone. The best studied receptor for cAMP in the eukaryotes is a cAMP-dependent protein kinase. There is only one cAMP-dependent protein kinase, and there are at least four well-defined calmodulin-dependent kinases. Moreover, calmodulin regulates many other enzyme systems, making Ca^{2+} much more versatile than cAMP.

The response of the Ca^{2+} system is inherently faster than that of the cAMP system because the signal does not have to be synthesized from a precursor. With cAMP, there must be enzymatic synthesis before the signal is transmitted to the affector protein.

Calmodulin is both a mediator of Ca^{2+} functions and a regulator of Ca^{2+}-dependent adenylate cyclase and phosphodiesterase, and it provides a molecular link between these messengers (Fig. 12). Most hormones allow extracellular communication, whereas cAMP and Ca^{2+} permit communication between intracellular organelles. The response time and the duration of hormonal action range from minutes to days. Those of cAMP, by contrast, range from seconds to minutes, whereas those of Ca^{2+} are probably in the millisecond range. Thus, the two messengers complement one another in the distance the signal travels and in the time of response and duration of action. Since the metabolism and function of Ca^{2+} and cAMP are interconnected, it is perhaps more accurate to refer to them simply as cellular messengers or regulators rather than as second messengers.

The high level of coordination of functions of the various cell compnents is amazing. The simplicity and efficiency with which the cell coordinates its activities throughout life affirms an elegant functional design. Cellular messengers control almost all aspects of cell activity, and it is a formidable challenge to elucidate the entire regulatory web at the molecular level.

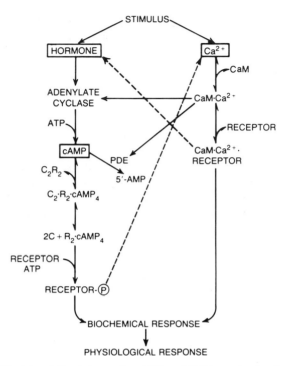

FIG. 12. The interrelation between the cAMP- and Ca^{2+}-regulated pathways in cellular processes. CaM, calmodulin. The dashed lines indicate relationships that are not yet well defined (from 91).

VIII. ACTIVATION OF CALMODULIN BY METAL CATIONS AS A FUNCTION OF IONIC RADIUS

We have noted that Tb^{3+}, which has an ionic radius (0.92 Å) comparable to that of Ca^{2+} (0.99 Å), effectively substitutes for Ca^{2+} in calmodulin (44). The question arises whether other cations having comparable ionic radii also replace Ca^{2+}. We chose Be^{2+}, Mg^{2+}, Sr^{2+}, and Ba^{2+} from the alkaline earth metals; Mn^{2+}, Co^{2+}, Ni^{2+}, Zn^{2+}, Cd^{2+}, Hg^{2+}, and Pb^{2+} from the fourth, fifth, and sixth periods; and La^{3+}, Sm^{3+}, and Tb^{3+} from the lanthanide series. The ionic radii of these cations range from 0.35 Å for Be^{2+} to 1.34 Å for Ba^{2+} (Table

TABLE IX

Influence of Ionic Radius of Metal Cations on Tyrosine Fluorescence, Electrophoretic Mobility, Calmodulin Activity, and Ca^{2+} Binding[a]

Cation	Radius (Å)	Fluorescence change (%)	Mobility change		Phosphodiesterase activity (%)	Ca^{2+} binding inhibition (%)
			Native gel	SDS gel		
Be^{2+}	0.35	6	−	−	33	3 ± 2
Mg^{2+}	0.65	8	−	−	35	3 ± 7
Ni^{2+}	0.69	8	−	−	33	0 ± 3
Co^{2+}	0.72	20	−	−	27	2 ± 1
Zn^{2+}	0.74	52	−	−	67	21 ± 6
Mn^{2+}	0.80	54	+	+	70	33 ± 6
Tb^{3+}	0.92	67	+	+	89	96 ± 2
Cd^{2+}	0.97	81	+	+	90	69 ± 5
Ca^{2+}	0.99	100	+	+	100	−
Sm^{3+}	1.00	66	+	+	98	99 ± 1
La^{3+}	1.02	70	+	+	94	95 ± 3
Hg^{2+}	1.10	75	−	−	73	0 ± 3
Sr^{2+}	1.13	72	+	±	86	27 ± 6
Pb^{2+}	1.20	47	+	+	92	63 ± 5
Ba^{2+}	1.34	4	−	−	23	4 ± 3

[a] Ionic radius refers to the crystal structure of corresponding salts. The tyrosine fluorescence and phosphodiesterase activity are expressed as a percentage of Ca^{2+}, which is taken as 100. Mobility change is indicated by +; slight change by ±; and no change by − (from 28).

IX). We used several criteria to examine the ability of these cations to substitute for Ca^{2+} in calmodulin.

First, we noted the ability of cations to enhance intrinsic tyrosine fluorescence of calmodulin. Bovine brain calmodulin possesses two tyrosines, residues 99 and 138, and no tryptophan. Binding of Ca^{2+} to calmodulin results in a conformational change which increases the quantum yield of tyrosine fluorescence. We monitored the emission spectra of calmodulin with the excitation wavelength set at 280 nm; a peak at 307 nm is characteristic of the tyrosine fluorescence, which increased with the addition of Ca^{2+} (44). The effect of the other cations on the tyrosine fluorescence was then measured.

When the ionic radii of these metals are compared with their ability to enhance fluorescence, the results indicate that cations with ionic radii comparable to Ca^{2+} increase fluorescence of calmodulin (Table IX), whereas those with significantly different radii were less effective.

Second, cations differ in their ability to induce in calmodulin a conformational change which can also be seen as an electrophoretic mobility change in polyacryamide gel. Calmodulin migrates more slowly on a polyacrylamide gel under nondenaturing conditions in the presence of Ca^{2+} than in the presence of EGTA, presumably because of a decrease in net charge upon binding Ca^{2+}. In the presence of Mn^{2+}, Tb^{3+}, Cd^{2+}, Sm^{3+}, La^{3+}, Sr^{2+}, or Pb^{2+}, calmodulin also migrated more slowly; in the presence of Be^{2+}, Mg^{2+}, Ni^{2+}, Co^{2+}, Zn^{2+}, Hg^{2+}, or Ba^{2+}, no significant change in mobility was seen. The effect of these cations on calmodulin mobility was further examined by SDS–polyacrylamide gel electrophoresis. Under this condition, calmodulin migrated faster in the presence of Mn^{2+}, Tb^{3+}, Cd^{2+}, Ca^{2+}, Sm^{3+}, La^{3+}, or Pb^{2+} than in the presence of EGTA. The greater mobility probably results from a change toward a more compact conformation. No change of mobility was seen with the other metal cations. Sr^{2+} appears to be a borderline case which induced only a slight change.

According to the effect on tyrosine fluorescence, Zn^{2+} and Hg^{2+} should also induce an electrophoretic mobility change in the acrylamide gel. The apparent lack of change may reflect a difference in the experimental conditions. During electrophoresis, calmodulin migrates toward the anode, while the free cations migrate toward the cathode. The cation-induced conformation in calmodulin depends upon the affinity of the cation for calmodulin. A cation with a low affinity may be released from calmodulin during the course of electrophoresis. Zn^{2+} may be such an example. Hg^{2+}, which has strong affinity for the amino group of glycine in the running buffer during electrophoresis, is most probably not available to form a complex with calmodulin.

Third, we studied the ability of different cations to support calmodulin-stimulated phosphodiesterase activity. Using phosphodiesterase as an assay, we tried to determine whether the change in conformation caused by the metal cations correlated with their ability to activate calmodulin. Be^{2+}, Mg^{2+}, and Ba^{2+} were essentially inactive. Sr^{2+} activated phosphodiesterase to 85% of the maximal activity by Ca^{2+}; Ni^{2+} and Co^{2+} were essentially inactive. Zn^{2+} and Mn^{2+} supported calmodulin-stimulated activity with a biphasic response. Cd^{2+} and Hg^{2+} gave qualitatively similar responses. Zn^{2+}, Cd^{2+}, and Hg^{2+} inhibited basal phosphodiesterase activity at high cation concentrations; this inhibition could explain their biphasic profiles. Pb^{2+}, which inhibits many enzymes as does Hg^{2+}, activated phosphodiesterase effectively. La^{3+}, Sm^{3+}, and Tb^{3+} stimulated phosphodiesterase at low concentrations and inhibited phosphodiesterase at high concentrations.

Fourth, we determined the ability of metal cations to affect the binding of $^{45}Ca^{2+}$ to calmodulin. The ability of cation metals to substitute for Ca^{2+} in the activation of calmodulin implies that these cations bind to the same Ca^{2+} sites on calmodulin. Be^{2+}, Mg^{2+}, Ba^{2+}, Co^{2+}, and Ni^{2+} did not significantly affect the binding of $^{45}Ca^{2+}$, whereas Sr^{2+}, Mn^{2+}, Zn^{2+}, Cd^{2+}, Pb^{2+}, and the lanthanides La^{3+}, Sm^{3+}, and Tb^{3+} decreased binding of $^{45}Ca^{2+}$. In general, cations that stimulate calmodulin inhibit $^{45}Ca^{2+}$ binding. An exception is Hg^{2+}, which was quite effective in activating calmodulin, but virtually ineffective in inhibiting $^{45}Ca^{2+}$ binding, possibly because of its potential interaction with the Tris buffer and dialysis membrane used in equilibrium dialysis. These results strongly suggest but do not prove that the effective metals bind to calmodulin at the Ca^{2+} sites.

Fifth, we studied the reversal of cation/calmodulin-stimulated phosphodiesterase activity by trifluoperazine. In the presence of Ca^{2+}, calmodulin exhibits a high affinity for trifluoperazine. Binding of the drug prevents calmodulin from interacting with and activating phosphodiesterase (86). Trifluoperazine at a concentration that did not affect basal phosphodiesterase activity suppressed the cation/caldmodulin-dependent phosphodiesterase activities to their basal levels in a manner qualitatively similar to the effect of Ca^{2+}. These results support the notion that other metal cations substitute for Ca^{2+} in calmodulin.

These data are summarized in Table IX and they indicate that all cations having ionic radii between Zn^{2+} (0.74 Å) and Pb^{2+} (ionic radius 1.20 Å) enhance intrinsic fluorescence. These cations show approximately equal activities for the induction of mobility changes in calmodulin in acrylamide gel, as expected from their effects on fluorescence enhancement. The possible exceptions were Zn^{2+} and Hg^{2+}, and their apparent lack of effect is probably due to calmodulin's difficulty in retaining them during electrophoresis. The ability of cations to stimulate calmodulin-supported phosphodiesterase activity appears to correlate quite well with the ability to induce tyrosine fluorescence changes. Indeed, all these attributes bear a close relationship to the cation's ability to inhibit Ca^{2+} binding to calmodulin.

Collectively, these data demonstrate a good correlation between the ionic radii of the cations and their ability to substitute for Ca^{2+} in calmodulin. Metal cations with ionic radii in the range of 1 ± 0.2 Å induce the right conformation in calmodulin and allow it to activate phosphodiesterase. It should be added that Na^+, whose ionic radius is 0.95 Å, did not cause any change in tyrosine fluorescence, nor did it support calmodulin-dependent phosphodiesterase activity. Thus, the metal cation has to possess at least two charges to activate calmodulin.

These data also show that Ca^{2+} is not specific for calmodulin and that other cations, with ionic radii comparable to that of calcium, are effective to different extents. For example, Sm^{3+}, whose ionic radius is nearly identical to that of Ca^{2+}, is nearly as effective in stimulating calmodulin-dependent phosphodiesterase activity, whereas Ba^{2+}, whose ionic radius is 30% larger than Ca^{2+}, is virtually inactive.

The apparent effectiveness of some of these cations does not necessarily mean that they serve a physiological function. In fact, Cd^{2+}, Hg^{2+}, and Pb^{2+} are not normal constituents of tissues; they represent serious environmental pollutants in certain industrial regions and accumulate in various human tissues, causing neurological, muscular, renal, and bronchial disorders (98). It is not known whether an elevated tissue level of these cations does indeed activate calmodulin *in vivo*. Mammalian cells contain millimolar glutathione (99) which chelates Cd^{2+}, Pb^{2+}, and Hg^{2+}. Moreover, metallothioneins, whose synthesis is induced by heavy metals (100), effectively bind heavy metals, thus protecting the cell. If, however, some of the heavy metals do find their way to calmodulin, it is conceivable that they may activate this versatile regulator, and upset the activity of calmodulin normally regulated by the cellular flux of Ca^{2+}. This may account in part for the toxicity of these metals.

Although the idea that heavy metals exert their toxicity through the activation of calmodulin may appear attractive, these studies must be regarded as preliminary. It is necessary to examine the ability of these metals to substitute for Ca^{2+} in other calmodulin-dependent enzymes. More importantly, these studies need to be substantiated with an *in vivo* system.

IX. Epilogue

In many years of intensive research in Ca^{2+}, calmodulin remained the hidden, yet ever present, participant in Ca^{2+}-mediated processes. Ironically, it was the abundance of calmodulin that made it so elusive. Its presence was disclosed by something as mundane as the loss of an enzyme's activity during purification.

Research is not always predictable, and the story of calmodulin is a vivid example of how serendipity can contribute to scientific progress. It was beyond my wildest dreams that some pedestrian enzymology studies would lead to the discovery of the missing partner in calcium's action, a protein that now captures the attention and imagination of researchers from all disciplines of biology and medicine.

The road to scientific progress is frequently long and arduous, criss-crossed with uncharted passages and blind alleys. Some travelers may even lose their way. Nevertheless, their paths leave behind indelible footprints, and in time prove to be valuable signposts for subsequent travelers. Occasionally, guided by those footsteps, a traveler stumbles onto a trail, already cleared by predecessors, that opens the way to further exploration. I was such a lucky traveler.

Acknowledgments

I am indebted to my co-workers Y. M. Lin, Y. P. Liu, S. Y. Song, J. A. Smoake, S. M. Patrick, T. J. Lynch, E. A. Tallant, A.-L. Pichard, R. W. Wallace, S. H. Chao, Y. S. Suzuki, L. R. Ballou, J. R. Zysk, M. A. Winkler, D. L. Merat, and Z. Y. Hu for their experimental and intellectual contributions to various phases of our research; to my colleagues L. S. Bradham and M. E. Dockter for their collaborative effort; and to G. R. Schonbaum for many constructive ideas and advice over the years. I thank John Gilbert for editorial assistance and Pat Powell for typing the manuscript. The research in our laboratory has been supported by NIH grants and by ALSAC.

This paper is dedicated to the memory of Professor Shiro Kakiuchi.

REFERENCES

1. Robinson, G. A., Butcher, R. W., and Sutherland, E. W. (1971). "Cyclic AMP." Academic Press, New York.
2. Ringer, S. (1883). *J. Physiol. (London)* **4**, 29–42.
3. Heilbrunn, I. V., and Wiercinski, F. J. (1947). *J. Cell. Comp. Physiol.* **29**, 15–32.
4. Ebashi, S., Endo, M., and Oktsuki, I. (1969). *Q. Rev. Biophys.* **2**, 351–384.
5. Cheung, W. Y. (1966). *Biochim. Biophys. Acta* **115**, 235–239.
6. Butcher, R. W., and Sutherland, E. W. (1962). *J. Biol. Chem.* **237**, 1244–1250.
7. Sutherland, E. W., Rall, T. W., and Menon, T. (1962). *J. Biol. Chem.* **237**, 1220–1227.
8. Kakiuchi, S., and Rall, T. W. (1968). *Mol. Pharmacol.* **4**, 367–378.
9. Kakiuchi, S., and Rall, T. W. (1968). *Mol. Pharmacol.* **4**, 379–388.
10. Cheung, W. Y. (1969). *Biochim. Biophys. Acta* **191**, 303–315.
11. Cheung, W. Y. (1971). *J. Biol. Chem.* **246**, 2859–2865.
12. Cheung, W. Y. (1971). *Biochim. Biophys. Acta* **242**, 395–409.
13. Cheung, W. Y. (1967). *Biochem. Biophys. Res. Commun.* **29**, 478–482.
14. Cheung, W. Y. (1970). *Biochem. Biophys. Res. Commun.* **38**, 533–538.
15. Smoake, J. A., Song, S. Y., and Cheung, W. Y. (1974). *Biochim. Biophys. Acta* **341**, 402–411.
16. Childers, S. R., and Siegel, F. L. (1975). *Biochim. Biophys. Acta* **405**, 99–108.
17. Cheung, W. Y. (1980). *Science* **207**, 19–27.
18. Cheung, W. Y. (1982). *Sci. Am.* **246**, 62–81.
19. Watterson, D. M., Sharief, F., and Vanaman, T. C. (1980). *J. Biol. Chem.* **255**, 462–475.
20. Kretsinger, R. H. (1976). *Annu. Rev. Biochem.* **45**, 239–266.
21. Cheung, W. Y. (1981). *J. Cyclic Nucleotide Res.* **7**, 71–84.
22. Grand, R. J. A., Perry, S. V., and Weeks, R. A. (1979). *Biochem. J.* **177**, 521–529.
23. Harper, J. F., Cheung, W. Y., Wallace, R. W., Huang, H. L., Levine, S. N., and Steiner, A. L. (1980). *Proc. Natl. Acad. Sci. U.S.A.* **77**, 366–370.
24. Wood, J. G., Wallace, R. W., Whitaker, J. N., and Cheung, W. Y. (1980). *J. Cell Biol.* **84**, 66–76.
25. Harper, J. F., Wallace, R. W., Cheung, W. Y., and Steiner, A. L. (1981). *Adv. Cyclic Nucleotide Res.* **14**, 581–591.
26. Chafouleas, J. G., Bolton, W. E., Hidaka, H., Boyd, A. E., III, and Means, A. R. (1982). *Cell* **28**, 41–50.
27. Levine, B. A., and Williams, R. J. P. (1982). *In* "Calcium and Cell Function" (W. Y. Cheung, ed.), Vol. 2, pp. 1–38. Academic Press, New York.

28. Chao, S. H., Suzuki, Y., Zysk, J. R., and Cheung, W. Y. (1984). *Mol. Pharmacol.*, **26**, 75–82.
29. Kakiuchi, S., Yamazaki, R., and Nakajima, H. (1970). *Proc. Jpn. Acad.* **46**, 587–592.
30. Cheung, W. Y. (1970). *In* "Role of Cyclic AMP in Cell Function" (P. Greengard and E. Costa, eds.), pp. 51–56. Raven, New York.
31. Teo, T. S., and Wang, J. H. (1973). *J. Biol. Chem.* **248**, 5950–5955.
32. Lin, Y. M., Liu, Y. P., and Cheung, W. Y. (1974). *J. Biol. Chem.* **249**, 4943–4954.
33. Teshima, Y., and Kakiuchi, S. (1974). *Biochem. Biophys. Res. Commun.* **56**, 489–495.
34. Brostrom, C. O., and Wolff, D. J. (1974). *Arch. Biochem. Biophys.* **165**, 715–727.
35. Liu, Y. P., and Cheung, W. Y. (1976). *J. Biol. Chem.* **251**, 4193–4198.
36. LaPorte, D. C., Wierman, B. M., and Storm, D. R. (1980). *Biochemistry* **19**, 3814–3819.
37. Tanaka, T., and Hidaka, H. (1980). *J. Biol. Chem.* **255**, 11078–11080.
38. Lin, Y. M., Liu, Y. P., and Cheung, W. Y. (1975). *FEBS Lett.* **49**, 356–360.
39. LaPorte, D. C., Toscano, W. A., and Storm, D. R. (1979). *Biochemistry* **13**, 2820–2825.
40. Klee, C. B., Crouch, T. H., and Krinks, M. H. (1979). *Biochemistry* **18**, 722–729.
41. Lynch, T. J., Tallant, E. A., and Cheung, W. Y. (1976). *Biochem. Biophys. Res. Commun.* **68**, 616–625.
42. Blumenthal, D. K., and Stull, J. T. (1980). *Biochemistry* **19**, 5608–5614.
43. Huang, C. Y., Chau, V., Chock, P. B., Wang, J. H., and Sharma, R. K. (1981). *Proc. Natl. Acad. Sci. U.S.A.* **78**, 871–875.
44. Wallace, R. W., Tallant, E. A., Dockter, M. E., and Cheung, W. Y. (1982). *J. Biol. Chem.* **257**, 1845–1854.
45. Lynch, T. J., Tallant, E. A., and Cheung, W. Y. (1977). *Arch. Biochem. Biophys.* **182**, 124–133.
46. Pichard, A.-L., and Cheung, W. Y. (1977). *J. Biol. Chem.* **252**, 4872–4875.
47. Lynch, T. J., and Cheung, W. Y. (1979). *Arch. Biochem. Biophys.* **194**, 165–170.
48. Tallant, E. A., and Cheung, W. Y. (1984). *Arch. Biochem. Biophys.* **232**, 269–279.
49. Bradham, L. S. (1972). *Biochim. Biophys. Acta* **276**, 434–443.
50. Brostrom, C. O., Huang, Y. C., Breckenridge, B.McL., and Wolff, D. J. (1975). *Proc. Natl. Acad. Sci. U.S.A.* **72**, 64–68.
51. Cheung, W. Y., Bradham, L. S., Lynch, T. J., Lin, Y. M., and Tallant, E. A. (1975). *Biochem. Biophys. Res. Commun.* **66**, 1055–1062.
52. Cheung, W. Y. (1982). *Prog. Brain Res.* **56**, 237–253.
53. Piascik, M. T., Wisler, P. L., Johnson, C. L., and Potter, J. D. (1980). *J. Biol. Chem.* **255**, 4176–4181.
54. Bond, G. H., and Clough, D. L. (1973). *Biochim. Biophys. Acta* **323**, 592–599.
55. Gopinath, R. M., and Vincenzi, F. F. (1977). *Biochem. Biophys. Res. Commun.* **77**, 1203–1209.
56. Jarret, H. W., and Penniston, J. T. (1977). *Biochem. Biophys. Res. Commun.* **77**, 1210–1216.

57. Cheung, W. Y., Lynch, T. J.,and Wallace, R. W. (1978). *Adv. Cyclic Nucleotide Res.* **9,** 233–251.
58. Walsh, M. P., and Hartshorne, D. J. (1982). *In* "Calcium and Cell Function" (W. Y. Cheung, ed.), Vol. 3, pp. 223–269. Academic Press, New York.
59. Krebs, E. G., DeLange, R. J., Kemp, R. G., and Riley, W. D. (1966). *Pharmacol. Rev.* **18,** 163–171.
60. Cohen, P., Burchell, A., Foulkes, J. G., Cohen, P. T. W., Vanaman, T. C., and Nairn, A. C., (1978). *FEBS Lett.* **92,** 287–293.
61. Payne, M. E., and Soderling, T. J. (1980). *J. Biol. Chem.* **255,** 8054–8056.
62. Greengard, P. (1978). *Science* **199,** 146–152.
63. Schulman, H., and Greengard, P. (1978). *Proc. Natl. Acad. Sci. U.S.A.* **75,** 5432–5436.
64. Bennet, M. K., Erondu, N. F., and Kennedy, M. B. (1978). *J. Biol. Chem.* **258,** 12735–12744.
65. Burke, B. E., and DeLorenzo, R. J. (1981). *Proc. Natl. Acad. Sci. U.S.A.* **78,** 991–995.
66. DeLorenzo, R. J. (1982). *In* "Calcium and Cell Function" (W. Y. Cheung, ed.), Vol. 3, pp. 271–309. Academic Press, New York.
67. Yamauchi, T., and Fijisawa, H. (1979). *Biochem. Biophys. Res. Commun.* **90,** 28–35.
68. Yamauchi, T., and Fijisawa, H. (1980). *Biochem. Int.* **1,** 98–104.
69. Anderson, J. M. and Cormier, M. (1978). *Biochem. Biophys. Res. Commun.* **84,** 595–602.
70. Epel, D., Patton, C., Wallace, R. W., and Cheung, W. Y. (1981). *Cell* **23,** 543–549.
71. Nagao, S., Suzuki, Y., Watanabe, Y., and Nozawa, Y. (1979). *Biochem. Biophys. Res. Commun.* **90,** 261–268.
72. Kakiuchi, S., Sobue, K., Yamazaki, R., Nagao, S., Umeki, S., Nozawa, Y., Yazawa, M., and Yagi, K. (1981). *J. Biol. Chem.* **256,** 19–22.
73. Walsh, M. J., Dedman, J. R., Brinkley, B. R., and Means, A. R. (1978). *Proc. Natl. Acad. Sci. U.S.A.* **75,** 1867–1871.
74. Marcum, J. M., Dedman, J. R., Brinkley, B. R., and Means, A. R. (1978). *Proc. Natl. Acad. Sci. U.S.A.* **75,** 3771–3775.
75. Margolis, R. L. (1983). *In* "Calcium and Cell Function" (W. Y. Cheung, ed.), Vol. 4, pp. 313–335. Academic Press, New York.
76. Winkler, M. A., Merat, D. L., Tallant, E. A., Hawkins, S., and Cheung, W. Y. (1984). *Proc. Natl. Acad. Sci. U.S.A.* **81,** 3054–3058.
77. Klee, C. B., Crouch, T. H., and Krinks, M. H. (1979). *Proc. Natl. Acad. Sci. U.S.A.* **76,** 6270–6273.
78. Aitken, A., Klee, C. B., and Cohen, P. (1984). *Eur. J. Biochem.* **139,** 663–671.
79. Wallace, R. W., Tallant, E. A., and Cheung, W. Y. (1980). *Biochemistry* **19,** 1831–1837.
80. Tallant, E. A., and Cheung, W. Y. (1983). *Biochemistry* **22,** 3630–3635.
81. Bradham, L. S., and Cheung, W. Y. (1982). *Prog. Nucleic Acid Res. Mol. Biol.* **27,** 189–231.

82. Penniston, J. T. (1983). *In* "Calcium and Cell Function" (W. Y. Cheung, ed.), Vol. 4, pp. 99–149. Academic Press, New York.
83. Cormier, M. J., Anderson, J. M., Charbonneau, H., Jones, H. P., and McCann, R. O. (1980). *In* "Calcium and Cell Function" (W. Y. Cheung, ed.), Vol. 1, pp. 201–218. Academic Press, New York.
84. Malencik, D. A., and Fischer, E. H. (1982). *In* "Calcium and Cell Function" (W. Y. Cheung, ed.), Vol. 3, pp. 161–188. Academic Press, New York.
85. Soderling, T. R., and Khatra, B. S. (1982). *In* "Calcium and Cell Function" (W. Y. Cheung, ed.), Vol. 3, pp. 189–221. Academic Press, New York.
86. Levin, R. M., and Weiss, B. (1976). *Mol. Pharmacol.* **12**, 581–589.
87. Dabrowska, R., Sherry, J. M. F., Aromatorio, D. K., and Hartshorne, D. (1978). *Biochemistry* **17**, 253–258.
88. Yagi, K., Yazawa, M., Kakiuchi, S., Oshima, M., and Uenishi, K. (1978). *J. Biol. Chem.* **253**, 1338–1340.
89. Stewart, A. A., Ingebritsen, T. S., Manalan, A., Klee, C. B., and Cohen, P. (1982). *FEBS Lett.* **137**, 80–84.
90. Yang, S. D., Tallant, E. A., and Cheung, W. Y. (1982). *Biochem. Biophys. Res. Commun.* **106**, 1419–1425.
91. Cheung, W. Y. (1982). *Fed. Proc., Fed. Am. Soc. Exp. Biol.* **41**, 2253–2257.
92. Asano, M., and Hidaka, H. (1984). *In* "Calcium and Cell Function" (W. Y. Cheung, ed.), Vol. 5., pp. 123–164. Academic Press, New York.
93. Sellinger-Barnette, M., and Weiss, B. (1984). *Adv. Cyclic Nucleotide Res.* **16**, 261–276.
94. Malencik, D. A., and Anderson, S. R. (1983). *Biochem. Biophys. Res. Commun.* **114**, 50–56.
95. Berridge, M. J. (1975). *Adv. Cyclic Nucleotide Res.* **6**, 1–98.
96. Rasmussen, H. (1981). "Calcium and cAMP as Synarchic Messengers." Wiley, New York.
97. Adelstein, R. S., and Klee, C. B. (1980). *In* "Calcium and Cell Function" (W. Y. Cheung, ed.), Vol. 1, pp. 167–182. Academic Press, New York.
98. Dreisbach, R. H. (1983). "Handbook of Poisoning," 11th Ed. Lange.
99. Kosower, N. S., and Kosower, E. M. (1978). *Int. Rev. Cytol.* **54**, 109–160.
100. Webb, M. (1979). *In* "Topics in Environmental Health" (M. Webb, ed.), Vol. 2, pp. 195–266. Elsevier, Amsterdam.

TISSUE-SPECIFIC GENE EXPRESSION AND CHROMATIN STRUCTURE*

HAROLD WEINTRAUB

Hutchinson Cancer Research Center
Seattle, Washington

I. QUESTIONS, BIASES, AND HYPOTHESES

WHY do particular cell types reproducibly appear at specific times and in particular locations during the development of an organism? This fascinating problem is made all the more mysterious when one considers that the information for this process is stored in a single cell, the zygote, and must be differentially parceled out to its progeny, both in space and in time. The spatial component to development is often discussed in terms of "pattern" or "position" and it is clear that the position of a cell in a developing embryo often seems to dictate subsequent cell type. However, position may not be an absolute require ment for cytodifferentiation; rather, the role of position might be to influence an endogenous nuclear program for generating diversity, and consequently, to increase the probability that specific cell types emerge at specific locations. This view (which is by no means original, e.g., see the work of Holtzer *et al.*, 1975) emphasizes the notion that the zygote is a metastable cell and that there is a program within the zygote nucleus that can differentially parcel out cell type-specific information to daughter cells, more or less influenced by external cues in the form of a cell's position, but basically independent of such external cues (e.g., see Weintraub *et al.*, 1977). This is not to say that such cues would not be crucial for coherently organizing an organism, but they would be modulators of a more unique and fascinating program for a continuous readout and partitioning of information between daughter nuclei. While there are many examples, I think that perhaps the best evidence that there is an inherent capacity for cells to differentiate into many cell

*Lecture delivered May 17, 1984.

types independent of position comes from two observations: (1) that single somatic cells from plants, when grown in culture, will eventually give rise to all of the differentiated cells of the organism and, indeed, to a perfectly formed plant (see Braun, 1975) and (2) that teratocarcinoma cells will differentiate into multiple cell types without any obvious signs of recreating the pattern of a normal embryo. In both cases, it is difficult to see how the equivalent of a normal cell position is recreated in these tissue masses and it is also hard to see how localized, specific cytoplasmic determinants are reassembled so as to dictate subsequent cytodifferentiation.

Obviously, this is an extreme and personal view based on rather flimsy experimental support. However, it is equally true that when trying to understand the generation of embyronic diversity, alternative explanations are only marginally better or worse given our primitive understanding of the problem. It is possible to model early development using assumptions based upon localized, specific cellular determinants combined with bacterial type regulatory mechanisms (e.g., see Ptashne, 1981) and the possibility that early embyronic cells can send specific signals to each other to turn genes on and off. While possibly correct, this view does not easily account for many experiments in the developmental literature (see above).

At an experimental level, we initially decided to work backward. This decision was dictated largely by the inacessibility of early embryos to biochemical manipulation. Our strategy was to study the regulation of a specific differentiated gene product in a specific cell type, globin in a red blood cell, and to progressively step backward in the red cell lineage to try to understand how a red cell precursor became committed to activating the globin genes in its progeny. With the advent of recombinant DNA and cloning we now believe that the biochemical tools are available to approach the problem in a forward direction, from the early embryo, and later in this article I will discuss our recent and preliminary attempts to do this.

II. WHY CHROMOSOME STRUCTURE?

Ten years ago, when I first became interested in eukaryotic chromosomes, I was struck by two related, but different facts that had emerged from the genetic and cytogenetic literature. Both had their appeal in suggesting that eukaryotic gene regulation had unique elements that were going to be profound and also different from prokaryotic control. The two observations were illustrated in two systems: (1) the inactive X chromosome and (2) position–effect variegation. Both systems illustrate two principles. The first is that there is clearly a relationship between the epigenetic inactivation of a gene and a "condensed chromatin structure." That is, a primary function of chromatin may be to turn genes off. Consequently, subsequent genetic activation may be viewed, at least in part, in terms of mechanisms responsible for removing the inhibiting function of chromatin. Once this occurs "bacterial type" mechanisms for both positive and negative control would then be able to operate effectively. I will return to this theme later. A second even more striking phenomenon illustrated by X chromosome inactivation and position–effect variegation is that the genetic inactivity can be faithfully propagated to daughter cells. This propagation is apparently very different from most forms of regulation in prokaryotes since the repression is propagated to both daughter chromosomes in "cis." This follows from the fact that genetic markers on the homologous chromosome remain active in progeny cells, while markers on the inactive chromosome remain inactive in clonally derived cells. The parallel between this cytogenetic phenomenon and cell commitment during development is difficult to ignore, since early embryonic cells appear to make specific commitment decisions and these decisions are usually stably inherented by their progeny.

A. DNase I Sensitivity of Large Domains of Active Chromatin

The cytogenetic data suggesting a correlation between genetic transcription and chromosome structure initially suggested that active and inactive chromatin might have different structures and that these differences might be probed in insolated nuclei using nucleases, specifically, DNase I. We found that in red cell nuclei, the globin genes were more sensitive to DNase I than inactive genes such as ovalbumin; however, in cells that did not express globin, the globin genes were resistant (Weintraub and Groudine, 1976). Figure 1 shows a Southern blot with DNA digested in red cell nuclei with increasing concentrations of DNase I. Ev-1 is an inactive endogeneous retrovirus; Ev-3 is more sensitive to DNase and is known to be an active endogenous retrovirus that is basically the same sequence as Ev-1. Their respective activities

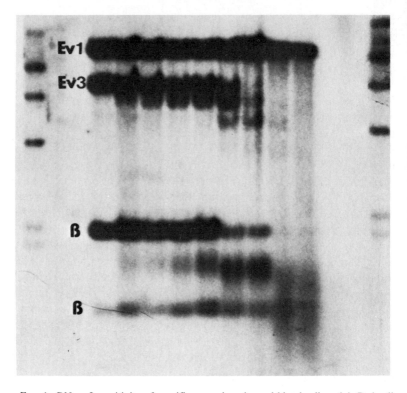

FIG. 1. DNase I sensitivity of specific genes in avian red blood cell nuclei. Red cell nuclei were digested with increasing levels of DNase I (left to right) and the DNA purified and digested with *Sac*I and then blot hybridized to either an Ev-1, Ev-3, or β-globin probe as indicated. The new bands that appear with DNase digestion represent chromosomal hypersensitive sites. Note that Ev-3 and the β-globin sequences are more sensitive than the inactive Ev-1 gene.

are probably reflected in the respective positions in the chromosome where they have integrated. β-Globin is also more sensitive than Ev-1. DNase I sensitivity of an active genetic locus usually extends beyond the transcribed region of the gene and may be as large as 50–100 kb depending on the locus. For β-globin, a border with resistant chromatin has been found some 10 kb 5′ to the 5′-most β-globin gene. Regions flanking the coding region may be somewhat less sensitive; however, this seems to vary from gene to gene. DNase I sensitivity over the transcribed region of an active domain is lost if the chromatin is eluted with 0.35 M NaCl; however, sensitivity is restored if two of the eluted nuclear proteins, HMG 14 and 17, are added back (Weisbrod and Weintraub, 1979), indicating that these proteins are responsible for DNase I sensitivity (Fig. 2). Similarly, actively transcribed nucleosomes can be purified on HMG 14 and 17 columns (Weisbrod and Weintraub, 1981), which preferentially bind nucleosomes associated with transcribed regions. The reason for this preferential binding is unclear. It is also not known how or why discrete borders for DNase sensitivity are established and maintained. The role of HMGs is a mystery. Several possibilities are that they allow the DNA in the nucleosome to be read by RNA polymerase; that they prevent higher order chromatin condensation by H1; that they are used during replication to propagate an active structure to daughter chromosomes. During early chick development, red cell precursors have been isolated (Fig. 3) and in these cells the globin genes are DNase resistant. It has not been possible yet to clearly demonstrate that transcription follows the appearance of DNase I sensitivity during gene activation; thus, it is still a formal possibility that the initial binding of HMGs depends on transcription. Nevertheless, continued transcription is not required for DNase sensitivity since mature nucleated avian erythrocytes not synthesizing Hb preserve the DNase I sensitivity of their globin genes.

B. DNase I Hypersensitivity

DNase I Hypersensitivity is observed in discrete regions of 200–400 bp (see Elgin, 1981). These regions behave as if they are lacking histones. They are assayed by the appearance of new bands after very mild DNase I digestion, for example, in Fig. 1 the new band below Ev-3 comes from a specific cut at an enhancer–promoter region (LTR) while the new band between the β-globin genes maps to a promoter region. Hypersensitive sites are usually found at the 5′ and 3′ ends of transcription units, near enhancer sequences, near steroid hormone binding sites, and they are often associated with regions of recombination. It is likely that hypersensitive sites reflect the binding of specific proteins to specific DNA sequences. In addition there are suggestions that nucleosomes themselves have a lower affinity for the DNA at such sites. This may be required so that specific recognition can occur. Both of these properties

A

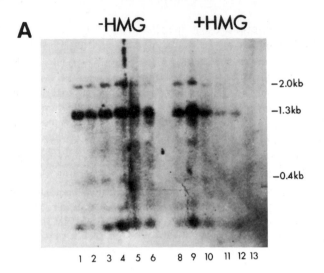

B <u>RBC</u>

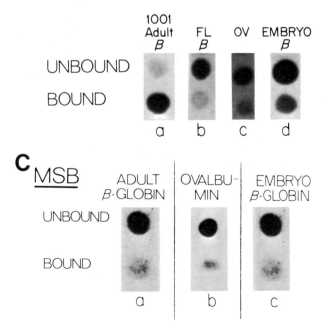

C <u>MSB</u>

(decreased nucleosome affinity and specific protein recognition) might reflect the finding that the DNA associated with hypersensitive sites in chromatin seems to be in an altered conformation since it is sensitive to a large number of probes (e.g., S1 nuclease) that detect non-B form DNA (Fig. 4). Interestingly, many of these sequences are also sensitive to these probes when harbored in supercoiled (but not relaxed) plasmid DNA, suggesting that superhelical tension might be required to drive these DNA sequences into an altered form. That superhelical strain is required for transcription is indicated by the observation that closed circular DNA but not linear DNA supports transcription after injection into frog oocytes (Harland *et al.,* 1983). Moreover, if circular DNA is injected, transcription is initiated normally, but if the template is linearized by a subsequent injection of a specific restriction enzyme, transcription ceases (Fig. 5).

FIG. 2. (A) Reconstitution of DNase I sensitivity of the globin gene with HMG 14 and 17. HMG-depleted and reconstituted chromatin was digested with increasing concentrations of DNase I and the purified DNA was digested with MSP, separated on 1.4% agarose gels, transferred to nitrocellulose paper, and hybridized to a ^{32}P nick-translated β-globin cDNA clone. Lanes 1–6 represent depleted chromatin digested with 0, 0.01, 0.03, 0.06, 0.1, and 0.3 μg/ml DNase I. Lanes 8–13 represent HMG-reconstituted chromatin digested similarly. Controls showed that at these levels of DNase I the inactive ovalbumin gene was not digested in either series. (B) Dot hybridization analysis of DNA from bound and unbound nucleosome monomers after HMG–agarose chromotography. Monomer nucleosome particles were obtained from avain red blood cell nuclei and depleted of HMG 14 and 17. They were then passed over an HMG 14 and 17 column; 80% of the nucleosomes did not bind, but the 20% that did could be eluted with 0.35 M NaCl. The figure shows the hybridization of 5 μg each of unbound monomer DNA and bound monomer DNA to (a) The adult β-globin cDNA clone; (b) an 11-kb *Bam* fragment flanking (FL) the coding sequence for the adult β-globin gene; (c) ovalbumin (OV) cDNA; (d) a 1-kb *Sac*I embryonic globin fragment that is not expressed. The DNA was covalently linked to DBM paper. The larger size of the hybridizing "dots" is due to the spread of the signal and not to the deposition of the DNA onto a larger area. (C) Analysis of MSB (T cells)-bound and unbound monomers by dot blot hybridization. The analysis is as described in (B) above, but the cells were a T-cell line (MSB) that does not make Hb; 5 μg each of bound DNA and unbound DNA were spotted onto DBM paper and hybridizied to the indicated probes.

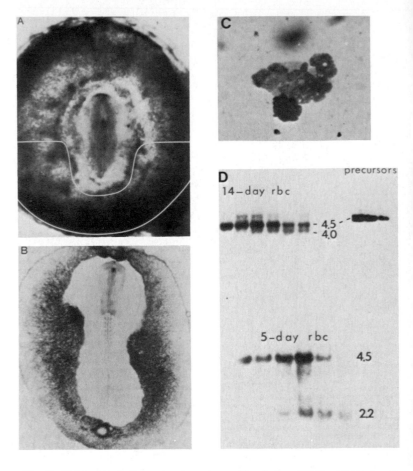

Fig. 3. Chicken blastoderms at various stages of incubation. (A) Head fold, stage 6, 23 hours; area outlined in white shows the precursor region that is cut out for the biochemical analysis. Most analysis is done with 20- to 22-hour embryos. (B) Stage 11, 40–45 hr, containing blood island. (C) *In vitro* erythroid colonies. The encircled region in (A) was cut out and plated in tissue culture as single cells. (C) shows a high power field at 3 days. The slide was stained for Hb with benzidine (brownish-yellow cells) and counter-stained with Giemsa (blue cells) to detect nonerythroid cells. (D) Absence of DNase I-hypersensitive sites in globin chromatin from precursor cells. Nuclei from primitive erythroblasts (from 5-day embryos) making embryonic Hb, definitive erythroblasts (from 14-day embryos) making adult Hb, and precursor cells (500 embryos) were digested with increasing concentrations of DNase I. The DNA was purified, restricted with *Hind*III and blot hybridized to an embryonic β-globin gene probe. Fourteen-day red cell-hypersensitive sites yield a 4-kb subband; 5-day cells (which express embryonic and not adult β-globin) yield a 2.2-kb subband; precursors show no subbands.

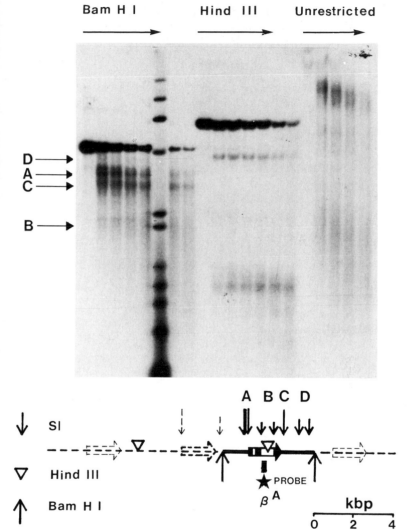

FIG. 4. S1-sensitive regions in adult red cell nuclei. Nuclei from adult definitive line red cells from 12-day embryos were digested with increasing concentrations of S1 nuclease (0, 12, 25, 50, and 100 units/μg). The probe is indicated by the star and the subbands are correlated with the position of the hypersensitive site in the map below. The dotted and continuous arrows above the map indicate the approximate position of the S1 cuts. Markers are λ-*Hind*III and OX *Hae*III fragments.

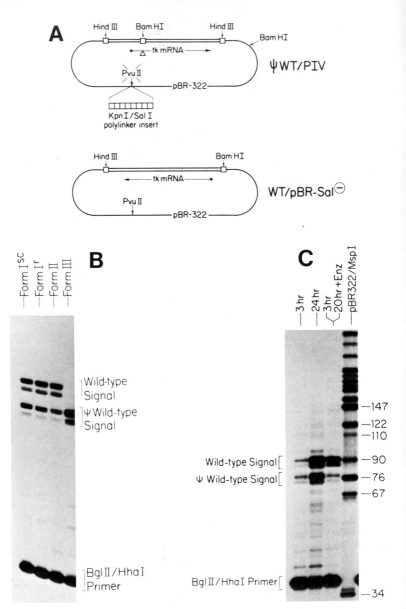

C. A Relaxed Higher Order Nucleosome Structure Is Associated with Active Chromatin

Expression of tissue-specific eukaryotic genes is strikingly suppressed in the inappropriate cell type. This suppression is greater than $10^{-7}–10^{-9}$ when comparing expressing and nonexpressing cell types (Ivarie et al., 1983; Groudine and Weintraub, 1975). This degree of suppression is over six orders of magnitude more extreme than repression in prokaryotes, which is about 10^{-3} for induced vs repressed states. Suppression of gene activity in eukaryotes is even more remarkable when one considers that fibroblast extracts will actively support globin gene transcription in vitro (Luse and Roeder, 1980). While generally believed to be the case, there has been almost no biochemical demonstration that active and inactive chromatin is differently organized with respect to its higher order structure. It is a good guess that the condensed chromatin structure seen morphologically is, in fact, partially responsible for genetic suppression. If so, then a crucial, perhaps a primary focus for gene activation during development may be the mechanism by which this suppression is relieved or removed. For these

---

FIG. 5. The requirement of continued circularity for transcription. (A) Two tk plasmids, which can be distinguished by size, tk transcript, and susceptibility to restriction endonucleases. The wild-type and pseudowild-type plasmids (missing 10 bases of coding sequence) produce distinguishable transcripts, but were further modified so that 1 (the pseudowild type) could be cut by the restriction enzymes chosen, and the other (wild type) would remain uncut. The enzymes KpnI and SalI were reconstituted from lyophilized stocks. The pseudowild type plasmid was designed so that all the KpnI and SalI sites of this gene are located at a single site, well removed from the tk coding sequences. (B) Transcripts were determined by primer extension after injection of wild-type DNA templates of the indicated topology. Form I^{sc}, form II, and form I^{r} become supercoiled after injection while form III (linear) does not. As a control, supercoiled pseudowild-type DNA was coinjected with each form of DNA. Transcription signals are seen from all forms, but not from form III linears. (C) An equimolar mixture of the wild-type and pseudowild-type plasmids was injected into oocytes. After 3 hours both plasmids were supercoiled, and continued to be so for 24 hours. If restriction enzymes (SalI and KpnI) were injected at 3 hours the pseudowild-type DNA was cut, and the wild-type DNA was left intact. Transcripts were observed from both genes after 3 hours, and continued to accumulate to a higher level at 24 hours. Transcripts of the linearized pseudowild-type gene (20 hours + Enz) did not seem to accumulate appreciably beyond the level of mRNA observed 3 hours postinjection.

reasons we have recently focused on the nature of the higher order interactions between nucleosomes.

When large chromatin (isolated by mild nuclease digestion of red cell nuclei) is electrophoresed through an agarose gel it migrates as a rather discrete band. Surprisingly, with additional digestion, little change in mobility is observed. When the average DNA size approaches 4 kb, three types of particles are observed, "a, b, and c" particles (Fig. 6A). The a particles migrate similarly to the particles produced at the lowest nuclease concentrations. By blotting these gels, we have shown that a particles contain inactive genes, b particles contain active genes and their flanking sequences (up to 10 kb 5′ of the β-globin transcription unit), and c particles contain nucleosome momomer DNA from both active and inactive sequences. (These nucleosomes probably dissociated from the higher order structures and they will not be considered.) The integrity of a particles depends on the presence of histone H1 which is thought to be responsible for supranucleosome structure. Thus a number of procedures known to be relatively specific for removing or inactivating HI also destroy the integrity of a particles as assayed by electrophoresis.

The DNA sizes in a and b particles can be examined by soaking the nucleoprotein gel in SDS and protease K and then electrophoresing the

---

FIG. 6. Higher order structure of chromatin in avian red cells. Avian red cell nuclei were digested with increasing levels of micrococcal nuclease and the chromatin isolated as nucleoprotein (NP) or DNA and electrophoresed in a 1% agarose gel as chromatin particles or as pure DNA (A and B). Note that even though the DNA decreases from over 24 kb to less than 1 kb, the particles remain fairly uniform. At the higher levels of nuclease, "a, b, and c" particles are seen. In (C), a, b, and c particles are separated on 1% agarose (top) and then analyzed on a second dimension SDS–protein gel showing that a and b particles contain all histone species while c particles are missing HI and HV. In (D) the DNA from a, b, and c particles (top) is analyzed on 1% SDS agarose gels; a particles contain DNA of sizes between 10 kb and 400 bp; b particles contain roughly the same DNA size distribution, but the DNA falls along a *diagonal*, indicating that the smaller the DNA fragment in b particles, the faster the mobility of the particle; c particles contain monomer length DNA. The fact that a particles contain DNA of such broad size range indicates that the particles are held together. Additional experiments removing HI and HV indicate that these histones are responsible for holding the cleaved chromatin together in a particles. In (E), a gel similar to the ones shown in (D) was hybridized to either β-globin (an active gene) or vitellogenin (an inactive gene). Both probes hybridized to monomer DNA, but the vitellogenin probe hybridized along the vertical (a particles) and the β-globin probe, along the diagonal (b particles).

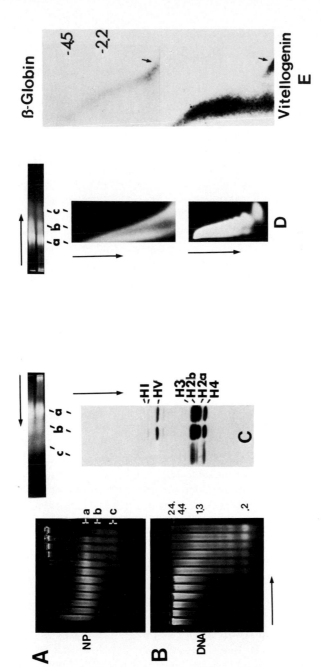

A NP

a
b
c

B DNA

2.4
4.4

1.3

.2

C

H1
HV

H3
H2b
H2a
H4

c'
b'
a'

D

a b c

E

β-Globin

-45
-22

Vitellogenin

DNA in a second dimension (Fig. 6D); a particles contain a set of DNA fragments between 500 bp and 4–6 kb; b particles contain fragments of about the same size distribution, but the larger fragments migrate more slowly than the smaller fragments in both the nucleoprotein dimension as well as the DNA dimension. When these two-dimensional gels are blot hybridized to specific probes, active genes such as globin or chicken thymidine kinase hybridize along the diagonal where b particle DNA resides, while inactive vitellogenin sequences are found along the vertical where a particle DNA resides (Fig. 6E). Both active and inactive DNA is found with the monomer c particles.

Our interpretation of these data is the following: For a particles, the DNA can be internally cleaved yet H1 will hold the particle together. For b particles, internal cleavage leads to scission of the polynucleosomal chromatin fiber and the release of faster migrating particles. Second dimension analysis on SDS–protein gels reveals that both a and b particles contain equivalent amounts of all four inner histones as well as H1 and the erythrocyte-specific analog of H1, H5 (Fig. 6C). Since H1 and H5 are responsible for the integrity of a particles we presume that over the active chromatin which is represented in b particles, H1 is modified or perhaps replaced by a polymorphic form of H1 not readily distinguished by our gels.

On the basis of these results we believe that H1 may be associated with a chromosomal structural conformation that is responsible for genetic inactivation. Presumably, one of the first events that occurs during the process of gene activation is the removal, replacement, or modification of H1. Once a chromosome fiber is relaxed, specific factors might then operate to enhance or modulate transcription from a specific transcription unit. How the initial events might occur are unclear and how the active structure, or more precisely, the uninhibited structure, is maintained and propagated to daughter cells is also unclear.

D. H1 Cooperativity

How do large domains of chromatin become structurally modified? This is not known; however, an interesting hypothesis comes from the observation that H1 binds cooperatively to DNA and to chromatin (Renz, 1975; Renz and Day, 1976). Consistent with cooperativity is the

the fact that H1 forms chains of homopolymers when crosslinked in nuclei (Bonner and Pollard, 1975; Thomas and Khabaza, 1980). The cooperative nature of H1 binding suggests a mechanism by which inactive structures might be propagated to daughter chromosomes as well as a mechanism by which the inactive, H1-dependent structure might be diassembled for gene activity. The cooperative character of H1 binding might be used to rapidly "fill in" the spaces for new H1 binding as the chromosome duplicates and old H1 molecules are distributed to the daughter chromosomes. Also, it is not difficult to imagine that the cooperative binding of H1 could be altered by a specific "defect" in the cooperative unit. Thus, a specific protein bound to a specific sequence might act as a "roadblock" for H1 polymerization and since the binding is cooperative, the association of all of the H1 in a large region would be altered. How could the initial interaction between a sequence-specific protein and an inactive chromatin structure occur? One obvious opportunity would be during DNA replication. Alternatively, it is known that even though H1 is tightly and cooperatively bound and the supranucleosome structure is stable, H1 monomers are continuously exchanging (Caron and Thomas, 1981; Weintraub, 1984). Thus, it is possible that during this exchange process, specific recognition could occur.

E. Propagation of Some DNase I Hypersensitive Sites in the Absence of Inducers

A fascinating feature of development is the process of determination, whereby the developmental potential of a cell becomes more restricted. Alternatively, determination could be considered in a more positive sense and might reflect the process by which the cell becomes committed to a specific lineage. Once this commitment occurs (either by some endogenous clock or by cues from the environment), the committed cell and its progeny remember their determined state even when placed in a totally new environment. Some sort of stable regulatory circuit must have been established to assure the continued differentiative potential of the determined cell.

The relative stability of the determined state suggest to us that it may be encoded in a chromosome structure and we decided to test the possibility that once induced, DNase I-hypersensitive sites are stably propagated to daughter cells in the absence of inducer (Groudine and Weintraub, 1981). Previously, we demonstrated that after transformation by Rous sarcoma virus (RSV), chick embryo fibroblasts turned on low levels of transcription from the globin genes and these genes acquired DNase I-hypersensitive sites. Using a temperature-sensitive mutant of the RSV transforming gene, *src*, as well as a deletion mutant of *src* we could demonstrate that this globin transcription from RSV–CEF was *src* dependent and, indeed, many genes were turned on and others turned off.

The experimental design to test whether DNase I-hypersensitive sites could be propagated relied on our ability to use a temperature-sensitive *src* gene product and hence (1) to induce globin DNase I-hypersensitive sites in CEF; (2) to inactivate *src* by temperature shift; and (3) to then ask whether cells retained the globin-hypersensitive sites after multiple rounds of replication in the absence of an active inducer, that is, in the absence of an active *src* gene product. The results demonstrated that globin-hypersensitive sites could be stably propagated.

More recently, we have demonstrated a similar phenomenon in an estrogen-induced gene, the vitellogenin gene in male livers (Burch and Weintraub, 1983). Here a group of three DNase I-hypersensitve sites is induced by estrogen at the 5′ end of the vitellogenin gene. One of these at −760 bp is dependent on the continued presence of hormone; hence, it is an example of a hypersensitive site that is not stably propagated. The other two, at −250 and 0 bp, are initially induced by estrogen, but with estrogen removal they are stably propagated to daughter cells. Thus, in contrast to RSV activation of globin, the estrogen induction and stabilization of vitellogenin-hypersensitve sites represents a natural condition where the propagation of these sites can be observed.

Mechanisms whereby the structural information present in hypersensitive sites could be propagated have been discussed at length (see Weintraub, 1979). In general, the most appealing models have the requirement for a multicomponent protein complex bound at the hypersensitive site whose individual members retain an affinity for one or the other of the two parental DNA strands as the replication fork copies the DNA. Each component segregates with the two parental DNA strands and the complementary components then "fill in" the empty binding sites.

Whether these hypersensitive sites actually encode the determined state is presently only a speculation. Alternative mechanisms (for example, involving positively controlled self-regulatory circuits) are also very possible and much more information is clearly needed.

F. Multiple Independent Chromosomal Events Are Required for Full Activation

Thus far, I have outlined a number of differences in chromatin structure found between active and inactive segments of chromatin. These include DNase I- and S1-hypersensitive sites at 5' and 3' borders of the transcription unit, sometimes in the middle of genes, sometimes far upstream, and sometimes far downstream. Active nucleosomes are preferentially associated with HMG 14 and 17, possibly with acetylated histones, possibly with ubiquitinated histones, possibly with topoisomerases, probably with rather specific stable transcription complex factors, etc. (see review by Weisbrod, 1982). Also, the DNA in actively transcribed regions (especially the 5' end of genes) is usually less modified by methylation. And finally H1 binding seems to be modified since the higher order structure of active chromatin is not held intact by these proteins. This might result from direct modification of H1 or by modification of the chromatin to which H1 is bound or both.

When we first compared the globin chromatin in red cell precursors (Weintraub *et al.*, 1982) with chromatin from red cells, many of our assays revealed that the chromatin was totally inactive in precursors and we therefore thought it reasonable that activation would require a single initiating event and then a cascade of dependent events would ensue until the active structure was completely built. However, subsequent work with red cell precursors arrested by transformation with avian erythroblastosis virus (AEV) showed that states of active chromatin could exist in these cells where some (but not all) features of active globin chromatin were present, but transcription was not occurring. These results led to the suggestion that full activation of the globin genes required multiple, independent events. Presumably, these events were encoded in genes and presumably, they effected different features of globin chromatin structure as well as "trans-acting" regulatory factors. These conclusions received additional support by the finding that globin genes activated in CEF by RSV yielded only low levels of transcription compared to red cells and globin genes activated in CEF by NaCl shock yield no detectable transcripts, yet displayed some globin-associated DNase I-hypersensitive sites. Thus, partial states of activation can occur and an obligatory cascade of events cannot explain the data.

If one assumes that multiple independent chromosomal events are necessary, then it is possible to ask whether all of these events are cell lineage specific or are these "events" used combinationally in different lineages. Current data are still fragmentary, but two observations suggest both possibilities. First Emerson and Felsenfeld (1984) have identified a protein that is responsible, at least in part, for generating a 5' β-globin DNase I-hypersensitive site. Suprisingly, this activity cannot be found in nonerythroid cells, suggesting that this putative regulatory gene produce is tissue specific.

Results from the vitellogenin system, however, suggest that combinatorial processes can also occur (Burch and Weintraub, 1983). In the presence of estrogen, the vitellogenin gene is transcribed in liver, but not in oviduct. The combinatorial nature of controls is best revealed by the associated hypersensitive sites. In liver from unstimulated males, hypersensitive sites are found within the gene and at the 3' end of the gene. We presume that these sites (termed "A" sites) mark some developmentally determined "preactivation" state since these sites are not seen in most nonresponsive tissue. Interestingly, A sites are observed in the oviduct, which is another estrogen-responsive tissue; however, in the oviduct vitellogenin is not induced, but ovalbumin is. A second class of sites, "C" sites, located about 760 bp 5' to the transcription start site is observed when hormone is present. Interestingly, this site is also seen in stimulated liver as well as oviduct. Why then doesn't the oviduct transcribe vitellogenin? One possibility is that a third class of sites, "B" sites, located at about -250 and 0 bp, is seen only in liver and not in oviduct. We believe that the inability of oviduct to encode such a site precludes active transcription. Hence, while liver can encode three "events" as reflected in A, B, and C sites, oviduct can encode only two, and red cells, none. Obviously, as our analysis becomes more exhaustive additional features will emerge that also distinguish different partially activated gene states. Ultimately, it will be crucial to correlate those with the activity of specific genes in different tissues. Also, the mutual dependency of the different states is important to understand. For example, in the vitellogenin system, do B and C sites require the previous changes reflected in the presence of A sites? Moreover, inhibitory events could also be important. In the vitellogenin system, a unique hypersensitive site (termed "X") is seen in oviduct, but not in liver or erythroid cells. For partially activated genes such as the vitellogenin gene in oviduct, could X reflect an inhibitory event required to keep the gene inactive?

G. Changes in Chromatin Structures: Cause or Effect?

A number of well-characterized differences are now known between the structure of chromatin that is transcribed and chromatin that is not (see above). For genes that are expressed in a tissue-specific way, these differences in structure are also tissue specific. Are these differences a cause or a result of the gene activation process? While it is probably safe to say that attempts to alter chromatin structure (genetically or biochemically) usually also alter expression and vice versa, perhaps the most compelling evidence that alterations in chromatin structure are prerequisites for transcriptional activation is the observation in a number of systems that DNase I-hypersensitive sites appear in development before transcriptional activation (Weintraub et al., 1982; Burch and Weintraub, 1983). Additional support comes from observations that retroviral proviruses usually become transcriptionally active (or not) depending on the activity of their chromosomal sites of integration (Yamamoto et al., 1983; Jaenisch et al., 1981). In one analogous case, an insertion element integrated into a Drosophila glue gene becomes expressed in a tissue-specific way under the control of the glue gene locus (Shermoen and Beckindorf, 1982).

Independent but less compelling evidence that chromatin structure may be a determinant for expression comes from studies of TK^- revertants of TK^+ transformed L cells. Here, a large number of revertant clones (which revert and rerevert at high frequency) lose DNase I sensitivity coordinately with TK expression (Davies et al., 1982; Rogihski et al., 1983). Similarly, introduction of the TK gene into L cells without selection results in clones that contain the gene, but most of these clones do not express TK, suggesting that when selection does not occur, most integrations are inactive, presumably because of integration into inactive chromatin (Luciw et al., 1983). So-called long-range, or position effects also are compatible with a role for chromosome structure as a participant in controlling gene activity. These are best illustrated by the effect of various DNA deletions in heriditary persistance of fetal hemoglobin (HPFH) (see Stamatoyannopoulos and Nienhuis, 1982) and the control by MAR or SIR over the activity of the inactive mating type cassettes (see review by Nasmythe, 1982), and the requirement for enhancer sequences for full expression (Banerji *et al.*, 1981; Benoist and Chambon, 1981) of transfected genes.

Our current working hypothesis for the contribution of chromosome structure to gene activation is the following: The idea of a large domain (20–100 kb) is central. The domain can be either relaxed or closed. A relaxed domain could be envisioned as having a loosened higher order nucleosome structure. As a result individual nucleosomes bind largely according to their own intrinsic binding constants to a particular stretch of DNA since nucleosome–nucleosome packing forces are diminished. Data from a wide variety of experiments indicate that intrinsic histone binding to particular DNA sequences is likely to vary considerably. We would guess that the relaxation of a domain would involve the removal, replacement, or modification of histone H1 (see above). It is likely that the cooperative nature of H1 binding is instrumental is causing such a large domain to relax. Once relaxed, the preferential loss of a nucleosome from specific sites would allow specific (or nonspecific stabilizing factors to bind. We suspect this occurs at DNase I- or S1-hypersensitive sites and is mediated through an altered DNA conformation induced locally by the superhelical tension generated by the loss of a nucleosome. Once stabilized, the hypersensitive structure can often be faithfully propagated, either because associated proteins preserve the structure or because the domain irreversibly remains open. It is possible that this may be one role of HMG 14 and 17, i.e., to prevent or alter H1 binding. Once formed, the hypersensitive site is perhaps an entry site for the transcription machinery, possibly by virtue of its single-stranded character. The hypersensitive sites might also be a record of the determined state of the cell.

This particular view portrays the role of chromatin largely in negative terms; that is, to inhibit gene activity, and therefore subsequent gene activity would require specific mechanisms to remove this inhibition. The mechanism by which this suppression is removed is likely to be fundamentally the same for constitutively expressed genes as for tissue-specific genes. The differences will likely reside in whether or not controlling elements are themselves constitutive or not. For constitutively expressed genes we presume that the gametes are pre-programmed to have these genes on (see Groudine and Canklin, 1985).

Although much of the underlying structure for potential transcription may be superficially suppressed, in the case of sperm by the protamines, it is supposed that these constitutively expressed genes are physically prepared for transcription: their domains would be relaxed, appropriate sites would be unmethylated, and the components needed for hypersensitive sites would be in place. Whether this structural information is transmitted from the gametes to the zygote in a way that is similar to the way hypersensitive sites are sometimes propagated in somatic cells (see above) is not known. How tissue-specific genes are activated in specific descendants of the zygote is just as unclear as ever. Specific determinants localized in specific regions of the fertilized egg is probably the most popular explanation. Another possibility emphasizes DNA structure. Here we view the developing zygote as a matrix of rather nonspecific gradients. We know from the behavior of pure supercoiled DNA that the ability of particular sequences to flip into an altered B-conformation is very dependent on the physical and chemical environment (Larsen and Weintraub, 1982). We think this inherent property of DNA may be used for differentially "reading" the points in an embryonic gradients. Once the embryonic gradients are read other factors, specific or nonspecific (e.g., single strand-specific binding proteins or HMGs), might stabilize the structure and allow for its propagation to progeny cells.

III. The Genetic Logic of Development

A. Specific Regulatory Factors vs Combinations of Less Specific Factors

A popular paradigm suggests that the appearance of a specific cell type during development, say a red blood cell, is the consequence of a series of commitment steps. Thus, the red blood cell does not just appear *de novo*, but is determined in large part by a sequential set of decisions made by its ancestors and passed on to their progeny. In order to understand fully how the globin genes become specifically activated in red cells, it is a reasonable guess that we must first understand the logic that governs how the red cell lineage unfolds and how particular precursor cells at specific times in development become committed to globin gene activation some time later in their red cell progeny. A classical approach to this type of problem is to first ask how many genes are *specifically* (and only) required for (causally) determining the red cell lineage. Ideally one would wish to know how many genes exist whose null alleles produce normal embryos lacking red cells. In such a hypothetical analysis, it might be argued that mutations in genes that produce normal red cells lacking certain specific "structural" products such as Hb- or red cell-specific spectrin should be excluded from this count. Immediately one's conception of the problem becomes unfocused since it is certainly possible that red cell-specific spectrin (for example) may be active in red cell precursors and since it imparts a certain degree of integrity to the cell surface, it is actually an absolute requirement for future differentiation. Hence, what might be a rather trivial (from the point of view of regulation) structural protein becomes defined as a crucial *genetic* regulatory element. It is likely that certain *Drosophila* developmental mutants such as *rudimentary* (which codes for aspartate transcarbarylase) might fall into this category. In such a case, the challenge is to understand how a metabolic mutation becomes transduced biochemically into a specific developmental defect. Since specific "regulatory" mutations effecting only a *single* well-defined cellular lineage (e.g., the myogenic or hematopoietic lineages) are rare, it is possible that the "logic" of development takes advantage of combinations of rather ordinary gene products (e.g., ATCase) to encode major developmental decisions. The role of specific proteins that bind to specific genes and activate or inactivate specific developmental pathways is just beginning to be documented by current experimentation and it is the major conceptual model used to design or explain new experiments.

It would seem that if every tissue-specific gene were governed by a unique regulatory molecule, the circuitry of development would be much too complex. On the other hand, there is the notion that batteries of genes could be regulated by a single gene, perhaps a master switch for red cell-specific gene products. In a related model (Kaufman, 1973), combinations of a set number of such genes are thought to code for these types of decisions. Sequence analysis of DNA near the α and β-globin genes, however, has not revealed any striking unique homologies between these genes. Moreover, studies with avian red cell precursors arrested in different developmental compartments clearly show that transcription of the red cell-specific histone H5 gene can occur before (and independent of) transcription of the globin genes (Beug *et al.*, 1982). Moreover, α-globin gene transcription can precede transcription from the β-globin genes (unpublished observations). Thus in many cases, batteries of tissue-specific genes are activated discoordinately. The simple notion of a single tissue-specific activator is also complicated by examples of tissue-specific genes active in different cell types. For example, in liver, both vitellogenin and conalbumen (transferrin) are active; yet, in oviduct, vitellogenin is off, and ovalbumen and conalbumen are on.

The main goal of our laboratory over the next years will be to try to understand the logic of how developmental commitments are made during embryogenesis. For the most part, we will focus on developing red blood cells. Largely, because of the phenotypic stability of these commitment decisions, it has been our bias that they are recorded in a biological structure, e.g., some aspect of nuclear organization, perhaps the higher order arrangement of nucleosomes, perhaps a stable transcription complex. Thus, specific genes may indeed be crucial for determining specific cell lineages; on the other hand, specific and heritable responses to combinations of rather nonspecific states might be important. The rather personal thoughts outlined in this section reflect this uncertainty and given the current level of understanding there seems to be no *a priori* reason to favor one model over the other.

B. Functional Identification of Regulatory Genes Using Antisense Transcription

It is unlikely that biochemical and molecular approaches to development and chromosome function will prove successful without genetics. Unfortunately, this tool is not available for many organisms and in those where genetic analysis can be done, the analysis is often slow and cumbersome; certain classes of interesting mutants (e.g., those that might effect only one cell type) are difficult to obtain (perhaps for reasons that may turn out to be profound); and conditional developmental mutants are relatively rare.

In an effort to deal with this problem, we have been trying to use the power of recombinant DNA technology to identify genes that function to control the emergence of the red cell lineage during development. Our strategy is to introduce a DNA sequence into cells in a way that would inhibit the function of the corresponding endogenous sequences. In the long term, we hope to be able to introduce cDNA clones representative of tissue or stage-*specific* mRNA sequences to try to functionally identify members from this class of genes that would inhibit subsequent differentiation of specific cell lineages.

Our initial approach considered several strategies: (1) to overexpress the cDNA clone in the hope that overexpression might lead to a dominant phenotype; (2) to make truncated or mutated cDNA in the hope that an altered gene product would be produced and function as a dominant mutation when expressed; (3) to provide a "compartmental" insertion signal on the expressed cDNA in the hope that such a hybrid protein might form a normal association with species with which it would have to interact *in situ,* but the interaction would funnel these species to the wrong cellular compartment; and (4) to construct the inhibitory cDNA expression vector so that anti-mRNA (i.e., RNA complementary to the normal RNA) would be transcribed in the hope that such an antimessage would duplex with the normal mRNA and prevent either nuclear processing or mRNA translation. Since the literature contained clues that the antimessage approach might be successful (reviewed in Izant and Weintraub, 1983), we decided to focus our efforts on this particular technique and chose the herpes simplex virus thymidine kinase gene (HSV-TK) as a model system.

Our strategy was to microinject plasmid DNA harboring the HSV-TK gene into LTK$^-$ cells (thymidine kinase negative cells) and to assay the activity by the acquired ability of these cells to make thymidine kinase and incorporate [^{3}H]TdR into nuclei as assayed by radioautography (Fig. 7). We reasoned that if an antisense TK construction (that is, a vector that produced antisense TK mRNA) were simultaneously injected, the number of TK-positive cells and the grain density per cell might be reduced. Our results showed that this was in fact the case. Control experiments showed that the antisense herpes vector did not inhibit expression of a sense chicken TK gene. Since the herpes and chicken TK genes share no sequence homology, these results attest to the sequence specificity of the inhibition. Moreover, an antisense chicken TK gene inhibited chicken TK, but not the herpes TK gene. In more recent experiments, we have found that only 50 bp of 5′ untranslated antisense transcript can inhibit TK activity. This result suggests the future possibility of using this approach for gene replacement procedures. We have also demonstrated that the same results with HSV-TK and chicken TK can be obtained using calcium phosphate transfection methods; moreover, an antisense β-actin construction, when introduced

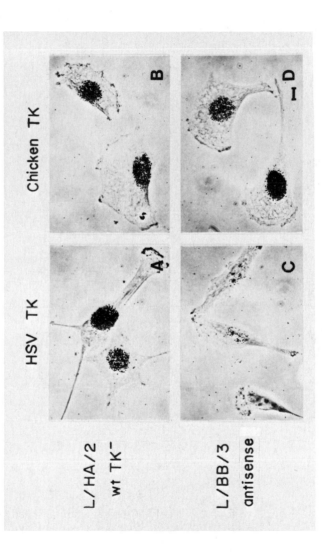

Fig. 7. Autoradiography of cells injected with HSV and chicken thymidine kinase genes. A line of LTK⁻ cells (L/HA/2) was transformed with an antisense-producing HSV⁻ TK plasmid (L/BB/3) under APRT selection. Representative micrographs of parental L/HA/mouse L cells (A) and (B) and antisense cell line L/BB/3 cells (C) and (D). Neighboring cells on the same coverslip were injected with either HSV-TK (A and C) or chicken TK plasmid (B and D). The autoradiographic grain density is, on the average, less in the antisense cells injected with HSV-TK than in those injected with chicken TK. Bar = 10 μm. (×350.)

into cells, causes a lethal phenotype, presumably by inhibiting normal endogenous actin expression.

Our initial results using antisense transcription to inhibit gene function seem promising, but they are still preliminary. We do not know the detailed mechanism of inhibition and most important, we do not know whether the approach will be general for all genes. Conceivably subtle features of mRNP structure, RNA compartmentalization, RNA concentration, and RNA secondary structure could be crucial and also unique to specific mRNAs. The stability of the antisense transcript is also a potential problem, especially since there is some suggestion that antisense TK mRNA is relatively unstable (Izant and Weintraub, 1984).

Our long-term strategy is to use antisense transcription to identify genes that control specifically the appearance of the red cell lineage. Expression vectors that encode cDNA sequences specific to red cells or red cell precursors might be introduced into early frog embryos with the hope that several such vectors might prevent subsequent red cell formation, but not effect global development of the tadpole. If such genes exist, the proposed assay is not unreasonable since it is known that the extirpation of the ventral mesoderm from early frog embryos prevents subsequent red cell formation, but does not affect the overall development of the tadpole (Goss, 1928). Thus, tadpoles without red cells are fully viable. Preliminary work by Dr. Richard Harland supports this observation and, in addition, suggests that antisense transcription (using HSV-TK as a model) is effective in frog oocytes. Additonal work by Dr. D. Melton (personal communication) using antisense RNA produced *in vitro* with SP6 RNA polymerase also shows that antisense inhibition can work in frog oocytes. The SP6 technique also provides an alternate, and in some cases, a more direct methodology than antisense transcription vectors for generating antisense RNA.

The use of antisense transcription provides a new and powerful tool for studying questions in cell biology and development and perhaps, for certain clinically related problems; however, there are still many important questions to be answered before the usefulness and generality of the approach can be fully evaluated. Moreover, it should be recalled that this is only one of a series of methodologies by which the power of recombinant DNA technology can be used to influence the expression of celular genes.

IV. Conclusions and Prospects

By analyzing in detail the chromatin structure of tissue-specific genes, we have now shifted our initial focus from why specific genes become activated in specific places and at specific times during development to the question of how *chromatin domains* containing these genes become *"relaxed"* (e.g., see Fig. 6) at specific times and in specific positions in the embryo. Since a variety of partially activated chromosomal states can be seen, we presume that *combinations* of events must occur before full activation occurs. How this is encoded genetically may eventually be approached using the emerging *antisense* genetic technology. Although the detailed mechanism by which DNase I-hypersensitive sites *propagate* chromosome structures to daughter cells is not known, the fact that this occurs for some hypersensitive sites suggests that these structures may be the vehicle by which the *determined state* is transmitted in any given cell lineage. As such, the accumulation of the information reflected in several of these structures may also be involved in determining the time at which a given cell type will emerge in a developing embryo. By a variety of assays, hypersensitive sites in chromatin contain an *altered DNA configuration* that can often be mimicked by pure supercoiled DNA. The induction of this altered conformation in supercoiled DNA is extremely dependent on solution conditions and we have speculated that this dependence may be used by nuclear DNA to read its position in an *embryonic field*. Once "read" the memory of that event must be imprinted in that cell and its progeny again, possibly by the ability of hypersensitive sites to be propagated.

Acknowledgments

Mark Groudine has been a wonderful collaborator and friend over these years and Howard Holtzer has been instrumental in emphasizing what I think are the key problems in development. I am also indebted to a large number of colleagues and collaborators, both in Seattle and in Princeton.

References

Banerji, J., Rusconi, S., and Schaffner, W. (1981). *Cell* **27,** 229–308.
Benoist, C., and Chambon, P. (1981). *Nature (London)* **290,** 304–310.
Beug, H., Palmieri, S., Freudenstein, C., Zentraf, H., and Graf, T. (1982). *Cell* **28,** 907.
Bogenhagen, D. F., Wormington, W. M., and Brown, D. D. (1982). *Cell* **28,** 413–421.
Bonner, W. M., and Pollard, H. B. (1975). *Biochem. Biophys. Res. Comm.* **64,** 282–288.

Braun, A. C. (1975). In "Cancer: A Comprehensive Treatise" (F. F. Becker, ed.), Vol. 3, pp. 3–20. Plenum, New York.

Burch, J. B. E., and Weintraub, H. (1983). *Cell* **33**, 65–76.

Caron, F., and Thomas, J. O. (1981). *J. Mol. Biol.* **146**, 513–537.

Davies, R., Fuhrer-Krusi, S., and Kucherlapati, R. (1982). *Cell* **31**, 521–529.

Elgin, S. C. R. (1981). *Cell* **27**, 413–415.

Emerson, B. M., and Felsenfeld, G. (1984). *Proc. Natl. Acad. Sci. U.S.A.* **81**, 95–99.

Goss, C. M. (1982). *J. Exp. Zool.* **52**, 45–63.

Groudine, M., and Canklin (1985). *Science* **228**, 1061–1068.

Groudine, M., and Weintraub, H. (1975). *Proc. Natl. Acad. Sci. U.S.A.* **72**, 4464–4468.

Groudine, M., and Weintraub, H. (1980). *Proc. Natl. Acad. Sci. U.S.A.* **77**, 5351–5354.

Groudine, M., and Weintraub, H. (1981). *Cell* **24**, 393–401.

Harland, R., Weintraub, H., and McKnight, S. (1983). *Nature (London)* **301**, 38–43.

Holtzer, H., Rubinstein, N., Fellinci, S., Yeoh, G., Chi, J., Birnbaum, J., and Okayama, M. (1975). *Q. Rev. Biophys.* **8**, 523–557.

Ivarie, R., Schacter, B., and O-Farrell, P. (1983). *Mol. Cell. Biol.* **3**, 1460–1467.

Izant, J. G., and Weintraub, H. (1984). *Cell* **36**, 1007–1015.

Jaenisch, R., Jahner, D., Nobis, P., Simon, I., Lohler, J., Harbers, K., and Grotkopp, D. (1981). *Cell* **24**, 519.

Kaufman, S. (1973). *Science* **181**, 310–318.

Larsen, A., and Weintraub, H. (1982). *Cell* **29**, 609–622.

Luciw, P., Bishop, M., Varmus, H., and Capecchi, M. (1983). *Cell* **33**, 705–716.

Luse, D. S., and Roeder, R. G. (1980). *Cell* **20**, 691–699.

Nasmythe, K. (1982). *Annu. Rev. Genet.* **16**, 439–501.

Ptashne, M. (1981). *Nature (London)* **294**, 217–223.

Renz, M. (1975). *Proc. Natl. Acad. Sci. U.S.A.* **72**, 733–736.

Renz, M., and Day, L. A. (1976). *Biochemistry* **15**, 3220–3228.

Rogihski, R. S., Skoultchi, A., Henthorn, P., Smithies, O., Hsiung, N., and Kucherlapati, R. (1983). *Cell* **35**, 149–155.

Shermoen, A., and Beckendorf, S. (1982). *Cell* **29**, 601.

Stamatoyannopoulos, G., and Nienhuis, A. W., eds. (1981). In "Organization and Expression of Globin Genes." Alan R. Liss, Inc., New York.

Thomas, J. O., and Khabaza, A. (1980). *Eur. J. Biochem.* **112**, 501–511.

Weintraub, H. (1979). *Nucleic. Acids Res.* **7**, 781–792.

Weintraub, H. (1984). *Cell,* in press.

Weintraub, H., and Groudine, M. (1976). *Science* **93**, 848–858.

Weintraub, H., Flint, S. J., Leffak, I. M., Groudine, M., and Grainger, R. M. (1977). *Cold Spring Harbor Symp. Quant. Biol.* **42**, 401–407.

Weintraub, H., Beug, H., Groudine, M., and Graf, T. (1982). *Cell* **28**, 931–940.

Weisbrod, S. (1982). *Nature (London)* **297**, 28–295.

Weisbrod, S., and Weintraub, H. (1979). *Proc. Natl. Acad. Sci. U.S.A.* **76**, 630–634.

Weisbrod, S., and Weintraub, H. (1981). *Cell* **23**, 391–400.

Yamamoto, K., Payvar, F., Firestone, G. L., Maler, B., Wrange, O., Carlstedt-Duke, J., Gustafsson, J. A., and Chandler, V. L. (1983). *Cold Spring Harbor Symp. Quant. Biol.* **47**, 977–984.

FORMER OFFICERS OF THE HARVEY SOCIETY

1905–1906

President: GRAHAM LUSK
Vice-President: SIMON FLEXNER
Treasurer: FREDERIC S. LEE
Secretary: GEORGE B. WALLACE

Council:
   C. A. HERTER
   S. J. MELTZER
   EDWARD K. DUNHAM

1906–1907

President: GRAHAM LUSK
Vice-President: SIMON FLEXNER
Treasurer: FREDERIC S. LEE
Secretary: GEORGE B. WALLACE

Council:
   C. A. HERTER
   S. J. MELTZER
   JAMES EWING

1907–1908

President: GRAHAM LUSK
Vice-President: JAMES EWING
Treasurer: EDWARD K. DUNHAM
Secretary: GEORGE B. WALLACE

Council:
   SIMON FLEXNER
   THEO. C. JANEWAY
   PHILIP H. HISS, JR.

1908–1909

President: JAMES EWING
Vice-President: SIMON FLEXNER
Treasurer: EDWARD K. DUNHAM
Secretary: FRANCIS C. WOOD

Council:
   GRAHAM LUSK
   S. J. MELTZER
   ADOLPH MEYER

1909–1910*

President: JAMES EWING
Vice-President: THEO. C. JANEWAY
Treasurer: EDWARD K. DUNHAM
Secretary: FRANCIS C. WOOD

Council:
   GRAHAM LUSK
   S. J. MELTZER
   W. J. GIES

1910–1911

President: SIMON FLEXNER
Vice-President: JOHN HOWLAND
Treasurer: EDWARD K. DUNHAM
Secretary: HAVEN EMERSON

Council:
   GRAHAM LUSK
   S. J. MELTZER
   JAMES EWING

---

* At the Annual Meeting of May 18, 1909, these officers were elected. In publishing the 1909–1910 volume their names were omitted, possibly because in that volume the custom of publishing the names of the incumbents of the current year was changed to publishing the names of the officers selected for the ensuing year.

1911–1912

President: S. J. MELTZER
Vice-President: FREDERIC S. LEE
Treasurer: EDWARD K. DUNHAM
Secretary: HAVEN EMERSON

Council:
GRAHAM LUSK
JAMES EWING
SIMON FLEXNER

1912–1913

President: FREDERIC S. LEE
Vice-President: WM. H. PARK
Treasurer: EDWARD K. DUNHAM
Secretary: HAVEN EMERSON

Council:
GRAHAM LUSK
S. J. MELTZER
WM. G. MACCALLUM

1913–1914

President: FREDERIC S. LEE
Vice-President: WM. G. MACCALLUM
Treasurer: EDWARD K. DUNHAM
Secretary: AUGUSTUS B. WADSWORTH

Council:
GRAHAM LUSK
WM. H. PARK
GEORGE B. WALLACE

1914–1915

President: WM. G. MACCALLUM
Vice-President: RUFUS I. COLE
Treasurer: EDWARD K. DUNHAM
Secretary: JOHN A. MANDEL

Council:
GRAHAM LUSK
FREDERIC S. LEE
W. T. LONGCOPE

1915–1916

President: GEORGE B. WALLACE*
Treasurer: EDWARD K. DUNHAM
Secretary: ROBERT A. LAMBERT

Council:
GRAHAM LUSK
RUFUS I. COLE
NELLIS B. FOSTER

1916–1917

President: GEORGE B. WALLACE
Vice-President: RUFUS I. COLE
Treasurer: EDWARD K. DUNHAM
Secretary: ROBERT A. LAMBERT

Council:
GRAHAM LUSK†
W. T. LONGCOPE
S. R. BENEDICT
HANS ZINSSER

1917–1918

President: EDWARD K. DUNHAM
Vice-President: RUFUS I. COLE
Treasurer: F. H. PIKE
Secretary: A. M. PAPPENHEIMER

Council:
GRAHAM LUSK
GEORGE B. WALLACE
FREDERIC S. LEE
PEYTON ROUS

* Dr. William G. MacCallum resigned after election. On Doctor Lusk's motion Doctor George B. Wallace was made President—no Vice-President was appointed.

† Doctor Lusk was made Honorary permanent Counsellor.

1918–1919

President: GRAHAM LUSK
Vice-President: RUFUS I. COLE
Treasurer: F. H. PIKE
Secretary: K. M. VOGEL

Council:
  GRAHAM LUSK
  JAMES W. JOBLING
  FREDERIC S. LEE
  JOHN AUER

1919–1920

President: WARFIELD T. LONGCOPE
Vice-President: S. R. BENEDICT
Treasurer: F. H. PIKE
Secretary: K. M. VOGEL

Council:
  GRAHAM LUSK
  HANS ZINSSER
  FREDERIC S. LEE
  GEORGE B. WALLACE

1920–1921*

President: WARFIELD T. LONGCOPE
Vice-President: S. R. BENEDICT
Treasurer: A. M. PAPPENHEIMER
Secretary: HOMER F. SWIFT

Council:
  GRAHAM LUSK
  FREDERIC S. LEE
  HANS ZINSSER
  GEORGE B. WALLACE

1921–1922

President: RUFUS I. COLE
Vice-President: S. R. BENEDICT
Treasurer: A. M. PAPPENHEIMER
Secretary: HOMER F. SWIFT

Council:
  GRAHAM LUSK
  HANS ZINSSER
  H. C. JACKSON
  W. T. LONGCOPE

1922–1923

President: RUFUS I. COLE
Vice-President: HANS ZINSSER
Treasurer: CHARLES C. LIEB
Secretary: HOMER F. SWIFT

Council:
  GRAHAM LUSK
  W. T. LONGCOPE
  H. C. JACKSON
  S. R. BENEDICT

1923–1924

President: EUGENE F. DUBOIS
Vice-President: HOMER F. SWIFT
Treasurer: CHARLES C. LIEB
Secretary: GEORGE M. MACKENZIE

Council:
  GRAHAM LUSK
  ALPHONSE R. DOCHEZ
  DAVID MARINE
  PEYTON ROUS

---

* These officers were elected at the Annual Meeting of May 21, 1920 but were omitted in the publication of the 1919–1920 volume.

1924–1925

President: EUGENE F. DUBOIS
Vice-President: PEYTON ROUS
Treasurer: CHARLES C. LIEB
Secretary: GEORGE M. MACKENZIE

Council:
  GRAHAM LUSK
  RUFUS COLE
  HAVEN EMERSON
  WM. H. PARK

1925–1926

President: HOMER F. SWIFT
Vice-President: H. B. WILLIAMS
Treasurer: HAVEN EMERSON
Secretary: GEORGE M. MACKENZIE

Council:
  GRAHAM LUSK
  EUGENE F. DUBOIS
  WALTER W. PALMER
  H. D. SENIOR

1926–1927

President: WALTER W. PALMER
Vice-President: WM. H. PARK
Treasurer: HAVEN EMERSON
Secretary: GEORGE M. MACKENZIE

Council:
  GRAHAM LUSK
  HOMER F. SWIFT
  A. R. DOCHEZ
  ROBERT CHAMBERS

1927–1928

President: DONALD D. VAN SLYKE
Vice-President: JAMES W. JOBLING
Treasurer: HAVEN EMERSON
Secretary: CARL A. L. BINGER

Council:
  GRAHAM LUSK
  RUSSEL L. CECIL
  WARD J. MACNEAL
  DAVID MARINE

1928–1929

President: PEYTON ROUS
Vice-President: HORATIO B. WILLIAMS
Treasurer: HAVEN EMERSON
Secretary: PHILIP D. MCMASTER

Council:
  GRAHAM LUSK
  ROBERT CHAMBERS
  ALFRED F. HESS
  H. D. SENIOR

1929–1930

President: G. CANBY ROBINSON
Vice-President: ALFRED F. HESS
Treasurer: HAVEN EMERSON
Secretary: DAYTON J. EDWARDS

Council:
  GRAHAM LUSK
  ALFRED E. COHN
  A. M. PAPPENHEIMER
  H. D. SENIOR

1930–1931

President: ALFRED E. COHN
Vice-President: J. G. HOPKINS
Treasurer: HAVEN EMERSON
Secretary: DAYTON J. EDWARDS

Council
  GRAHAM LUSK
  O. T. AVERY
  A. M. PAPPENHEIMER
  S. R. DETWILER

1931–1932

President: J. W. JOBLING
Vice-President: HOMER W. SMITH
Treasurer: HAVEN EMERSON
Secretary: DAYTON J. EDWARDS

Council:
GRAHAM LUSK
S. R. DETWILER
THOMAS M. RIVERS
RANDOLPH WEST

1932–1933

President: ALFRED F. HESS
Vice-President: HAVEN EMERSON
Treasurer: THOMAS M. RIVERS
Secretary: EDGAR STILLMAN

Council:
GRAHAM LUSK
HANS T. CLARKE
WALTER W. PALMER
HOMER W. SMITH

1933–1934

President: ALFRED HESS*
Vice-President: ROBERT K. CANNAN
Treasurer: THOMAS M. RIVERS
Secretary: EDGAR STILLMAN

Council:
STANLEY R. BENEDICT
ROBERT F. LOEB
WADE H. BROWN

1934–1935

President: ROBERT K. CANNAN
Vice-President: EUGENE L. OPIE
Treasurer: THOMAS M. RIVERS
Secretary: RANDOLPH H. WEST

Council:
HERBERT S. GASSER
B. S. OPPENHEIMER
PHILIP E. SMITH

1935–1936

President: ROBERT K. CANNAN
Vice-President: EUGENE L. OPIE
Treasurer: THOMAS M. RIVERS
Secretary: RANDOLPH H. WEST

Council:
ROBERT F. LOEB
HOMER W. SMITH
DAVID MARINE

1936–1937

President: EUGENE L. OPIE
Vice-President: PHILIP E. SMITH
Treasurer: THOMAS M. RIVERS
Secretary: McKEEN CATTELL

Council:
GEORGE B. WALLACE
MARTIN H. DAWSON
JAMES B. MURPHY

1937–1938

President: EUGENE L. OPIE
Vice-President: PHILIP E. SMITH
Treasurer: THOMAS M. RIVERS
Secretary: McKEEN CATTELL

Council:
GEORGE B. WALLACE
MARTIN H. DAWSON
HERBERT S. GASSER

---

*Dr. Hess died December 5, 1933.

1938–1939

President: PHILIP E. SMITH
Vice-President: HERBERT S. GASSER
Treasurer: KENNETH GOODNER
Secretary: McKEEN CATTELL

Council:
HANS T. CLARKE
JAMES D. HARDY
WILLIAM S. TILLETT

1939–1940

President: PHILIP E. SMITH
Vice-President: HERBERT S. GASSER
Treasurer: KENNETH GOODNER
Secretary: THOMAS FRANCIS, JR.

Council:
HANS T. CLARKE
N. CHANDLER FOOT
WILLIAM S. TILLETT

1940–1941

President: HERBERT S. GASSER
Vice-President: HOMER W. SMITH
Treasurer: KENNETH GOODNER
Secretary: THOMAS FRANCIS, JR.

Council:
N. CHANDLER FOOT
VINCENT DU VIGNEAUD
MICHAEL HEIDELBERGER

1941–1942

President: HERBERT S. GASSER
Vice-President: HOMER W. SMITH
Treasurer: KENNETH GOODNER
Secretary: JOSEPH C. HINSEY

Council:
HARRY S. MUSTARD
HAROLD G. WOLFF
MICHAEL HEIDELBERGER

1942–1943

President: HANS T. CLARKE
Vice-President: THOMAS M. RIVERS
Treasurer: KENNETH GOODNER
Secretary: JOSEPH C. HINSEY

Council:
ROBERT F. LOEB
HAROLD G. WOLFF
WILLIAM C. VON GLAHN

1943–1944

President: HANS T. CLARKE
Vice-President: THOMAS M. RIVERS
Treasurer: COLIN M. MACLEOD
Secretary: JOSEPH C. HINSEY

Council:
ROBERT F. LOEB
WILLIAM C. VON GLAHN
WADE W. OLIVER

1944–1945

President: ROBERT CHAMBERS
Vice-President: VINCENT DU VIGNEAUD
Treasurer: COLIN M. MACLEOD
Secretary: JOSEPH C. HINSEY

Council:
WADE W. OLIVER
MICHAEL HEIDELBERGER
PHILIP D. McMASTER

1945–1946

President: ROBERT CHAMBERS
Vice-President: VINCENT DU VIGNEAUD
Treasurer: COLIN M. MACLEOD
Secretary: EDGAR G. MILLER, JR.

Council:
PHILIP D. McMASTER
EARL T. ENGLE
FRED W. STEWART

1946–1947

President: VINCENT DU VIGNEAUD
Vice-President: WADE W. OLIVER
Treasurer: COLIN M. MACLEOD
Secretary: EDGAR G. MILLER, JR.

Council:
EARL T. ENGLE
HAROLD G. WOLFF
L. EMMETT HOLT, JR.

1947–1948

President: VINCENT DU VIGNEAUD
Vice-President: WADE W. OLIVER
Treasurer: HARRY B. VAN DYKE
Secretary: MACLYN MCCARTY

Council:
PAUL KLEMPERER
L. EMMETT HOLT, JR.
HAROLD G. WOLFF

1948–1949

President: WADE W. OLIVER
Vice-President: ROBERT F. LOEB
Treasurer: HARRY B. VAN DYKE
Secretary: MACLYN MCCARTY

Council:
PAUL KLEMPERER
SEVERO OCHOA
HAROLD L. TEMPLE

1949–1950

President: WADE W. OLIVER
Vice-President: ROBERT F. LOEB
Treasurer: JAMES B. HAMILTON
Secretary: MACLYN MCCARTY

Council:
WILLIAM S. TILLETT
SEVERO OCHOA
HAROLD L. TEMPLE

1950–1951

President: ROBERT F. LOEB
Vice-President: MICHAEL HEIDELBERGER
Treasurer: JAMES B. HAMILTON
Secretary: LUDWIG W. EICHNA

Council:
WILLIAM S. TILLETT
A. M. PAPPENHEIMER, JR.
DAVID P. BARR

1951–1952

President: RENÉ J. DUBOS
Vice-President: MICHAEL HEIDELBERGER
Treasurer: JAMES B. HAMILTON
Secretary: LUDWIG W. EICHNA

Council:
DAVID P. BARR
ROBERT F. PITTS
A. M. PAPPENHEIMER, JR.

1952–1953

President: MICHAEL HEIDELBERGER
Vice-President: SEVERO OCHOA
Treasurer: CHANDLER MCC. BROOKS
Secretary: HENRY D. LAUSON

Council:
ROBERT F. PITTS
JEAN OLIVER
ALEXANDER B. GUTMAN

1953–1954

President: SEVERO OCHOA
Vice-President: DAVID P. BARR
Treasurer: CHANDLER MCC. BROOKS
Secretary: HENRY D. LAUSON

Council:
JEAN OLIVER
ALEXANDER B. GUTMAN
ROLLIN D. HOTCHKISS

1954–1955

President: DAVID P. BARR
Vice-President: COLIN M. MACLEOD
Treasurer: CHANDLER McC. BROOKS
Secretary: HENRY D. LAUSON

Council:
  ALEXANDER B. GUTMAN
  ROLLIN D. HOTCHKISS
  DAVID SHEMIN

1955–1956

President: COLIN M. MACLEOD
Vice-President: FRANK L. HORSFALL, JR.
Treasurer: CHANDLER McC. BROOKS
Secretary: RULON W. RAWSON

Council:
  ROLLIN D. HOTCHKISS
  DAVID SHEMIN
  ROBERT F. WATSON

1956–1957

President: Frank L. HORSFALL, JR.
Vice-President: WILLIAM S. TILLETT
Treasurer: CHANDLER McC. BROOKS
Secretary: RULON W. RAWSON

Council:
  DAVID SHEMIN
  ROBERT F. WATSON
  ABRAHAM WHITE

1957–1958

President: WILLIAM S. TILLETT
Vice-President: ROLLIN D. HOTCHKISS
Treasurer: CHANDLER McC. BROOKS
Secretary: H. SHERWOOD LAWRENCE

Council:
  ROBERT F. WATSON
  ABRAHAM WHITE
  JOHN V. TAGGART

1958–1959

President: ROLLIN D. HOTCHKISS
Vice-President: ANDRE COURNAND
Treasurer: CHANDLER McC. BROOKS
Secretary: H. SHERWOOD LAWRENCE

Council:
  ABRAHAM WHITE
  JOHN V. TAGGART
  WALSH McDERMOTT

1959–1960

President: ANDRE COURNAND
Vice-President: ROBERT F. PITTS
Treasurer: EDWARD J. HEHRE
Secretary: H. SHERWOOD LAWRENCE

Council:
  JOHN V. TAGGART
  WALSH McDERMOTT
  ROBERT F. FURCHGOTT

1960–1961

President: ROBERT F. PITTS
Vice-President: DICKINSON W. RICHARDS
Treasurer: EDWARD J. HEHRE
Secretary: ALEXANDER G. BEARN

Council:
  WALSH McDERMOTT
  ROBERT F. FURCHGOTT
  LUDWIG W. EICHNA

1961–1962

President: DICKINSON W. RICHARDS
Vice-President: PAUL WEISS
Treasurer: I. HERBERT SCHEINBERG
Secretary: ALEXANDER G. BEARN

Council:
  ROBERT F. FURCHGOTT
  LUDWIG W. EICHNA
  EFRAIM RACKER

1962–1963

President: PAUL WEISS
Vice-President: ALEXANDER B. GUTMAN
Treasurer: I. HERBERT SCHEINBERG
Secretary: ALEXANDER G. BEARN

Council:
LUDWIG W. EICHNA
EFRAIM RACKER
ROGER L. GREIF

1963–1964

President: ALEXANDER B. GUTMAN
Vice-President: EDWARD L. TATUM
Treasurer: SAUL J. FARBER
Secretary: ALEXANDER G. BEARN

Council:
EFRAIM RACKER
ROGER L. GREIF
IRVING M. LONDON

1964–1965

President: EDWARD TATUM
Vice-President: CHANDLER McC. BROOKS
Treasurer: SAUL J. FARBER
Secretary: RALPH L. ENGLE, JR.

Council:
ROGER L. GREIF
LEWIS THOMAS
IRVING M. LONDON

1965–1966

President: CHANDLER McC. BROOKS
Vice-President: ABRAHAM WHITE
Treasurer: SAUL J. FARBER
Secretary: RALPH L. ENGLE, JR.

Council:
IRVING M. LONDON
LEWIS THOMAS
GEORGE K. HIRST

1966–1967

President: ABRAHAM WHITE
Vice-President: RACHMIEL LEVINE
Treasurer: SAUL J. FARBER
Secretary: RALPH L. ENGLE. JR.

Council:
LEWIS THOMAS
GEORGE K. HIRST
DAVID NACHMANSOHN

1967–1968

President: RACHMIEL LEVINE
Vice-President: SAUL J. FARBER
Treasurer: PAUL A. MARKS
Secretary: RALPH L. ENGLE, JR.

Council:
GEORGE K. HIRST
DAVID NACHMANSOHN
MARTIN SONENBERG

1968–1969

President: SAUL J. FARBER
Vice-President: JOHN V. TAGGART
Treasurer: PAUL A. MARKS
Secretary: ELLIOTT F. OSSERMAN

Council:
DAVID NACHMANSOHN
MARTIN SONENBERG
HOWARD A. EDER

1969–1970

President: JOHN V. TAGGART
Vice-President: BERNARD L. HORECKER
Treasurer: PAUL A. MARKS
Secretary: ELLIOTT F. OSSERMAN

Council:
MARTIN SONENBERG
HOWARD A. EDER
SAUL J. FARBER

1970–1971

President: Bernard L. Horecker
Vice-President: Maclyn McCarty
Treasurer: Edward C. Franklin
Secretary: Elliott F. Osserman

Council:
Howard A. Eder
Saul J. Farber
Solomon A. Berson

1971–1972

President: Maclyn McCarty
Vice-President: Alexander G. Bearn
Treasurer: Edward C. Franklin
Secretary: Elliott F. Osserman

Council:
Saul J. Farber
Solomon A. Berson
Harry Eagle

1972–1973

President: Alexander G. Bearn
Vice-President: Paul A. Marks
Treasurer: Edward C. Franklin
Secretary: John Zabriskie

Council:
Harry Eagle
Jerard Hurwitz

1973–1974

President: Paul A. Marks
Vice-President: Igor Tamm
Treasurer: Edward C. Franklin
Secretary: John B. Zabriskie

Council:
Harry Eagle
Charlotte Friend
Jerard Hurwitz

1974–1975

President: Igor Tamm
Vice-President: Gerald M. Edelman
Treasurer: Stephen I. Morse
Secretary: John B. Zabriskie

Council:
Jerard Hurwitz
H. Sherwood Lawrence
Charlotte Friend

1975–1976

President: Gerald M. Edelman
Vice-President: Elvin A. Kabat
Treasurer: Stephen I. Morse
Secretary: John B. Zabriskie

Council:
Paul A. Marks
H. Sherwood Lawrence
Charlotte Friend

1976–1977

President: Elvin A. Kabat
Vice-President: Fred Plum
Treasurer: Stephen I. Morse
Secretary: Donald M. Marcus

Council:
H. Sherwood Lawrence
Paul A. Marks
Bruce Cunningham

1977–1978

President: FRED PLUM
Vice-President: CHARLOTTE FRIEND
Treasurer: STEPHEN I. MORSE
Secretary: DONALD M. MARCUS

Council:
  PAUL A. MARKS
  BRUCE CUNNINGHAM
  VITTORIO DEFENDI

1978–1979

President: CHARLOTTE FRIEND
Vice-President: MARTIN SONENBERG
Treasurer: ALFRED STRACHER
Secretary: DONALD M. MARCUS

Council:
  BRUCE CUNNINGHAM
  VITTORIO DEFENDI
  DEWITT S. GOODMAN

1979–1980

President: MARTIN SONENBERG
Vice-President: KURT HIRSCHHORN
Treasurer: ALFRED STRACHER
Secretary: EMIL C. GOTSCHLICH

Council:
  VITTORIO DEFENDI
  DEWITT S. GOODMAN
  ORA ROSEN

1980–1981

President: KURT HIRSCHHORN
Vice President: GERALD WEISSMANN
Treasurer: ALFRED STRACHER
Secretary: EMIL C. GOTSCHLICH

Council:
  RALPH NACHMAN
  DEWITT S. GOODMAN
  ORA ROSEN

1982 1983

President: DEWITT S. GOODMAN
Vice President: MATTHEW D. SCHARFF
Treasurer: ALFRED STRACHER
Secretary: EMIL C. GOTSCHLICH

Council:
  KURT HIRSCHHORN
  RALPH L. NACHMAN
  GERALD WEISSMANN

1983–1984

President: MATTHEW D. SCHARFF
Vice President: HAROLD S. GINSBERG
Treasurer: RICHARD A. RIFKIND
Secretary: EMIL C. GOTSCHLICH

Council:
  KURT HIRSCHHORN
  GERALD WEISSMANN
  JAMES P. QUIGLEY

CUMULATIVE AUTHOR INDEX*

DR. JOHN J. ABEL, 1923–24 (d)
PROF. J. D. ADAMI, 1906–07 (d)
DR. ROGER ADAMS, 1941–42 (d)
DR. THOMAS ADDIS, 1927–28 (d)
DR. JULIUS ADLER, 1976–77 (h)
DR. E. D. ADRIAN, 1931–32 (h)
DR. FULLER ALBRIGHT, 1942–43 (h)
DR. FRANZ ALEXANDER, 1930–31 (h)
DR. FREDERICK ALLEN, 1916–17 (a)
DR. JOHN F. ANDERSON, 1908–09 (d)
DR. R. J. ANDERSON, 1939–40 (d)
DR. CHRISTOPHER H. ANDREWS, 1961–62 (h)
DR. CHRISTIAN B. ANFINSEN, 1965–66 (h)
PROF. G. V. ANREP, 1934–35 (h)
DR. CHARLES ARMSTRONG, 1940–41 (d)
DR. LUDWIG ASCHOFF, 1923–24 (d)
DR. LEON ASHER, 1922–23 (h)
DR. W. T. ASTBURY, 1950–51 (h)
DR. EDWIN ASTWOOD, 1944–45 (h)
DR. JOSEPH C. AUB, 1928–29 (d)
DR. K. FRANK AUSTEN, 1977–78 (h)
DR. RICHARD AXEL, 1983–84 (a)
DR. JULIUS AXELROD, 1971–72 (h)
DR. E. R. BALDWIN, 1914–15 (d)
DR. DAVID BALTIMORE, 1974–75 (h)
PROF. JOSEPH BARCROFT, 1921–22 (d)
DR. PHILIP BARD, 1921–22 (h)
DR. H. A. BARKER, 1949–50 (h)
PROF. LEWELLYS BARKER, 1905–06 (d)
DR. JULIUS BAUER, 1932–33 (d)
PROF. WILLIAM M. BAYLISS, 1921–22 (d)
DR. FRANK BEACH, 1947–48 (h)
DR. GEORGE W. BEADLE, 1944–45 (h)
DR. ALEXANDER G. BEARN, 1974–75 (a)
DR. ALBERT BEHNKE, 1941–42 (h)
DR. BARUJ BENACERRAF, 1971–72 (a)

PROF. F. G. BENEDICT, 1906–07 (d)
DR. STANLEY BENEDICT, 1915–16 (d)
DR. D. BENNETT, 1978–79 (a)
DR. M. V. L. BENNETT, 1982–83 (a)
PROF. R. R. BENSLEY, 1914–15 (d)
DR. SEYMOUR BENZER, 1960–61 (h)
DR. PAUL BERG, 1971–72 (h)
DR. MAX BERGMANN, 1935–36 (d)
DR. SUNE BERGSTRÖM, 1974–75 (h)
DR. ROBERT W. BERLINER, 1958–59 (h)
DR. SOLOMON A. BERSON, 1966–67 (a)
DR. MARCEL C. BESSIS, 1962–63 (h)
DR. C. H. BEST, 1940–41 (h)
DR. A. BIEDL, 1923–24 (h)
DR. RUPERT E. BILLINGHAM, 1966–67 (h)
DR. RICHARD J. BING, 1954–55 (a)
DR. J. MICHAEL BISHOP, 1982–83 (a)
DR. JOHN J. BITTNER, 1946–47 (d)
PROF. FRANCIS G. BLAKE, 1934–35 (d)
DR. ALFRED BLALOCK, 1945–46 (d)
DR. GÜNTER BLOBEL, 1980–81 (a)
DR. KONRAD BLOCH, 1952–53 (a)
DR. WALTER R. BLOOR, 1923–24 (d)
DR. DAVID BODIAN, 1956–57 (h)
DR. WALTER F. BODMER, 1976–77 (h)
DR. JAMES BONNER, 1952–53 (h)
DR. JULES BORDET, 1920–21 (h)
DR. WILLIAM T. BOVIE, 1922–23 (d)
DR. EDWARD A. BOYSE, 1971–72, 1975–76 (h)
DR. STANLEY E. BRADLEY, 1959–60 (a)
DR. DANIEL BRANTON, 1981–82 (a)
DR. ARMIN C. BRAUN, 1960–61 (h)
DR. EUGENE BRAUNWALD, 1975–76 (h)
PROF. F. BREMER, (h)†
PROF. T. G. BRODIE, 1909–10 (d)
DR. DETLEV W. BRONK, 1933–34 (d)
DR. B. BROUWER, 1925–26 (d)

*(h), honorary; (a), active; (d) deceased.
†Did not present lecture because of World War II.

257

Dr. M. F. Perutz, 1967–68 (h)
Dr. John P. Peters, 1937–38 (d)
Dr. W. H. Peterson, 1946–47 (d)
Dr. David C. Phillips, 1970–71 (h)
Dr. Ernst P. Pick, 1929–30 (h)
Dr. Ludwig Pick, 1931–32 (d)
Dr. Gregory Pincus, 1966–67 (d)
Dr. Clemens Pirquet, 1921–22 (d)
Dr. Colin Pitendrigh, 1960–61 (h)
Dr. Robert Pitts, 1952–53 (d)
Dr. A. Policard, 1931–32 (h)
Prof. George J. Popjak, 1969–70 (h)
Dr. Keith R. Porter, 1955–56 (a)
Prof. Rodney R. Porter, 1969–70 (h)
Dr. W. T. Porter, 1906–07, 1917–19 (d)
Dr. Mark Ptashne, 1973–74 (h)
Dr. T. T. Puck, 1958–59 (h)
Dr. J. J. Putnam, 1911–12 (d)
Dr. Efraim Racker, 1955–56 (a)
Dr. Hermann Rahn, 1958–59 (h)
Dr. Charles H. Rammelkamp, Jr., 1955–56 (h)
Dr. S. Walter Ranson, 1936–37 (d)
Dr. Kenneth B. Raper, 1961–62 (h)
Dr. Alexander Rich, 1982–83 (a)
Dr. Arnold R. Rich, 1946–47 (d)
Prof. Alfred N. Richards, 1920–21, 1934–35 (a)
Dr. Dickinson W. Richards, 1943–44 (a)
Prof. Theodore W. Richards, 1911–12 (d)
Dr. Curt P. Richter, 1942–43 (h)
Dr. D. Rittenberg, 1948–49 (d)
Dr. Thomas M. Rivers, 1933–34 (d)
Dr. William Robbins, 1942–43 (h)
Dr. O. H. Robertson, 1942–43 (d)
Prof. William C. Rose, 1934–35 (h)
Dr. M. J. Rosenau, 1908–09 (d)
Dr. Russell Ross, 1981–82 (a)
Dr. Jesse Roth, 1981–82 (a)
Dr. F. J. W. Roughton, 1943–44 (h)
Dr. Peyton Rous, 1935–36 (d)
Dr. Wallace P. Rowe, 1975–76 (h)
Dr. Harry Rubin, 1965–66 (h)
Prof. Max Rubner, 1912–13 (d)

Dr. Frank H. Ruddle, 1973–74 (h)
Dr. John Runnstrom, 1950–51 (h)
Major Frederick F. Russell, 1912–13 (d)
Dr. F. R. Sabin, 1915–16 (d)
Dr. Leo Sachs, 1972–73 (h)
Dr. Ruth Sager, 1982–83 (a)
Dr. Bengt Samuelsson, 1979–80 (a)
Dr. Wilbur A. Sawyer, 1934–35 (d)
Dr. Howard Schachman, 1972–73 (h)
Prof. E. A. Schafer, 1907–08 (d)
Dr. Robert T. Schimke, 1980–81 (a)
Dr. Matthew D. Scharff, 1973–74 (a)
Dr. Harold A. Scheraga, 1967–68 (h)
Dr. Bela Schick, 1922–23 (h)
Dr. Oscar Schloss, 1924–25 (d)
Dr. Stuart F. Schlossman, 1983–84 (a)
Prof. Adolph Schmidt, 1913–14 (d)
Dr. Carl F. Schmidt, 1948–49 (h)
Dr. Knut Schmidt-Neilsen, 1962–63 (h)
Dr. Francis O. Schmitt, 1944–45 (h)
Dr. R. Schoeneheimer, 1936–37 (d)
Dr. P. F. Scholander, 1961–62 (h)
Dr. Nevin S. Scrimshaw, 1962–63 (h)
Dr. William H. Sebrell, 1943–44 (h)
Prof. W. T. Sedgwick, 1911–12 (d)
Dr. Walter Seegers, 1951–52 (h)
Dr. J. Edwin Seegmiller, 1969–70 (h)
Dr. Michael Sela, 1971–72 (h)
Dr. Philip A. Shaffer, 1922–23 (d)
Dr. James A. Shannon, 1945–46 (a)
Dr. David Shemin, 1954–55 (a)
Dr. Henry C. Sherman, 1917–19 (d)
Dr. Richard Shope, 1935–36 (d)
Dr. Ephraim Shorr, 1954–55 (d)
Dr. Robert L. Sinsheimer, 1968–69 (h)
Dr. E. C. Slater, 1970–71 (h)
Dr. G. Elliot Smith, 1930–31 (d)
Dr. Emil L. Smith, 1966–67 (h)
Dr. Homer W. Smith, 1939–40 (d)

ACTIVE MEMBERS

Dr. Bent Aasted
Dr. Ruth Gail Abramson
Dr. Steven B. Abramson
Dr. S. A. Acharya
Dr. Frederic J. Agate
Dr. Edward H. Ahrens
Dr. Agop Aintablian
Dr. Philip Aisen
Dr. Salah Al-Askari
Dr. Qais Al-Awqati
Dr. Anthony A. Albanese
Dr. Michael Harris Alderman
Dr. Robert Alexander
Dr. Emma Gates Allen
Dr. Fred H. Allen, Jr.
Dr. Jona Allerhand
Dr. Fred Allison, Jr.
Dr. Robert D. Allison
Dr. Norman R. Alpert
Dr. Blanche F. Alter
Dr. Norman Altszuler
Dr. Burton M. Altura
Dr. Richard P. Ames
Dr. A. F. Anderson*
Dr. Charles Anderson*
Dr. Helen M. Anderson
Dr. Karl E. Anderson
Dr. Giuseppe A. Andres
Dr. Muriel M. Andrews
Dr. Alfred Angrist*
Dr. Reginald M. Archibald*
Dr. Francis P. Arena
Dr. Diana C. Argyros
Dr. Irwin M. Arias
Dr. Donald Armstrong
Dr. Aaron Arnold
Dr. Robert B. Aronson
Dr. Hiroshi Asanuma
Dr. Paul W. Aschner*
Dr. Amir Askari
Dr. Muvaffak A. Atamer

Dr. Dana W. Atchley*
Dr. Kimball Chase Atwood
Dr. Arleen D. Auerbach
Dr. Arthur H. Aufses, Jr.
Dr. Joseph T. August
Dr. Peter A. M. Auld
Dr. Felice B. Aull
Dr. Robert Austrian
Dr. Avram Avramides
Dr. Theodore W. Av Ruskin
Dr. Richard Axel
Dr. D. Robert Axelrod
Dr. Stephen M. Ayres
Dr. L. Fred Ayvazian
Dr. Henry A. Azar
Dr. Efrain C. Azmitia
Dr. Rostom Bablanian
Dr. Radoslav Bachvaroff
Dr. Mortimer E. Bader
Dr. Richard A. Bader
Dr. George Baehr*
Dr. Leslie Baer
Dr. Silvio Baez
Dr. John C. Baiardi
Dr. Robert D. Baird*
Mrs. Katherine J. Baker
Dr. Sulamita Balagura
Dr. John C. Balardi*
Dr. David S. Baldwin
Dr. Horace S. Baldwin*
Dr. M. Earl Balis
Dr. Amiya K. Banerjee
Dr. S. Banerjee*
Dr. Arthur Bank
Dr. Norman Bank
Dr. Alvan L. Barach*
Dr. W. H. Barber*
Dr. Jose Luis Barbosa-Saldivar
Dr. Marion Barclay
Dr. S. B. Barker*
Dr. Lane Barksdale

*Life member.

267

Dr. W. A. BARNES
Dr. HARRY BARON
Dr. HOWARD BARON
Dr. JEREMIAH A. BARONDESS
Dr. DAVID P. BARR*
Dr. BRUCE A. BARRON
Dr. GUY T. BARRY
Dr. CLAUDIO BASILICO
Dr. C. ANDREW L. BASSETT
Dr. JEANNE BATEMAN*
Dr. JACK R. BATTISTO
Dr. STEPHEN G. BAUM
Dr. LEONA BAUMGARTNER*
Dr. ELIOT F. BEACH*
Dr. JOSEPH W. BEARD*
Dr. ALEXANDER G. BEARN
Dr. CARL BECKER
Dr. E. LOVELL BECKER
Dr. JOSEPH W. BECKER
Dr. WILLIAM H. BECKER
Dr. PAUL B. BEESON*
Dr. RICHARD E. BEHRMAN
Dr. BRIAN BEIMAN
Dr. JULIUS BELFORD
Dr. BERTRAND BELL
Dr. FRITZ KARL BELLER
Dr. BARUJ BENACERRAF
Dr. MORRIS BENDER*
Dr. AARON BENDICH
Dr. BERNARD BENJAMIN*
Dr. BRY BENJAMIN
Dr. IVAN L. BENNETT
Dr. M. V. L. BENNETT
Dr. THOMAS P. BENNETT
Dr. HARVEY L. BENOVITZ
Dr. GORDON BENSON
Dr. RICHARD BERESFORD
Dr. BENJAMIN N. BERG*
Dr. KARE BERG
Dr. STANLEY S. BERGEN
Dr. ADOLPH BERGER
Dr. LAWRENCE BERGER
Dr. INGEMAR BERGGARD
Dr. JAMES BERKMAN

Dr. ALICE R. BERNHEIM*
Dr. ALAN W. BERNHEIMER
Dr. HARRIET BERNHEIMER
Dr. LESLIE BERNSTEIN
Dr. CAR A. BERNTSEN
Dr. GEORGE PACKER BERRY*
Dr. JOHN F. BERTLES
Dr. OTTO A. BESSEY*
Dr. JOSEPH J. BETHEIL
Dr. MARGARET BEVANS
Dr. SHERMAN BEYCHOK
Dr. RAJESH M. BHATNAGAR
Dr. CELSO BIANCO
Dr. JOHN T. BIGGER, JR.
Dr. R. J. BING*
Dr. CARL A. L. BINGER*
Dr. FRANCIS BINKLEY
Dr. J. MICHAEL BISHOP
Dr. MARK W. BITENSKY
Dr. IRA BLACK
Dr. WILLIAM A. BLANC
Dr. KENNETH C. BLANCHARD*
Dr. DAVID H. BLANKENHORN
Dr. SHELDON P. BLAU
Dr. RICHARD W. BLIDE
Dr. ANDREW BLITZER
Dr. GUNTER BLOBEL
Dr. KONRAD E. BLOCH
Dr. ARTHUR D. BLOOM
Dr. BARRY BLOOM
Dr. RICHARD S. BOCKMAN
Dr. OSCAR BODANSKY*
Dr. DIETHELM BOEHME
Dr. BRUCE I. BOGART
Dr. MORTON D. BOGDONOFF
Dr. ALFRED J. BOLLET
Dr. RICHARD J. BONFORTE
Dr. ROY W. BONSNES*
Dr. ROBERT M. BOOKCHIN
Dr. ELLEN BORENFREUND
Dr. FRANK BOSCHENSTEIN
Dr. ADELE L. BOSKEY
Dr. BARBARA H. BOWMAN
Dr. LINN J. BOYD*

*Life member.

Dr. Robert J. Boylan
Dr. Richard C. Bozian
Dr. Robert Brackenbury
Dr. Stanley Bradley*
Dr. Thomas B. Bradley
Dr. Leon Bradlow
Dr. J. Leonard Brandt
Dr. Lawrence J. Brandt
Dr. Daniel Branton
Dr. Jo Anne Brasel
Dr. Thomas A. Brastitus
Dr. Goodwin Breinin
Dr. Esther Breslow
Dr. Jan L. Breslow
Dr. Robin Briehl
Dr. Stanley A. Briller
Dr. Anne E. Briscoe
Dr. Susan Broder
Dr. Felix Bronner
Dr. Chandler McC. Brooks
Dr. Dana C. Brooks
Dr. Clinton D. Brown
Dr. D. E. S. Brown*
Dr. John Lyman Brown
Dr. Ted Brown
Dr. Howard C. Bruenn*
Dr. Elmer Brummer
Dr. J. Marion Bryant
Dr. J. Robert Buchanan
Dr. Nancy M. Buckley
Dr. Joseph A. Buda
Dr. Elmer D. Bueker
Dr. George E. Burch*
Dr. Joseph H. Burchenal
Dr. Richard Burger
Dr. Dean Burk*
Dr. Edward R. Burka
Dr. E. A. Burkhardt*
Dr. John J. Burns
Dr. Earl O. Butcher*
Dr. Vincent P. Butler, Jr.
Dr. Joel N. Buxbaum
Dr. Abbie Knowlton Calder
Dr. Peter T. B. Caldwell

Dr. Lawrence A. Caliguiri
Dr. Berry Campbell*
Dr. Robert E. Canfield
Dr. Paul Jude Cannon
Dr. Guilio L. Cantoni
Dr. Charles R. Cantor
Dr. Eric T. Carlson
Dr. Peter Wagner Carmel
Dr. Fred Carpenter
Dr. Malcolm B. Carpenter
Dr. Hugh J. Carroll
Dr. Steven Carson
Dr. Anne C. Carter
Dr. Sidney Carter
Dr. J. Casals-Ariet*
Dr. David B. Case
Dr. Robert B. Case
Dr. Albert E. Casey*
Dr. Joan I. Casey
Dr. William D. Cash
Dr. McKeen Cattell*
Dr. William Caveness*
Dr. Peter P. Cervoni
Dr. Raju S. K. Chaganti
Dr. R. W. Chambers
Dr. Philip C. Chan
Dr. W. Y. Chan
Dr. J. P. Chandler*
Dr. Merrill W. Chase*
Dr. Norman E. Chase
Dr. Herbert Chasis*
Dr. Kirk C. S. Chen
Dr. Tehodore Chenkin
Dr. Wai Yiu Cheung
Dr. David S. Chi
Dr. Marie T. Chiao
Dr. Shu Chien
Dr. C. Gardner Child*
Dr. Francis P. Chinard
Dr. Herman Chmel
Dr. Yong Sung Choi
Dr. Purnell W. Choppin
Dr. Charles L. Christian
Dr. Ronald V. Christie*

*Life member.

Dr. Judith K. Christman
Dr. Nicholas P. Christy
Dr. Jacob Churg
Dr. Duncan W. Clark*
Dr. Frank H. Clarke
Dr. Albert Claude*
Dr. Hartwig Cleve
Dr. Leighton E. Cluff
Dr. Jaime B. Coelho
Dr. Bernard Cohen
Dr. Cal K. Cohn
Dr. Mildred Cohn*
Dr. Zanvil A. Cohn
Dr. Henry Colcher
Dr. Randolph P. Cole
Dr. Morton Coleman
Dr. Neville Colman
Dr. Spencer L. Commerford
Dr. Richard M. Compans
Dr. Neal J. Conan, Jr.
Dr. Lawrence A. Cone
Dr. Stephen C. Connolly
Dr. James H. Conover
Dr. Jean L. Cook
Dr. John S. Cook
Dr. Stuart D. Cook
Dr. George Cooper
Dr. Norman S. Cooper
Dr. Jack M. Cooperman
Dr. W. M. Copenhaver*
Dr. George N. Cornell
Dr. James S. Cornell
Dr. George Corner*
Dr. Armand F. Cortese
Dr. Daniel L. Costa
Dr. Thomas Costantino
Dr. Richard Costello
Dr. Lucien J. Cote
Dr. Andre Cournand*
Dr. David Cowen
Dr. Herold R. Cox*
Dr. George Craft
Dr. John P. Craig

Dr. B. B. Crohn*
Dr. Richard J. Cross
Dr. Mary K. Crow
Dr. Bruce Cunningham
Dr. Dorothy J. Cunningham
Dr. Edward C. Curnen*
Dr. Mary G. McCrea Curnen
Dr. T. J. Curphey*
Dr. Samuel W. Cushman
Dr. Samuel Dales
Dr. Marie Maynard Daly
Dr. Joseph Dancis
Dr. John A. Dancus
Dr. Betty S. Danes
Dr. Farrington Daniels, Jr.
Dr. R. C. Darling*
Dr. James E. Darnell, Jr.
Dr. Fredric Daum
Dr. Fred M. Davenport
Dr. Charles M. David
Dr. John David
Dr. Leo M. Davidoff*
Dr. Murray Davidson
Dr. Nicholas O. Davidson
Dr. Earl W. Davie
Dr. Jean Davignon
Dr. Bernard D. Davis
Dr. Robert P. Davis
Dr. Emerson Day
Dr. Noorbibi K. Day
Dr. Stacey B. Day
Dr. Peter G. Dayton
Dr. Norman Deane
Dr. Robert H. De Bellis
Dr. Vittorio Defendi
Dr. Paul F. de Gara*
Dr. Thomas J. Degnan
Dr. A. C. DeGraff*
Dr. John E. Deitrick*
Dr. C. E. de la Chapelle*
Dr. Nicholas Delhias
Dr. R. J. Dellenback
Dr. Felix E. Demartini

*Life member.

Dr. Quentin B. Deming
Dr. Felix de Narvaez
Dr. Robert Desnick
Dr. Dickson D. Despommier
Dr. Ralph A. Deterling, Jr.
Dr. Wolf-Dietrich Dettbarn
Dr. Ingrith J. Deyrup
Dr. Elaine Diacumakos
Dr. Herbert S. Diamond
Dr. Leroy S. Dietrich
Dr. George W. Dietz, Jr.
Dr. Mario Di Girolamo
Dr. Alexander B. Dimich
Dr. Peter Dineen
Dr. J. R. Di Palma
Dr. P. A. Di Sant'Agnese
Dr. Zacharias Dische
Dr. Ann M. Dnistrian
Dr. Charles A. Doan*
Dr. William Dock*
Dr. Alvin M. Donnenfeld
Dr. David Donner
Dr. Philip J. Dorman
Dr. Louis B. Dotti*
Dr. Gordon W. Douglas
Dr. R. Gordon Douglas, Jr.
Dr. Steven D. Douglas
Dr. Charles V. Dowling
Dr. Peter C. Dowling
Dr. Alan W. Downie*
Dr. Cora Downs*
Dr. Arnold Drapkin
Dr. David A. Dreiling
Dr. Paul Driezen
Dr. David T. Dresdale
Dr. Lewis M. Drusin
Dr. Ronald E. Drusin
Dr. René J. Dubos*
Dr. Allan Dumont
Dr. Bo Dupont
Dr. Vincent Du Vigneaud*
Dr. Murray Dworetzky
Dr. D. Dziewiatkowski

Dr. Harry Eagle
Dr. Lila W. Easley
Dr. John C. Eccles*
Dr. Gerald M. Edelman
Dr. Norman Edelman
Dr. Howard A. Eder
Dr. Adrian L. E. Edwards
Dr. Richard M. Effros
Dr. Hans J. Eggers
Dr. Kathryn H. Ehlers
Dr. Klaus Eichmann
Dr. Ludwig W. Eichna*
Dr. Max Eisenberg
Dr. Moises Eisenberg
Dr. William J. Eisenmenger
Dr. Robert P. Eisinger
Dr. Stuart D. Elliott
Dr. John T. Ellis
Dr. Rose-Ruth Tarr Ellison
Dr. Peter Elsbach
Dr. Samuel K. Elster
Dr. Charles A. Ely*
Dr. Kendall Emerson, Jr.*
Dr. Morris Engelman
Dr. Mary Allen Engle
Dr. Ralph L. Engle, Jr.
Dr. Leonard Epifano
Dr. Bernard F. Erlanger
Dr. Solomon Estren
Dr. Hugh E. Evans
Dr. Henry E. Evert
Dr. Ronald B. Faanes
Dr. Stanley Fahn
Dr. Gordon F. Fairclough, Jr.
Dr. Saul J. Farber
Dr. Mehdi Farhangi
Dr. Peter B. Farnsworth
Dr. John W. Farquhar
Dr. Lee E. Farr*
Dr. Aaron Feder*
Dr. Martha E. Fedorko
Dr. Muriel F. Feigelson
Dr. Philip Feigelson

*Life member.

Dr. Maurice Feinstein
Dr. Daniel Feldman
Dr. Colin Fell
Dr. Soldano Ferrone
Dr. Bernard N. Fields
Dr. Ronald R. Fieve
Dr. Arthur M. Figur
Dr. Howard Fillit
Dr. Laurence Finberg
Dr. Louis M. Fink
Dr. Stanley R. Finke
Dr. John T. Finkenstaedt
Dr. Edward E. Fischel
Dr. Saul H. Fischer*
Dr. Vincent A. Fischetti
Dr. Arthur Fishberg*
Dr. Paul B. Fisher
Dr. Patrick J. Fitzgerald
Dr. Martin FitzPatrick
Dr. Raul Fleischmajer
Dr. Alan R. Fleischman
Dr. Howard Fleit
Dr. Charles Flood*
Dr. Alfred L. Florman*
Dr. Kathleen M. Foley
Dr. Conrad T. O. Fong
Dr. Joseph Fortner
Dr. Arthur C. Fox
Dr. Lewis M. Fraad*
Dr. Tova Francus
Dr. Blas Frangione
Dr. Harry Meyer Frankel
Dr. Edward C. Franklin
Dr. John E. Franklin, Jr.
Dr. Richard C. Franson
Dr. Andrew G. Frantz
Dr. Carl E. Frasch
Dr. Blair A. Fraser
Dr. Irwin M. Freedberg
Dr. Aaron D. Freedman
Dr. Michael L. Freedman
Dr. Alvin Freiman
Dr. Matthew Jay Freund
Dr. Richard H. Freyburg*

*Life member.

Dr. Henry Clay Frick, II
Dr. Irwin Fridovich
Dr. Arnold J. Friedhof
Dr. Ralph Friedlander*
Dr. Eli A. Friedman
Dr. Ronald Friedman
Dr. Charlotte Friend
Dr. George W. Frimpter
Dr. William Frisell
Dr. Joseph S. Fruton*
Dr. Fritz F. Fuchs
Dr. Mildred Fulop
Dr. Robert F. Furchgott*
Dr. Palmer H. Futcher*
Dr. Jacques L. Gabrilove
Dr. Morton Galdston
Dr. W. Einar Gall
Dr. G. Gail Garnder
Dr. William A. Gardner*
Dr. Martin Gardy
Dr. Owen W. Garrigan
Dr. Lawrence Gartner
Dr. Nancy E. Gary
Dr. Jerald D. Gass
Dr. Frederick T. Gates, III
Dr. Sabastiano Gattoni
Dr. Mario Gaudino
Dr. Gerald E. Gaull
Dr. Malcolm Gefter
Dr. Walton B. Geiger
Dr. Lester M. Geller
Dr. Jeremiah M. Gelles
Dr. Donald Gerber
Dr. James L. German, III
Dr. Edward L. Gershey
Dr. E. C. Gerst
Dr. Menard Gertler
Dr. Melvin Gertner
Dr. Norman R. Gevirtz
Dr. Nimai Ghosh
Dr. Stanley Giannelli, Jr.
Dr. Allan Gibofsky
Dr. Irma Gigli
Dr. Fred Gilbert

Dr. Harriet S. Gilbert
Dr. Helena Gilder
Dr. Alfred Gilman
Dr. Sid Gilman
Dr. Charles Gilvarg
Dr. H. Earl Ginn
Dr. James Z. Ginos
Dr. Harold S. Ginsberg
Dr. Isaac F. Gittleman
Dr. Sheldon Glabman
Dr. Philip R. Glade
Dr. Herman Gladstone
Dr. Warren Glaser
Dr. George B. Jerzy Glass
Dr. Ephraim Glassmann*
Dr. Vincent V. Glaviano
Dr. Frank Glenn*
Dr. Marvin L. Gliedman
Dr. David L. Globus
Dr. Martin J. Glynn, Jr.*
Dr. David J. Gocke
Dr. Henry P. Godfrey
Dr. Gabriel C. Godman
Dr. G. Nigel Godson
Dr. Walther F. Goebel*
Dr. Edmond A. Goidl
Dr. Robert B. Golbey
Dr. Allen M. Gold
Dr. Leslie I. Gold
Dr. Jonathan W. M. Gold
Dr. Allan R. Goldberg
Dr. Burton Goldberg
Dr. Anna Goldfeder
Dr. Roberta M. Goldring
Dr. William Goldring*
Dr. Edward I. Goldsmith
Dr. Eli D. Goldsmith*
Dr. David A. Goldstein
Dr. Gideon Goldstein
Dr. Jack Goldstein
Dr. Marvin H. Goldstein
Dr. Robert Goldstein
Dr. Julius Golubow

Dr. Robert A. Good
Dr. Robert Goodhart*
Dr. DeWitt S. Goodman
Dr. Laurance D. Goodwin
Dr. Norman L. Gootman
Dr. Albert S. Gordon*
Dr. Alvin J. Gordon
Dr. Gary G. Gordon
Dr. Harry H. Gordon*
Dr. Irving Gordon*
Dr. Emil Claus Gotschlich
Dr. Eugene Gottfried
Dr. Otto Götze
Dr. Dicran Goulian, Jr.
Dr. Arthur W. Grace*
Dr. R. F. Grady
Dr. Irving Graef*
Dr. William R. Grafe
Dr. Samuel Graff*
Dr. Frank A. Graig
Dr. Lester Grant
Dr. Arthur I. Grayzel
Dr. Jack Peter Green
Dr. Peter H. R. Green
Dr. Robert H. Green
Dr. Saul Green
Dr. Lowell M. Greenbaum
Dr. Elias L. Greene
Dr. Lewis J. Greene
Dr. Olga Greengard
Dr. Ezra M. Greenspan
Dr. Isidor Greenwald*
Dr. Robert A. Greenwald
Dr. Mary R. Greenwood
Dr. Gregory Gregariadis
Dr. Anastasia Gregoriades
Dr. John D. Gregory
Dr. Roger I. Greif
Dr. Ira Greifer
Dr. Giancarlo Guideri
Dr. Joel Grinker
Dr. Arthur Grishman
Dr. David Grob

*Life member.

DR. HOWARD S. GROB
DR. ARTHUR P. GROLLMAN
DR. LIONEL GROSSBARD
DR. MELVIN GRUMBACH
DR. DEZIDER GRUNBERGER
DR. HARRY GRUNDFEST*
DR. ALAN B. GRUSKIN
DR. ALEXANDRA D. GRUSS
DR. JOSEPH J. GUARNERI
DR. RUTH M. GIBITS
DR. RICHARD S. GUBNER
DR. PETER GUIDA
DR. ANTHONY J. GRIECO
DR. GUIDO GUIDOTTI
DR. CONNIE M. GUION*
DR. STEPHEN J. GULOTTA
DR. SIDNEY GUTSTEIN
DR. GAIL S. HABICHT
DR. DAVID V. HABIF
DR. JOHN W. HADDEN
DR. SUSAN JANE HADLEY
DR. HANSPAUL HAGENMAIER
DR. JACK W. C. HAGSTROM
DR. KATHLEEN A. HAINES
DR. DAVID P. HAJJER
DR. SEYMOUR P. HALBERT
DR. BERNARD H. HALL*
DR. ROBERT I. HAMBY
DR. JAMES B. HAMILTON*
DR. JOHN HAMILTON
DR. LEONARD HAMILTON
DR. PAUL B. HAMILTON*
DR. WARNER S. HAMMOND*
DR. CHESTER W. HAMPEL*
DR. H. HANAFUSA
DR. EUGENE S. HANDLER
DR. EVELYN E. HANDLER
DR. LEONARD C. HARBER
DR. JAMES D. HARDY*
DR. KEN HAREWOOD
DR. PETER CAHNERS HARPEL
DR. ALBERT H. HARRIS*
DR. MICHAEL B. HARRIS

DR. RUTH C. HARRIS
DR. BENJAMIN HARROW*
DR. UNA HART
DR. REJANE HARVEY
DR. RUDY HASCHEMEYER
DR. GEORGE A. HASHIM
DR. SAM A. HASHIM
DR. GEORGE M. HASS*
DR. WILLIAM K. HASS
DR. A. BAIRD HASTINGS*
DR. VICTOR HATCHER
DR. A. DANIEL HAUSER
DR. RICHARD HAWKINS
DR. ARTHUR M. HAYES
DR. JOHN M. HEFTON
DR. RICHARD M. HAYES
DR. MICHAEL HEIDELBERGER*
DR. WILLIAM CARROLL HEIRD
DR. LEON HELLMAN
DR. LAWRENCE HELSON
DR. WALTER L. HENLEY
DR. PHILIP H. HENNEMAN
DR. VICTOR HERBERT
DR. ROBERT M. HEARBST*
DR. MICHAEL HERMAN
DR. MORRIS HERMAN*
DR. FREDERIC P. HERTER
DR. ROBERT B. HIATT
DR. PAUL J. HIGGINS
DR. MARGARET HILGARTNER
DR. CHARLES H. HILL
DR. LAWRENCE E. HINKLE, JR.
DR. JOSEPH C. HINSEY*
DR. CHRISTOPHE H. W. HIRS
DR. JACOB HIRSCH
DR. JAMES G. HIRSCH
DR. JULES HIRSCH
DR. ROBERT L. HIRSCH
DR. KURT HIRSCHHORN
DR. GEORGE K. HIRST*
DR. PAUL HOCHSTEIN
DR. PAUL F. A. HOEFER*
DR. THOMAS I. HOEN*

*Life member.

Dr. Alan F. Hofmann
Dr. Duncan A. Holiday
Dr. Raymond F. Holden*
Dr. Mary Jean C. Holland
Dr. Charles S. Hollander
Dr. Vincent Hollander
Dr. J. H. Holmes*
Dr. Peter R. Holt
Dr. Donald A. Holub
Dr. Robert S. Holzman
Dr. Edward W. Hook
Dr. Bernard L. Horecker
Dr. William H. Horner
Dr. Marshall S. Horwitz
Dr. Verne D. Hospelhorn
Dr. Rollin D. Hotchkiss*
Dr. S. D. Hotta
Dr. Michael Luray Howe
Dr. Howard H. T. Hsu
Dr. Konrad Chang Hsu
Dr. Ming-Ta Hsu
Dr. William N. Hubbard, Jr.
Dr. Lisa C. Hudgins
Dr. L. E. Hummel*
Dr. George H. Humphreys*
Dr. Jerard Hurwitz
Dr. Dorris Hutchinson
Dr. Thomas H. Hutteroth
Dr. Michael Iacobellis
Dr. Genevieve S. Incefy
Dr. Laura Inselman
Dr. Harry L. Ioachim
Dr. Henry D. Isenberg
Dr. Harold D. Itskovitz
Dr. Richard W. Jackson*
Dr. Jerry C. Jacobs
Dr. Eric A. Jaffe
Dr. Ernst R. Jaffe
Dr. Herbert Jaffe
Dr. S. Jakowska
Dr. George James
Dr. James D. Jamieson
Dr. Aaron Janoff

Dr. Alfonso H. Janoski
Dr. Henry D. Janowitz
Dr. Saul Jarcho*
Dr. Charles I. Jaworski
Dr. Jamshid Javid
Dr. Norman B. Javitt
Dr. S. Michel Jazwinski
Dr. Graham H. Jeffries
Dr. Alan J. Johnson
Dr. Dorothy D. Johnson
Dr. Walter D. Johnson, Jr.
Dr. Barbara Johnston
Dr. Kenneth H. Johnston
Dr. Thomas Jones
Dr. Alan S. Josephson
Dr. A. Jost*
Dr. Austin L. Joyner*
Dr. Ronald Kaback
Dr. Elvin A. Kabat*
Dr. Lawrence J. Kagen
Dr. Martin Kahn
Dr. Melvin Kahn
Dr. Thomas Kahn
Dr. Eric R. Kandel
Dr. Sungzong Kang
Dr. Stephen M. Kaplan
Dr. Alfred J. Kaltman
Dr. Mikio Kamiyama
Dr. William Kammerer
Dr. Sandra Kammerman
Dr. Yoshinobu Kanno
Dr. Thomas G. Kantor
Dr. F. F. Kao
Dr. Barry H. Kaplan
Dr. Attallah Kappas
Dr. S. J. Karakashian
Dr. Arthur Karanas
Dr. Arthur Karlin
Dr. Maxwell Karshan*
Dr. Stuart S. Kassan
Dr. Arnold M. Katz
Dr. Michael Katz
Dr. Mitchell A. Katz

*Life member.

Dr. George L. Kauer, Jr.*
Dr. David M. Kaufman
Dr. Hans Kaunitz
Dr. Herbert J. Kayden
Dr. Donald Kaye
Dr. D. Gordon I. Kaye
Dr. B. H Kean
Dr. Aaron Kellner
Dr. Stephen Kent
Dr. Alan J. Kenyon
Dr. Muriel Kerr
Dr. Lee Kesner
Dr. Richard H. Kessler
Dr. Gerald T. Keusch
Dr. Andre C. Kibrick*
Dr. John G. Kidd*
Dr. Edwin D. Kilbourne
Dr. Margaret Kilcoyne
Dr. Diana C. Killip
Dr. Thomas Killip
Dr. Yoon Berm Kim
Dr. Young Tai Kim
Dr. Thomas J. Kindt
Dr. Barry G. King*
Dr. Donald West King
Dr. Glenn C. King*
Dr. Lawrence C. Kingsland, Jr.
Dr. David W. Kinne
Dr. John M. Kinney
Dr. R. A. Kinsella*
Dr. Esben Kirk
Dr. D. M. Kirschenbaum
Dr. David Klapper
Dr. Arthur A. Klein
Dr. Bernard Klein
Dr. Herbert Klein
Dr. Robert S. Klein
Dr. David L. Kleinberg
Dr. Abraham M. Kleinman
Dr. A. K. Kleinschmidt
Dr. Percy Klingenstein
Dr. Jerome L. Knittle

Dr. W. Eugene Knox
Dr. Joseph A. Kochen
Dr. Shaul Kochwa
Dr. Samuel Saburo Koide
Dr. Kiyomi Koizumi
Dr. M. J. Kopac*
Dr. Levy Kopelovich
Dr. Arthur Kornberg
Dr. Peter Kornfeld
Dr. Leonard Korngold
Dr. Irvin M. Korr*
Dr. Charles E. Kossmann*
Dr. Ione A. Kourides
Dr. Arthur Kowalsky
Dr. O. Dhodanand Kowlessar
Dr. Philip Kozinn
Dr. Irwin H. Krakoff
Dr. Lawrence R. Krakoff
Dr. Alvan Krasna
Dr. Richard M. Krause
Dr. Richard Kravath
Dr. Norman Kretchmer
Dr. Howard P. Krieger
Dr. Robert A. Kritzler
Dr. Robert Schild Krooth
Dr. Stephen Krop*
Dr. Saul Krugman
Dr. Edward J. Kuchinskas
Dr. Friedrich Kueppers
Dr. I. Newton Kugelmass*
Dr. Ashok B. Kulkarni
Dr. Henry G. Kunkel
Dr. Sherman Kupfer
Dr. Herbert S. Kupperman
Dr. Marvin Kuschner
Dr. Henn Kutt
Dr. Sau-Ping Kwan
Dr. David M. Kydd
Dr. Chun-Yen Lai
Dr. Robert G. Lahita
Dr. Michael Lake*
Dr. Michael Lamm

*Life member.

Dr. Robert Landesman
Dr. Frank R. Landsberger
Dr. M. Daniel Lane
Dr. William B. Langan
Dr. Gertrude Lange
Dr. Kurt Lange
Dr. Louis Langman*
Dr. Philip Lanzkowsky
Dr. John H. Laragh
Dr. Nicholas F. LaRusso
Dr. Etienne Y. Lasfargues
Dr. Sigmund E. Lasker
Dr. Leonard Laster
Dr. Raffaelle Lattes
Dr. John Lattimer
Dr. Henry D. Lauson
Dr. Beverly Lavietes
Dr. Leroy S. Lavine
Dr. Christine Lawrence
Dr. H. S. Lawrence
Dr. Walter Lawrence, Jr.
Dr. Richard W. Lawton
Dr. Robert W. Leader
Dr. Stanley L. Lee
Dr. Sylvia Lee-Huang
Dr. Robert S. Lees
Dr. Albert M. Lefkovits
Dr. David Lehr*
Dr. Gerard M. Lehrer
Miss Grace Leidy
Dr. Edgar Leifer
Dr. Louis Leiter*
Dr. John Lenard
Dr. Edwin H. Lennette*
Dr. E. Carwile LeRoy
Dr. Stephen H. Leslie
Dr. Gerson J. Lesnick
Dr. Gerson T. Lesser
Dr. Harry Le Veen
Dr. Stanley M. Levenson
Dr. Arthur H. Levere
Dr. Ricahrd D. Levere

Dr. Harold A. Levey
Dr. Robert Levi
Dr. Aaron R. Levin
Dr. Louis Levin*
Dr. Philip Levine*
Dr. Rachmiel Levine
Dr. Robert A. Levine
Dr. Cyrus Levinthal
Dr. Marvin F. Levitt
Dr. Barnet M. Levy
Dr. David E. Levy
Dr. Harvey M. Levy
Dr. Lester Levy
Dr. Milton Levy*
Dr. Sharon Lewin
Dr. Arthur Lewis
Dr. James L. Lewis
Dr. N. D. C. Lewis*
Dr. Marjorie Lewisohn *
Dr. Allyn B. Ley
Dr. Herbert C. Lichtman
Dr. Charles S. Lieber
Dr. Kenneth Lieberman
Dr. Seymour Lieberman
Dr. Frederick M. Liebman
Dr. Martin R. Liebowitz
Dr. Fannie Liebson
Dr. Frank Lilly
Dr. Edith M. Lincoln*
Dr. Alfred S. C. Ling
Dr. George Lipkin
Dr. Martin Lipkin
Dr. Fritz Lipmann*
Dr. M. B. Lipsett
Dr. Julius Littman*
Dr. George Liu
Dr. Darrell T. Liu
Dr. Arthur Livermore
Dr. Rodolfo Llinas
Dr. David P. C. Lloyd*
Dr. Joseph LoBue
Dr. Michael D. Lockshin

*Life member.

Dr. John N. Loeb
Dr. Robert F. Loeb*
Dr. Werner R. Loewenstein
Dr. Irving M. London
Dr. R. Lorente de Nó*
Dr. Barbara W. Low
Dr. Jerome Lowenstein
Dr. Oliver H. Lowry*
Dr. Fred V. Lucas
Dr. Jean M. Lucas-Lenard
Dr. E. Hugh Luckey
Dr. A. Leonard Luhby
Dr. Daniel S. Lukas
Dr. Carol Lusty
Dr. Clara J. Lynch*
Dr. Harold Lyons
Dr. Michael Lyons
Dr. George I. Lythcott
Dr. Kenneth McAlpin*
Dr. Marsh McCall
Dr. W. S. McCann*
Dr. Kenneth S. McCarty
Dr. Maclyn McCarty
Dr. Robert McClusky
Dr. David J. McConnell
Dr. Donovan J. McCune*
Dr. Walsh McDermott
Dr. Fletcher McDowell
Dr. Robert C. McEvoy
Dr. Currier McEwen*
Dr John C. McGiff
Dr. Eleanor McGowan
Dr. Paul R. McHugh
Dr. Rustin McIntosh*
Dr. Cosmo G. MacKenzie*
Dr. Robert G. McKittrick
Dr. John MacLeod*
Dr. Donald J. McNamara
Dr. James J. McSharry
Dr. Charles K. McSherry
Dr. Robert M. McVie
Dr. Thomas Maack

Dr. Nicholas T. Macris
Dr. Melville G. Magida*
Dr. T. P. Magill*
Dr. Jacob V. Maizel, Jr.
Dr. Ole J. W. Malm
Dr. William M. Manger
Dr. Belur N. Manjula
Dr. Mart Mannik
Dr. James M. Manning
Dr. Wladyslaw Manski
Dr. Karl Maramorosch
Dr. Aaron J. Marcus
Dr. Donald M. Marcus
Dr. Philip I. Marcus
Dr. Norman Marine
Dr. Morri Markowitz
Dr. Morton Marks
Dr. Paul A. Marks
Dr. Robin Marks-Kaufman
Dr. Douglas A. Marsland*
Dr. Daniel S. Martin
Dr. Richard L. Masland
Dr. Bento Mascarenhas
Dr. Richard C. Mason*
Dr. Arthur M. Master*
Dr. Edmund B. Masurovsky
Dr. Leonard M. Mattes
Dr. Robert Matz
Dr. Paul H. Mauer
Dr. Evelyn A. Mauss
Dr. Morton H. Maxwell
Dr. Klaus Mayer
Dr. Aubre de L. Maynard
Dr E. W. Maynert
Dr. Rajarshi Mazumder
Dr. Abraham Mazur
Dr. Valentino Mazzia
Dr. John G. Mears
Dr. Edward Meilman
Dr. Harriet K. Meiss
Dr. Gilbert W. Mellin
Dr. Robert B. Mellins

*Life member.

Dr. Ismael Mena
Dr. Milton Mendlowitz*
Dr. Walter L. Mersheimer
Dr. Edward J. Messina
Dr. William Metcalf
Dr. Karl Meyer*
Dr. Leo M. Meyer*
Dr. Alexander J. Michie
Dr. Joseph Michl
Dr. Go Burroughs Mider*
Dr. Yves B. Mikol
Dr. Peter O. Milch
Dr. Donna Mildvan
Dr. A. T. Milhorat*
Dr. David K. Miller*
Dr. Frederick Miller
Dr. John A. P. Millett*
Dr. C. Richard Minick
Dr. George S. Mirick*
Dr. Ormond G. Mitchell
Dr. Peter Model
Dr. Walter Modell*
Dr. Carl Monder
Dr. Charles Moody
Dr. Dan H. Moore*
Dr. Stanford Moore
Dr. Brian L. G. Morgan
Dr. Anatol G. Morrell
Dr. Augusto Moreno
Dr. Gilda Morillo-Cucci
Dr. Akiro Morishima
Dr. Thomas Quinlan Morris
Dr. Kevin P. Morrissey
Dr. Alan N. Morrison
Dr. John Morrisson
Dr. Stephen I. Morse
Dr. Norman Moscowitz
Dr. Michael W. Mosesson
Dr. Melvin L. Moss
Dr. Harry Most*
Dr. Isabel M. Mountain*
Dr. Arden W. Moyer

Dr. Richard W. Moyer
Dr. Stuart Mudd*
Dr. G. H. Mudge
Dr. Meredith Mudgett
Dr. John V. Mueller
Dr. M. G. Mulinos*
Dr. Otto H. Muller*
Dr. Hans J. Müller-Eberhard
Dr. Ursula Müller-Eberhard
Dr. George E. Murphy
Dr. James S. Murphy
Dr. M. Lois Murphy
Dr. Carl Muschenheim*
Dr. W. P. Laird Myers
Dr. Martin S. Nachbar
Dr. Ralph L. Nachman
Dr. David D. Nachmansohn*
Dr. Ronald L. Nagel
Dr. Gabriel G. Nahas
Dr. Tatsuji Namba
Dr. William Nastuk
Dr. Benjamin H. Natelson
Dr. Samuel Natelson
Dr. Gerald Nathenson
Dr. M. Nathenson
Dr. Stanley G. Nathenson
Dr. Clayton L. Natta
Dr. Brian A. Naughton
Dr. Enid A. Neidle
Dr. Norton Nelson
Dr. Harold C. Neu
Dr. Maria M. New
Dr. Walter Newman
Miss Eleanor B. Newton*
Dr. Shih-hsun Ngai
Dr. Chi Nguyen-Huu
Dr. Warren W. Nichols
Dr. John F. Nicholson
Dr. John L. Nickerson*
Dr. Giorgio L. Nicolis
Dr. Julian Niemetz

*Life member.

Dr. Ross Nigrelli*
Dr. Jerome Nisselbaum
Dr. Charles Noback*
Dr. W. C. Noble*
Dr. M. R. Nocenti
Dr. Angelika Noegel
Dr. Robert Nolan
Dr. John H. Northrop
Dr. Robert A. Norum
Dr. Hymie L. Nossel
Dr. Richard Novick
Dr. Alex B. Novikoff
Dr. Abraham Novogrodsky
Dr. Ruth S. Nussenzweig
Dr. Victor Nussenzweig
Dr. Irwin Nydick
Dr. William B. Ober
Dr. Manuel Ochoa, Jr.
Dr. Severo Ochoa*
Dr. Herbert F. Oettgen
Dr. Michiko Okamoto
Dr. Arthur J. Okinaka
Dr. William M. O'Leary
Dr. Allen I. Oliff
Dr. Carl A. Olsson
Dr. Eng Bee Ong
Dr. Peter Orahovats
Dr. Irwin Oreskes
Dr. Marian Orlowski
Dr. Ernest V. Orsi
Dr. Louis G. Ortega
Dr. Eduardo Orti
Dr. Mary Jane Osborn
Dr. Elliott F. Osserman
Dr. Elena I. R. Ottolenghi
Dr. Zoltan Ovary
Dr. M. D. Overholser*
Dr. Norbert I. A. Overweg
Dr. Irvine H. Page*
Dr. George Palade
Dr. Photini S. Papageorgiou
Dr. George D. Pappas

Dr. A. M. Pappenheimer, Jr.
Dr. John R. Pappenheimer*
Dr. Jean Papps*
Dr. Frank S. Parker
Dr. Raymond C. Parker*
Dr. Robert J. Parsons*
Dr. Pedro Pasik
Dr. Tauba Pasik
Dr. Mark W. Pasmantier
Dr. Gavril W. Pasternak
Dr. Jaygonda R. Patil
Dr. Pierluigi Patriarca
Dr. Philip Y. Patterson
Dr. Mary Ann Payne
Dr. O. H. Pearson
Dr. Edmund D. Pellegrino
Dr. Abraham Penner
Dr. James M. Perel
Dr. George A. Perera*
Dr. Eli Perlman
Dr. Gertrude Perlmann*
Dr. Benvenuto G. Pernis
Dr. James H. Pert
Dr. Demetrius Pertsemlidis
Dr. Barry W. Peterson
Dr. Malcolm L. Peterson
Dr. Rudolph Peterson
Dr. Mitchell L. Petusevsky
Dr. Frederick S. Philips
Dr. Robert A. Philips*
Dr. Sidney Pestka
Dr. Lennart Philipson
Dr. Emanuel T. Phillips
Dr. Mildred Phillips
Dr. Julia M. Phillips-Quagliata
Dr. John G. Pierce
Dr. Cynthia H. Pierce-Chase
Dr. Lou Ann Pilkington
Dr. Joseph B. Pincus
Dr. Matthew Pincus
Dr. Johanna Pindyck
Dr. Kermit L. Pines

*Life member.

Dr. Xavier Pi-Sunyer
Dr. Margaret Pittman*
Dr. Charles Plank
Dr. Calvin F. Plimpton
Dr. Charles M. Plotz
Dr. Fred Plum
Dr. Norman H. Plummer*
Dr. Beatriz G. T. Pogo
Dr. Alan Paul Poland
Dr. Roberta R. Pollock
Dr. William Pollack
Dr. Margaret J. Polley
Dr. Edwin A. Popenoe
Dr. J. W. Poppell
Dr. Laura Popper
Dr. Hans Popper
Dr. Keith R. Porter
Dr. Jerome G. Porush
Dr. Jerome B. Posner
Dr. Edward L. Pratt
Dr. Rudolf Preisig
Dr. John B. Price, Jr.
Dr. Richard W. Price
Dr. Marshall P. Primack
Dr. John W. Prineas
Dr. R. B. Pringle
Dr. Philip H. Prose
Dr. John F. Prudden
Dr. Lawrence Prutkin
Dr. Charles B. Pryles
Dr. Maynard E. Pullman
Dr. Dominick P. Purpura
Dr. Franco Quagliata
Dr. Paul G. Quie
Dr. James P. Quigley
Dr. Michel Rabinovitch
Dr. Julian Rachele*
Dr. Efraim Racker
Dr. Shalom Rackovsky
Dr. Bertha Radar
Dr. C. A. Ragan, Jr.
Dr. Kanti R. Rai

Dr. Ilene Raisfeld
Dr. Morris L. Rakieten*
Dr. Henry T. Randall
Dr. Helen M. Ranney
Dr. Felix T. Rapaport
Dr. Howard G. Rapaport
Dr. Richard H. Rapkin
Dr. Fred Rapp
Dr. Maurice M. Rapport
Dr. Sarah Ratner*
Dr. Aaron R. Rausen
Dr. Rulon W. Rawson
Dr. Lawrence W. Raymond
Dr. Stanley E. Read
Dr. George G. Reader
Dr. Kutumba K. Reddi
Dr. Walter Redisch
Dr. Colvin Manuel Redman
Dr. S. Frank Redo
Dr. George Reed
Dr. George N. Reeke, Jr.
Dr. Gabrielle H. Reem
Dr. Westley H. Reeves
Dr. Carl Reich
Dr. Edward Reich
Dr. Lee Reichman
Dr. Marcus M. Reidenberg
Dr. Alexander Rich
Dr. Maurice N. Richter*
Dr. Christine Reilly
Dr. Joseph F. Reilly
Dr. Leopold Reiner
Dr. Donald J. Reis
Dr. Paul Reznikoff*
Dr. Abby M. Rich
Dr. Goetz W. Richter
Dr. Ronald F. Rieder
Dr. Harold Rifkin
Dr. Richard A. Rifkind
Dr. Robert R. Riggio
Dr. Walter F. Riker, Jr.
Dr. Vernon Riley

*Life member.

Dr. David Allen Ringle
Dr. Harris Ripps
Dr. Marcos Rivelis
Dr. Richard S. Rivlin
Dr. Carleton W. Roberts
Dr. Jay Roberts
Dr. Kathleen E. Roberts
Dr. Richard B. Roberts
Dr. Alan G. Robinson
Dr. William G. Robinson
Dr. Dudley F. Rochester
Dr. Olga M. Rochovansky
Dr. Morris Rockstein
Dr. Robert G. Roeder
Dr. William M. Rogers*
Dr. Ida Pauline Rolf*
Dr. Marie C. Rosati
Dr. Harry M. Rose*
Dr. Herbert G. Rose
Dr. Gerald Rosen
Dr. John F. Rosen
Dr. Ora Rosen
Dr. Murray D. Rosenberg
Dr. Philip Rosenberg
Dr. Richard E. Rosenfeld
Dr. Isadore Rosenfeld
Dr. Herbert S. Rosenkranz
Dr. Arthur F. Rosenthal
Dr. William S. Rosenthal
Dr. Paul M. Rosman
Dr. William Rosner
Dr. Herbert Ross
Dr. Russell Ross
Dr. Pedro Rosso
Dr. Eugene F. Roth
Dr. Jesse Roth
Dr. Alan B. Rothballer
Dr. Sidney Rothbard*
Dr. Edmund O. Rothschild
Dr. M. A. Rothschild
Dr. Bruce Rowe
Dr. Lewis P. Rowland
Dr. Paul Royce

Dr. S. Jaime Rozovski
Dr. Albert L. Rubin
Dr. Benjamin A. Rubin
Dr. Meryl S. A. Rubin
Dr. Ronald P. Rubin
Dr. Walter Rubin
Dr. Daniel Rudman
Dr. Maria A. Rudzinska
Dr. Paul Ruegeseggar
Dr. George D. Ruggieri
Dr. Mark G. Rush
Dr. Henry I. Russek
Dr. Gregory Russell-Jones
Dr. Urs. S. Rutishauser
Dr. David D. Rutstein*
Dr. David Sabatini
Dr. Ruth Sager
Dr. David B. Sachar
Dr. Harold A. Sackeim
Dr. Robert Safirstein
Dr. Stanley Walter Sajdera
Dr. Lester B. Salans
Dr. Gerald Salen
Dr. Letty G. M. Salentijn
Dr. Irving E. Salit
Dr. Lee Salk
Dr. Milton R. J. Salton
Dr. Abdol H. Samiy
Dr. Paul Samuel
Dr. Herbert Samuels
Dr. Stanley Samuels
Dr. John Sandson
Dr. B. J. Sanger*
Dr. Shigeru Sassa
Dr. Arthur Sawitsky
Dr. Philip N. Sawyer
Dr. Wilbur H. Sawyer
Dr. Brij Saxena
Dr. Robert G. Schacht
Dr. David Schachter
Dr. Russell W. Schaedler
Dr. Morris Schaeffer
Dr. Fenton Schaffner

*Life member.

Dr. Matthew D. Scharff
Dr. Joseph D. Schattner*
Dr. Frederick G. Schechter
Dr. Andreas S. Scheid
Dr. Margrit Scheid
Dr. Stephen S. Scheidt
Dr. Isaac Schenkein
Dr. Barbara M. Scher
Dr. William Scher
Dr. Donald Scherl
Dr. Lawrence Scherr
Dr. Peter B. Schiff
Dr. Gerald Schiffman
Dr. E. B. Schlesinger
Dr. R. W. Schlesinger*
Dr. Jeffrey Schlom
Dr. Detlef Schlondorff
Dr. Stuart F. Schlossman
Dr. Donald H. Schmidt
Dr. Willard C. Schmidt
Dr. Howard A. Schneider*
Dr. J. B. Schorr
Dr. Paul Schreibman
Dr. Steven Schutzer
Dr. Ernest Schwartz
Dr. Irving L. Schwartz
Dr. James H. Schwartz
Dr. Morton K. Schwartz
Dr. David Schwimmer
Dr. John J. Sciarra
Dr. James Sciubba
Dr. Morris J. Schoeneman
Dr. Ronald W. Schwizer
Dr. T. F. McNair Scott*
Dr. William Addison Scott
Dr. John C. Scott-Baker
Dr. Jean E. Sealey
Dr. Barry M. Segal
Dr. Sheldon J. Segal
Dr. George Seiden
Dr. Irving Seidman
Dr. Samuel Seifter

Dr. Stephen J. Seligman
Dr. Ewald Selkurt*
Dr. Indira Sen
Dr. Fabio Sereni
Dr. Aura E. Severinghaus*
Dr. David Schafritz
Dr. Robert E. Shank
Dr. James A. Shannon*
Dr. Harvey C. Shapiro
Dr. Herman S. Shapiro
Dr. L. L. Shapiro*
Dr. Lucille Shapiro
Dr. William R. Shapiro
Dr. Lewis Inman Sharp*
Dr. Aaron Shatkin
Dr. Elliott Shaw
Dr. Michael Shelanski
Dr. David Shemin*
Dr. Paul Sherlock
Dr. Raymond Lionel Sherman
Dr. Sol Sherry
Dr. Maurice E. Shils
Dr. Bong-Sop Shim
Dr. W. C. Shoemaker
Dr. Joyce E. Shriver
Dr. Charles D. Siegel
Dr. George Siegel
Dr. Morris Siegel*
Dr. Philip Siekevitz
Dr. Selma Silagi
Dr. Robert Silber
Dr. Maxmillian Silbermann*
Dr. Lawrence Silver
Dr. Richard T. Silver
Dr. Morris Silverman
Dr. Philip Silverman
Dr. William A. Silverman
Dr. Emanuel Silverstein
Dr. Martin E. Silverstein
Dr. Samuel C. Silverstein
Dr. Saul Silverstein
Dr. Michael Simberkoff

*Life member.

Dr. Eric J. Simon
Dr. Norman Simon
Dr. Joe L. Simpson
Dr. Melvin V. Simpson
Dr. Inder J. Singh
Dr. Gregory Siskind
Dr. William R. Sistrom
Dr. Anneliese L. Sitarz
Dr. Mark T. Skarstedt
Dr. Vladimir P. Skipski
Dr. Robert J. Slater
Dr. Daniel N. Slatkin
Dr. George K. Smelser*
Dr. Frank Rees Smith
Dr. James P. Smith
Dr. M. De Forest Smith*
Dr. Elizabeth M. Smithwick
Dr. Edna Sobel
Dr. Louis Soffer*
Dr. Richard Luber Soffer
Dr. John A. Sogn
Dr. Arthur Sohval
Dr. Leon Sokoloff
Dr. Louis Sokoloff
Dr. Samuel Solomon
Dr. Alex C. Solowey
Dr. Martin Sonenberg
Dr. Joseph A. Sonnabend
Dr. Hamilton Southworth*
Dr. Paul Spear
Dr. Abraham Spector
Dr. Francis Speer*
Dr. Robert Sisson Spiers
Dr. Frank C. Spencer
Dr. Gabriel Spergel
Dr. Morton Spivack
Dr. David Sprinson
Dr. Norton Spritz
Dr. Katherine Sprunt
Dr. Catherine L. Squires
Dr. P. R. Srinivasan
Dr. John M. Steele, Jr.

Dr. Neal H. Steigbigel
Dr. Richard M. Stein
Dr. William Stein*
Dr. Donald F. Steiner
Dr. Charles R. Steinman
Dr. Philip R. Steinmetz
Dr. Harry Steinberg
Dr. Herman Steinberg
Dr. Ralph M. Steinman
Dr. Kurt H. Stenzel
Dr. Kenneth Sterling
Dr. Joseph R. Stern
Dr. Marvin Stern
Dr. William Stern
Dr. Stephen Sternberg
Dr. Irmin Sternlieb
Dr. De Witt Stetten, Jr.*
Dr. Fred W. Stewart*
Dr. John M. Stewart
Dr. W. B. Stewart
Dr. Walter A. Stewart*
Dr. C. Chester Stock*
Dr. Richard J. Stockert
Dr. Walter Stoeckenius
Dr. Peter E. Stokes
Dr. Daniel J. Stone
Dr. Fritz Streuli
Dr. William T. Stubenbord
Dr. Jackson H. Stuckey
Dr. Horace W. Stunkard*
Dr. Osias Stutman
Dr. John Y. Sugg*
Dr. Barnet M. Sultzer
Dr. Martin I. Surks
Dr. Marcy Sussman
Dr. Joseph G. Sweeting
Dr. Roy C. Swingle
Dr. Margaret Prince Sykes
Dr. Wlodzimierz Szer
Dr. Milton Tabachnick
Dr. John Taggart*
Dr. Igor Tamm

*Life member.

Dr. Lilly S. Tang
Dr. Donald F. Tapley
Dr. Suresh S. Tate
Dr. Edward Lawrie Tatum
Dr. Harry Taube
Dr. Jurg Tauber
Dr. Sheldon B. Taubman
Dr. Howard Taylor, Jr.*
Dr. Alvin Teirstein
Dr. Constantin V. Teodoru
Dr. Robert D. Terry
Dr. Gail A. Theis
Dr. Henry M. Thomas
Dr. Lewis Thomas
Dr. David D. Thompson
Dr. Neils A. Thorn
Dr. David A. Tice
Dr. Edward Tolstoi*
Dr. Helene W. Toolan
Dr. William A. Triebel*
Dr. George L. Tritsch
Dr. Walter Troll
Dr. Jir Shiong Tsai
Dr. Orestes Tsolas
Dr. Gerard M. Turino
Dr. Gray H. Twombly*
Dr. Theodore Tyberg
Dr. Koji Uchizono
Dr. Sidney Udenfriend
Dr. Jonathan W. Uhr
Dr. John E. Ultmann
Dr. Harry F. Ungerleider*
Dr. Jay C. Unkeless
Dr. Arthur Canfield Upton
Dr. Morton Urivetzky
Dr. Virginia Utermohlen
Dr. Fred Valentine
Dr. Parker Vanamee
Dr. Ivo Van de Rijn
Dr. William G. Van der Kloot
Dr. Andre Varma
Dr. Mario Vassalle
Dr. Edward F. Vastola

Dr. Martha Vaughan
Dr. Frank Veith
Dr. Elliot S. Vesell
Dr. Carmine T. Vicale
Dr. Herman Villarreal, Jr.
Dr. F. Stephen Vogel
Dr. Mögens Volkert
Dr. William C. Von Glahn
Dr. Salome G. Waelsch
Dr. Bernard M. Wagner
Dr. Bonnie A. Wallace
Dr. Lila A. Wallis
Dr. Roderich Walter
Dr. John L. Wang
Dr. S. C. Wang
Dr. Lewis W. Wannamaker
Dr. George E. Wantz
Dr. Bettina Warburg*
Dr. Robert C. Warner
Dr. Louis R. Wasserman*
Dr. Norbert H. Wasserman
Dr. Alice M. Waterhouse*
Dr. Robert F. Watson*
Dr. Samuel Waxman
Dr. Annemarie Weber
Dr. Bruce Webster*
Dr. Richard P. Weeden
Dr. Rene Wegria
Dr. Richard Weil, III
Dr. Virginia L. Weimar
Dr. Leo Weiner
Dr. Herbert Weinfeld
Dr. I. Bernard Weinstein
Dr. Harel Weinstein
Dr. Stephen W. Weinstein
Dr. Irwin M. Weinstock
Dr. Harold Weintraub
Dr. John M. Weir
Dr. Gerson Weiss
Dr. Harvey J. Weiss
Dr. Paul A. Weiss
Dr. Herbert Weissbach
Dr. Bernard Weissman

*Life member.

Dr. Charles Weissmann
Dr. Gerald Weissmann
Dr. Babette Weksler
Dr. Francis M. Weld
Dr. Daniel Wellner
Dr. Gerhardt Werner
Dr. Sidney C. Werner*
Dr. W. Clarke Wescoe
Dr. C. D. West
Prof. Otto Westphal
Dr. Joseph P. Whalen
Dr. Abraham White
Dr. Abraham G. White
Dr. Ralph deVere White
Dr. John C. Whitsell, II
Dr. Edkhart Wiedeman
Dr. Stanley Wiener
Dr. Norman Wikler
Dr. Herbert B. Wilcox, Jr.*
Dr. David L. Williams
Dr. M. Henry Williams
Dr. John Wilson
Dr. Victor J. Wilson
Dr. Sidney J. Winawer
Dr. Erich E. Windhager
Dr. Myron Winick
Dr. Asher Winkelstein
Dr. Jonathan Winson
Dr. Robert M. Winters
Dr. Jonathan Wittenberg
Dr. Herbert Wohl
Dr. Abner Wolf*
Dr. David Wolf
Dr. George A. Wolf
Dr. Julius Wolf

Dr. Stewart G. Wolf, Jr.
Dr. James A. Wolff
Dr. Harvey Wolinsky
Dr. Sandra R. Wolman
Dr. Henry N. Wood
Dr. John A. Wood
Dr. John L. Wood*
Dr. James M. Woodruff
Dr. Kenneth R. Woods
Dr. Melvin H. Worth, Jr.
Dr. Walter D. Wosilait
Dr. Irving S. Wright*
Dr. Tze-Chein Wun
Dr. Melvin D. Yahr
Dr. Martin L. Yarmush
Dr. Sehchi Yasumura
Dr. Carol A. Yeadon
Dr. Chester L. Yntema*

Dr. Bruce Young
Dr. Stuart H. Young
Dr. Fuli Yu
Dr. Tasai-Fan Yu
Dr. Ralph Zalusky
Dr. Esmail D. Zanjani
Dr. Italo Zanzi
Dr. Charles G. Zaroulis
Dr. Vratislav Zbuzek
Dr. James E. Ziegler, Jr.*
Dr. Norton Zinder
Dr. Burton L. Zohman
Dr. Thomas R. Kozel
Dr. Joseph Zubin*
Dr. Marjorie B. Zucker
Dr. Dorothea Zucker-Franklin
Dr. Benjamin W. Zweifach

*Life member.